Queens

A collection of b
the world's leadi

We are proud to present a collection of
three novels featuring the
Summer sisters by international
bestselling author

CAROLE
MORTIMER

'TO HAVE A HUSBAND
by Carole Mortimer is an emotionally
charged tale dealing with betrayal, love at
first sight and passion.'
—*Romantic Times*

'Carole Mortimer pens a complex tale with
good character development.'
—*Romantic Times* on *To Make a Marriage*

'Carole Mortimer's TO BECOME A BRIDE
is an enjoyable tale with a very strong emotional
conflict, two fiery characters and a passionate
premise.' —*Romantic Times*

Available in the

Queens of Romance

collection

16th March 2007

20th April 2007

18th May 2007

15th June 2007

Collect all 4 superb books!

CAROLE MORTIMER

Meant to Wed

Containing

To Have a Husband
To Become a Bride
To Make a Marriage

*M&B™ and M&B™ with the Rose Device
are trademarks of the publisher.
Harlequin Mills & Boon Limited, Eton House,
18-24 Paradise Road,
Richmond, Surrey TW9 1SR*

Meant To Wed © by Harlequin Books S.A. 2007

To Have a Husband, To Become a Bride and *To Make a Marriage*
were first published in Great Britain by Harlequin Mills & Boon
Limited in separate, single volumes.

To Have a Husband © Carole Mortimer 2000
To Become a Bride © Carole Mortimer 2001
To Make a Marriage © Carole Mortimer 2001

ISBN: 978 0 263 85835 8

010-0507

*Printed and bound in Spain
by Litografia Rosés S.A., Barcelona*

To Have a Husband

CAROLE MORTIMER

Carole Mortimer began writing in 1978 and has now written over one hundred and twenty-five books for Harlequin Mills & Boon Ltd. Carole has four sons, Matthew, Joshua, Timothy and Peter, and a bearded collie called Merlyn. She says, 'I'm very happily married to Peter senior; we're best friends as well as lovers, which is probably the best recipe for a successful relationship.'

Look for Carole Mortimer's new novel
The Billionaire's Marriage Bargain
out in August from Mills & Boon
Modern Romance®.

My husband, Peter

PROLOGUE

'IF I cross your palm with silver, are you going to tell me I'm going to meet a tall, dark, beautiful stranger?'

Harriet's second reaction to this less than respectful remark to her role as Gypsy Rosa, Fortune-teller, was—you *are* a tall, dark, handsome stranger!

It had been her second reaction—because her first had been ouch!

After being stuck in this tent at the Summer Fête most of the afternoon—a typically damp, English June afternoon—these were the first free few minutes she'd had for a much-needed cup of tea. This man walking in here without warning had caused her to spill most of the hot liquid over her hand!

'You *are* Gypsy Rosa, aren't you?' the man prompted mockingly at her lack of reply.

Lord, she hoped so, otherwise her fashion sense badly needed working on! She certainly didn't usually wear flowery skirts that reached to her ankles, or low-necked white blouses designed to reveal rather than hide her cleavage. And her make-up wasn't usually so garish, the red gloss on her lips matching the varnish on her nails. She also wore huge hoop earrings at her lobes, and her hair was completely covered by a bright red scarf.

Her only saving grace, as far as she was concerned, was that the lack of lightning in the closed-in tent, as well as making it stifling hot, also made it impossible for anyone to see her properly, and so recognise her. At least, she hoped it did!

Her sister Andie usually took over this role at the Summer Fête, and loved every minute of it, but this morning her sister had woken with the beginnings of flu. Everyone else, it seemed, already had their role to play at the fête, and so it had been left to her to—reluctantly—become Gypsy Rosa.

Until the last few moments, it hadn't been too difficult. She'd lived in the village most of her life, and knew all of the people who lived here, so it wasn't too hard to predict romances, weddings, even births in some cases, and the rest of what was said she just made up to make it sound more interesting.

Until the last few moments...

Because even in the subdued lighting of the tent, she knew she had never seen this man before!

Although she could obviously see he was tall. And dark. And his physique seemed to imply he was muscular as well as handsome. He was certainly a stranger, of that she was sure!

'Please sit,' she invited in the husky voice she had adopted for her role of Gypsy Rosa, indicating the chair opposite hers at the table, surreptitiously putting her mug down on the grass at her feet before wiping her wet hand on her skirt beneath the table—otherwise she would be crossing his hand with tea!

Close up she could see him a little better; he had dark hair and light-coloured eyes, either blue or grey. His face all hard angles, his chin square and determined, he wore a dark suit and a white shirt. Well, she could tell one thing just from looking at him—the way he was dressed, he had no more expected to be at a village fête this afternoon than she had expected him to walk into her tent to have his fortune told!

'It started to rain again,' the man drawled, looking across at her, his brows raised derisively.

Ah. In other words, he wouldn't be in here at all if he

hadn't needed to step inside out of the rain that had dampened a lot of the afternoon!

She held back a smile at this disclosure: at least he was honest.

'I'm afraid it takes a little more than silver nowadays,' she murmured throatily. 'The board outside tells you it costs a pound.'

'That's inflation for you,' he acknowledged dryly as his hand went into his trouser pocket to pull out a pound coin and place it on the table between them.

'Would you pass it to me, please?' she invited—for what had to be the fiftieth time this afternoon!

It was amazing how many people, even though they knew it wasn't a real 'Gypsy Rosa' inside this tent, still came in here hoping she would tell them some good news. Although it seemed rather sad to her that it appeared to be the lottery most people hoped to win nowadays rather than wishing for anything else good that could possibly happen to them.

He raised his brows even further as he complied with her request, although his mouth twisted mockingly as, instead of taking the money, she took his hand into both of hers to look down intently into his palm.

She knew absolutely nothing about palm-reading, but as the afternoon had progressed she'd realised you really could tell quite a lot about a person from their hands. And this man was no different. For one thing, his hand was quite smooth, meaning he didn't physically work with his hands. It was also his left hand he had brought forward, a left hand bare of rings.

She glanced up at his face beneath lowered lashes. It was a hard, indomitable face, with a touch of ruthlessness if it should prove necessary to his plans.

No, she decided, that lack of a ring did not, in this man's case, mean that he was unmarried; he was just a man who would resist any show of ownership, even that of a wedding ring.

But while he obviously didn't do physical labour with his hand, it was nevertheless a strong hand. The nails were kept deliberately short; if he was a musician he certainly wasn't a guitar player. She remembered quite vividly from her youth having to keep the nails on one hand long so that she could pluck at the guitar strings!

Well, she had decided what he wasn't—now all she had to try and work out was what he was!

Quite honestly, she didn't have a clue. Wealthy, from the cut of his suit, and the silk material of his shirt. And, as she knew from his entrance, he was possessed of a mocking arrogance that spoke of a complete confidence in himself and his capabilities. Wealthy, then, she decided.

But that only made his presence at a small village fête all the more an enigma!

Or did it…?

Perhaps not, if her guess was correct.

She moved further over his hand, frowning down as if in deep thought. 'I see a meeting,' she murmured softly.

'That tall, dark, beautiful stranger?' he taunted mockingly.

She shook her head slowly. 'This is with another man. Although he is a stranger to you,' she continued, frowning. 'This meeting will take place soon. Very soon,' she added as she felt the sudden tension in the hand she held in hers.

'And?' he prompted harshly.

Yes—and? She had worked out by a process of elimination who this man might possibly be, and it seemed from his reaction to what she was saying that she was probably right, but what did she say to him now?

At this moment she felt, with the rain teeming down outside, as if only the two of them existed, that the rest of the world were a long, long way away. It was almost as if—

She blinked dazedly as the tent-flap was thrown back suddenly to admit the light—and a young lady who looked very like a drowned rat at this moment, with her red hair plastered over her face from the deluge of rain still falling outside.

She glared at the man sitting opposite 'Gypsy Rosa'. 'I've been looking everywhere for you,' she muttered accusingly, pushing the wet hair from her face.

The man stood up, smoothly taking his hand back as he did so. 'Well, now you've found me,' he drawled unconcernedly, although his eyes—now identifiable as aquablue—were narrowed coldly.

The young woman nodded. 'I've come to take you up to the house.' She indicated the umbrella in her hand—something she obviously hadn't taken the time to use on herself on her run over here! 'If you've finished here, that is?' she added with a derisive twist of her lips.

The man glanced back at 'Gypsy Rosa', those strange-coloured eyes gleaming with mocking humour. 'Yes, I believe I've finished here,' he said dismissively.

They'd barely begun, but as 'Gypsy Rosa' really had nothing else to tell him, perhaps it was as well this particular fortune-telling had been interrupted!

She stood up, holding out his pound coin. 'I believe you're a man who makes his own fortune,' she murmured dryly.

He gave an acknowledging inclination of his head, although he made no effort to take back the money she offered him. 'Keep it to put in the fête's funds; I believe it goes to a good cause.'

A party for the village children, where great fun was had by all. But she was surprised he'd bothered to find that out...

'Thank you.' She dropped the money into the jar with all the other pound coins she'd collected through the afternoon.

He turned back to the young woman standing near the entrance. 'Then I'm ready whenever you are,' he prompted.

The young woman with the red hair nodded tersely, turning outside to put up the umbrella, her impatience barely contained as she waited for the man to precede her out of the tent.

Uh-oh, 'Gypsy Rosa' winced inwardly as she watched the pair hurry across the lawn through the rain to the house. From her sister Danie's behaviour towards him just then he had already done something to upset her this afternoon, and Danie certainly wouldn't have kept that rancour to herself!

Which boded ill for the meeting that was about to take place inside the house…!

Talking of which, it was time that Harriet went back to being herself, and for 'Gypsy Rosa' to retire…

CHAPTER ONE

QUINN'S fingers tapped restlessly on the arm of the chair he sat in. Quite frankly, he was tired of waiting for the arrival of his host for the afternoon, Jerome Summer. Justifiably so, in his book.

He'd been flown in by helicopter to the Summer estate earlier this afternoon. After landing on the smooth lawn that backed onto the impressive manor house, he'd been informed by the pilot that the man he had come here to meet, Jerome Summer, had been called away elsewhere, but would hopefully be back later on this afternoon.

It had been that 'hopefully' that had rankled him the most about that statement. Jerome—Rome—Summer was obviously a busy man, hence this Saturday afternoon appointment in the first place, but Quinn's time was no less valuable, and hanging around at the country fête that was being held on the estate, for most of the afternoon, was not using that time effectively as far as he was concerned.

Besides, it was one of the most boring afternoons he had spent for a very long time!

Well…except for the fortune-teller; she might have proved interesting. But he'd hardly begun to talk to her before being interrupted—by the red-haired virago he was quickly learning to dislike!—with instructions that he was wanted up at the house—now.

Well, he had been up 'at the house' for fifteen minutes now, and Jerome Summer still hadn't put in an appearance. Quinn should have realised that the tea tray waiting for him in the sitting-room was rather ominous!

He would wait for another five minutes, he decided

coldly, and then he would ask to be flown back to London. Which wasn't in any way going to help solve the problem he'd come here to talk over with Jerome Summer, but at the same time Quinn refused to be treated offhandedly.

'Ah, my dear Mr McBride, so sorry to have kept you waiting!' greeted a jovial male voice seconds after Quinn had heard the door open behind him.

The man who'd entered the sitting-room was recognisable on sight as his host, Jerome Summer. The man's photograph as often as not adorned the pages of the newspaper Jerome owned, admittedly usually on the financial pages, about one successful business feat or another. He was tall, blond-haired, with a still boyishly handsome face despite his fifty-odd years—those photographs in no way portrayed the sheer power of the man, both physically and charismatically.

He smiled cheerfully as Quinn slowly stood up, holding out his hand in greeting. 'Estate business, I'm afraid,' Rome excused his tardiness dismissively. 'With a place this size, it's never-ending.' He shrugged good-naturedly.

Quinn knew something of the other man; he never liked to meet adversaries without being at least partially briefed. Jerome Summer had bought this estate, comprising the house and extensive grounds, including a deer-park, and half the cottages in the village itself, some twenty years ago. A widower for some years, he now lived here with his three children.

But, as Quinn also knew, those facts only told half the story. Jerome Summer was a self-made man. As the youngest son of a country doctor, he'd built up a financial empire over the last thirty years with various business enterprises, until now, aged fifty-four, he was one of the richest and most powerful men in England. And his complete ease of manner spoke of the confidence that wealth gave him.

It also explained why he'd felt no qualms about keeping

Quinn waiting about for hours; if Jerome Summer was half the man of shrewdness Quinn guessed him to be beneath that boyish charm, then *he* would also have done his homework on *him*. The McBride family, of which Quinn was now the head, chaired and was the major shareholder of one of the most prestigious banks in London. But it was a bank with which Jerome Summer had no personal or business dealings.

'Ah, good, you've been given tea.' Jerome Summer indicated the tea tray on the table.

For all of Jerome Summer's breezy attitude, Quinn was quite sure the other man was well aware of what his movements had been for the whole afternoon, tea being the last thing Jerome was interested in!

'It's probably cold by now,' he told the other man dryly as his host poured tea into the second cup that had been on the tray when he'd arrived—giving Quinn the hope at the time that Jerome Summer himself would appear at any moment!

The other man looked up to grin at him. 'Believe me, over the years I've become used to drinking tea in all sorts of guises.' As if to prove his point he straightened to take a swallow of the lukewarm brew.

Quinn was becoming impatient again. He'd come here because he had something he needed to talk to this man about, something of great importance to him, and with this man acting as if he'd just called in on the off chance of being offered afternoon tea it was becoming increasingly difficult to bring the conversation round to what he wanted—needed!—to talk to Jerome Summer about.

'Mr Summer—'

'Please call me Rome,' the other man invited lightly, relaxing back in one of the armchairs. 'And do sit down, dear boy; you're making me nervous towering over me like that!' He laughed softly up at Quinn as he still stood.

Quinn's eyes narrowed. 'I doubt that very much— Rome,' he bit out tersely, not fooled for a moment by the other man's apparent friendliness. And he certainly wasn't a 'boy', dear or otherwise. At thirty-nine, he'd controlled the McBride Bank for the last ten years, and very successfully too.

The other man continued to smile, giving an inclination of his head. 'Perhaps so,' he drawled in an amused voice. 'But humour me anyway.' He indicated the comfortable chair opposite his own across the coffee-table.

Quinn had an idea that most people humoured this man, for whatever reason. In his own case, he decided as he sat down, it was because the matter he wanted to talk to Jerome Summer about was urgent—and very personal. 'I really do need to talk with you, Rome.' He sat forward in his seat. 'You see—'

'Could you just wait a few more minutes, Quinn?' the other man asked. 'I'm expecting my lawyer to join us at any moment,' he explained at Quinn's frowning look.

Quinn stiffened in his chair. Lawyer? What the hell—?

'I believe I explained to your secretary, when I made this appointment to see you, that this was a private matter?' he bit out harshly. Damn it, he didn't want a lawyer involved in this!

Rome gave another gracious inclination of that leonine head. 'Of course, dear boy, but I've invariably found that the presence of a lawyer is always a good idea—in any situation,' he added hardly, revealing some of the steel Quinn had been sure lay beneath that surface charm.

Quinn's mouth tightened. This was personal, damn it. He didn't want a lawyer present.

'I can assure you that Harrie is the soul of discretion,' Rome added dismissively, bending confidently forward to help himself to one of the sandwiches Quinn had ignored earlier and which were now starting to curl a little at the edges.

Quinn had no doubt that, over the years, discretion was something this man's lawyer had been much in need of! Quinn's expression was grim. He had, he already felt, been jerked around enough by this man for one day. Of course, that had always been the danger when agreeing to meet Rome Summer on his own home ground, but when Quinn had originally been offered this meeting at the Summer estate it had seemed better than no meeting at all. Now he wished he'd tempered his impatience and waited until the other man were free to see him in town. Except, as he inwardly acknowledged, neither he nor Corinne had that time to wait…

Although he'd already learnt enough about this man to know any sign of weakness on his part would quickly be spotted—and as quickly taken advantage of!—by this shrewd adversary.

Quinn drew in a softly controlling breath, deliberately maintaining his own relaxed posture. 'I believe, in this case, you will find you have wasted your lawyer's time,' he drawled dismissively, his own eyes narrowed now, deciding he would hate to play chess with the other man!

Rome Summer shrugged. 'It's my time to waste,' he murmured pleasantly.

'But—' Quinn broke off as he heard the door open behind him, noting the pleasure that lit up the other man's face as he stood up. The shrewdness had gone from Rome Summer's face now as he grinned boyishly before crossing the room to greet the person who had just entered.

'Sorry I'm late; I was unavoidably detained,' murmured a huskily soft voice in apology.

A female voice, Quinn noted with a frown, turning in his chair before slowly standing up to get a better look at the woman who had just entered the room.

Only to find himself looking at the most beautiful woman he'd ever set eyes on!

She had long hair, the colour of midnight, which fell in soft tumbling curls down her back; while long lashes of the same colour surrounded eyes the colour of emeralds, her skin the colour of magnolia, her nose small and pert, covered by a sprinkling of freckles, her mouth wide and smiling, a poutingly sensual mouth, the red lip-gloss she wore a perfect match for the long painted nails on her slenderly expressive hands. She was tall and slender, the tailored grey suit and white blouse she wore adding to that impression of height; her legs were long and shapely beneath the knee-length skirt.

But it wasn't only the woman's obvious beauty that made Quinn stare across the room with narrowed eyes; Rome Summer had grasped both of those slender white hands in his, even as he bent down and kissed one pale magnolia cheek!

Quinn's brows rose knowingly. Obviously—despite their own appointment today!—life wasn't all business for the older man. But as Rome Summer had been a widower for the last ten years, and was obviously still a very attractive as well as powerful man, that wasn't surprising. Quinn just wished the other man's current girlfriend—for this young woman must be almost thirty years younger than Rome Summer—had waited until Quinn had finished his own business with the older man before disrupting their meeting!

Rome put his arm about the woman's slender shoulders as he brought her further into the room, his grin more boyish than ever. 'Come and say hello to Quinn McBride, darling,' he invited softly.

The woman walked like a dream too, Quinn thought contemptuously, her movements fluid while at the same time totally feminine. Sheer perfection, in one five-foot-eight-inch package, Quinn acknowledged grimly. But then, with Rome Summer's wealth, Quinn wouldn't have expected anything less of the current woman in his life!

'Mr McBride,' the woman greeted huskily, standing only inches away from Quinn now.

He found himself looking down at one of those artistically slender hands, at the same time becoming aware of the light headiness of her perfume, a perfume that jolted a memory for him from somewhere, although for the moment he couldn't remember where.

But one thing he was sure of, he'd never met this woman before; she wasn't the sort of woman any man would ever forget once having seen her!

He took the slender hand in the largeness of his own— and almost pulled it away again as quickly!

Something that felt very like an electric shock had passed from the woman's fingers through to his own; a slightly tingling sensation remained in his hand even now, although he resisted the urge to massage away that sensation with his other hand.

His eyes were narrowed to aqua-blue slits now as he looked at the woman for any sign in her own expression that she'd also felt that electrical charge. The gaze that steadily met his own was as cool and impersonal as the jewels they resembled.

Beautiful but cold as ice, Quinn decided, impatiently dismissing his own reaction as he turned to look at Rome Summer once again. 'I have to be back in town by early evening,' he prompted the other man pointedly.

'Of course,' the other man accepted lightly, indicating Quinn should resume his seat. 'Fire away,' he invited cheerfully once they were all seated, Rome having opted now to sit on the sofa beside the young woman.

Quinn gave her a frowning look. Okay, it was a weekend, and the other man obviously had other, more pleasurable plans to occupy his time, but Quinn still had no intention of discussing his private business in the presence of Rome Summer's girlfriend!

'I've already explained to you that my business is private,' he began tautly.

'And I've already assured you—' the other man nodded abruptly '—that anything you say in front of Harrie will be completely confidential.' He looked at Quinn challengingly.

It took tremendous effort of will on Quinn's part—helped by years of running and controlling a worldwide banking concern, where his own tremendous control could mean the difference in millions of pounds for his bank and investors alike—to keep his own expression bland.

Harrie! This woman, obviously an intimate friend of Rome Summer's, was the *lawyer* he'd said would be in on their meeting!

Quinn looked at the woman with fresh eyes, reassessing her businesslike appearance in the tailored suit and blouse, the cool beauty of her face, noting the confidence in her gaze that seemed to say, whatever her private relationship with the older man, she was nevertheless a lawyer, and a damned good one!

Strangely enough, despite her unprofessional intimacy with her employer, Quinn had a feeling she was, too!

He gave an acknowledging inclination of his head. 'This is, nevertheless, a private—very private—matter, to me,' he repeated grimly. 'One that doesn't require legal advice,' he added determinedly.

Not being in control of a situation wasn't something Quinn was particularly comfortable with, and this situation had already been out of control before he'd been made aware of it. Rome Summer, he felt, was the only one now who could put a halt to it in any effective way. If he chose to do so... And Quinn resented having to appeal to this man in the presence of a third party. Especially a third party who, as well as being Rome Summer's lawyer, was obviously the other man's mistress too!

'Quinn—I may call you that, I hope…?' Harrie looked at him enquiringly, the perfect black arc of her left brow raised questioningly.

He gave an acknowledging inclination of his head. 'Mr McBride' might put this meeting on a more formal level, but in the circumstances it was that very formality that he was trying to avoid.

She smiled in acknowledgement of his agreement, her teeth very white and even against the red lip-gloss. 'Then, Quinn, wouldn't it be better if you just told Rome what your problem is, and tried to forget my presence here altogether?' she suggested smoothly.

For one thing, she wasn't the sort of woman any man could easily ignore! 'Just what makes you think I have a "problem"—Harrie?' he bit out, his narrowed gaze levelled on her challengingly.

She blinked once. Just the once. But it was enough to tell Quinn he had briefly disarmed her. But the brief satisfaction he felt at that knowledge was as quickly dispersed as he inwardly admitted there was a problem, even if it wasn't of his own making. But it also made him wonder whether Rome Summer already knew exactly why he'd wanted to see him today… After all, Rome Summer was just as likely to have done his homework on *him* once the appointment had been made!

Harrie shrugged slender shoulders. 'I believe you told Audrey as much when you made this appointment. Rome's secretary,' she explained at his questioning look concerning the mention of the other woman.

He recalled the friendly efficiency of the other woman's voice when he had telephoned Rome Summer's head office yesterday. And, yes, he had told her that. He would never have got this appointment to see Rome Summer so quickly if he hadn't!

But he could also see that, with true legal guardedness, the beautiful Harrie had eluded actually answering his question…

Pompous ass, Harrie thought inwardly, knowing there would be no outward sign of her inner feelings as she continued to look across at Quinn McBride with cool impartiality.

He'd looked at her when she'd entered the room earlier, summed her up, pigeon-holed her as a frothy female friend of Rome's, and as quickly dismissed her as nothing more than an unwanted irritation. Until he'd realised she was Rome's lawyer.

Oh, he'd tried to hide his surprise when Rome had told him of her identity, a polite mask coming down over those handsome features, but it hadn't been quick enough to hide the brief shock that had been reflected in his eyes, the stunned disbelief, before he'd done another mental assessment of her role here today.

Not that his second summing up had been all that complimentary, she acknowledged ruefully; he obviously believed now that Rome was a man who mixed business with pleasure. But at the same time she could see he did accept her legal qualification too!

If he'd known Rome at all, which he obviously didn't, he would have realised the other man never confused his personal life with that of his business one; he may occasionally link them together, but he never, ever confused them…!

Rome had informed her when she'd arrived at the house earlier that this meeting with the banker, Quinn McBride, was planned for this afternoon, and in truth she'd been as puzzled as Quinn McBride obviously was that Rome should require her presence during the meeting. But she hadn't questioned the request in the way that Quinn McBride obviously had; she'd accepted that Rome always had a reason for everything he did.

Quinn McBride finally turned away from her dismissively, his mouth a grim line as he looked across at the older man. 'It appears I have little choice but to accept the situation,' he bit out harshly. 'But I do so on the understanding that what I have to say will be treated as completely confidential, that it is not for discussion with anyone outside of this room. And I do mean *anyone*!'

Harrie bridled with indignation. She was a lawyer, for goodness' sake; of course this conversation would be completely confidential.

'You have my word on it,' Rome drawled derisively, laughter gleaming in his blue eyes as he glanced briefly at Harrie.

Well at least one of them found Quinn McBride's attitude funny—because Harrie certainly didn't! She'd met too many men like Quinn McBride in her years of climbing up the legal ladder, men who took one look at her surface beauty and wrote off any chance of there being a brain under the tumbling black hair. Usually she took great delight in proving those men wrong, to their own detriment, but at the moment this situation with Quinn McBride was a complete unknown to her.

'Mine, too,' she added softly.

Quinn McBride didn't even glance at her this time, his expression grim as he glared down at the cooling teapot. 'My business here today concerns one of the reporters on your newspaper, Rome. And my sister,' he added harshly.

Harrie frowned. Rome owned a newspaper, yes, but she didn't think the minutiae of the lives of the people that worked on it would be of any interest to him. In fact, she was sure of it!

Rome obviously shared her view. 'Let me get this straight. One of the reporters from my newspaper is involved with your sister, and you want me—'

'Certainly not!' Quinn McBride cut in disgustedly. 'My sister is—engaged to marry someone else completely,' he rasped harshly. 'This…reporter—for want of another word,' he added contemptuously, 'has information concerning my sister's past—'

'Something detrimental?' Rome guessed, catching on fast to the other man's angry tone. As he usually did…

It was the key to his success, of course. Outwardly pleasant and amiable, Rome nevertheless possessed a sharp intelligence, and a certain knowledge of his fellow human beings that had saved him from disaster more than once. Anyone who underestimated Rome was heading for disaster.

Although somehow Harrie didn't think Quinn McBride fell into that category; she sensed the quiet respect with which he addressed the older man.

'As you say,' he gave an acknowledging inclination of his head. 'Something detrimental,' he said heavily. 'Not of particular relevance in normal circumstances,' he added firmly. 'But—'

'These aren't "normal circumstances",' Rome finished hardly. 'Am I right in assuming you only have the one sister, Quinn?' Blue eyes were narrowed shrewdly now.

Harrie looked at him thoughtfully, having a definite feeling that he already knew Quinn McBride had only the one sibling…

'Yes,' the other man confirmed abruptly. 'The situation is—delicate, to say the least, and—'

'I can understand your concern, Quinn,' Rome cut in smoothly. 'I just don't know what you want me to do about it. Information, bringing the truth to the general public, is what newspapers are about—'

'I'm not sure I altogether agree with you there,' Quinn scorned derisively. 'The truth, yes. Sensationalism, for the sake of it, no.'

' "…Let them that be without sin themselves cast the first stone" syndrome, hmm?' Rome accepted ruefully.

'Something like that.' Quinn's mouth twisted with distaste. 'I would lay odds on there being very few adults, over the age of say…twenty-five?—who don't have something in their past they would rather weren't made public knowledge!'

Rome nodded. 'And if I were a betting man—which, incidentally, I'm not—I think I would agree with you. How about you, Harrie?' He turned to her enquiringly. 'You're what…? Twenty-nine now? I'm sure there must have been something in your life already that you would rather were kept a secret?'

The conversation had been turned on her so suddenly Harrie didn't even have time to cover up her reaction to the bluntness of the question, her cheeks colouring fiery red under Rome's mocking gaze and Quinn McBride's scornful one.

Nevertheless, she managed to return Rome's challenging gaze. 'I don't believe we were talking about me,' she dismissed coolly.

'Perhaps not,' he conceded in an amused voice before turning back to the other man. 'To get back to the problem of your sister—' he frowned '—I'm not sure I have the right, even when asked as a personal favour to you, Quinn, to actually bury a story that the public may—'

'That's just the point, this reporter isn't—oh, damn!' Quinn McBride stood up impatiently to pace the room. 'You're a father yourself, Rome, I believe?' he prompted irritably.

'Yes…' Rome confirmed guardedly.

'My sister Corinne and I were left parentless fifteen

years ago, when our parents were killed in the crash of the light aircraft they were travelling in. I was twenty-four at the time, but Corinne was only fifteen.' He made the statement in a flat emotionless voice, but it was obvious he'd only achieved this with the passage of time. 'I, naturally, took over the care of my sister—'

'And the Chair of the bank,' Rome added quietly.

Once again Harrie gave him a narrow-eyed look. Just exactly what else did he know about Quinn McBride? The expression on Rome's face was as inscrutable as usual. Meaning he'd no intention of answering that particular question for her, either now or in the future! It was the way he worked, the way he'd always worked—alone!—and he wasn't about to change now.

'And the bank, eventually,' Quinn acknowledged dismissively. 'But that came five years later; at twenty-four I wasn't old enough or experienced enough to take on such a position. And that isn't the point at issue here,' he dismissed impatiently. 'My sister is thirty now, but it's those past tragic circumstances that make me protective of her still.' He sighed. 'I'm sure you know how it is, Rome, that you must feel the same way about your own children.' He grimaced knowingly at the older man.

Rome gave an answering smile. 'Three girls.' He nodded. 'They've given me my fair share of headaches over the years,' he conceded lightly.

Harrie gave him a frowning look beneath lowered dark lashes; he made those 'three daughters' sound like hellions! Something she knew they most certainly were not!

'But a lot of fun and happiness, too,' Rome added affectionately.

'Mmm,' Quinn agreed distractedly, still moving restlessly about the room. 'My sister married five years ago, but unfortunately her husband died of cancer two years later. Corinne was, naturally, devastated,' he murmured heavily. 'She was inconsolable for the first year after Paul died. And then, when she finally felt able to look at the world again, she—she made a mistake,' he added firmly, looking challengingly across the room as he did so.

For her own part, he could have saved himself the trouble, Harrie puzzled thoughtfully; she was no nearer knowing what point he was trying to make than she had been when she'd arrived a few minutes ago for this meeting! Although she very much doubted that Rome, despite his encouragingly friendly expression, was as uninformed…

'It happens to the best of us,' Rome conceded gently.

Quinn McBride's mouth set grimly. 'Not to the woman who is about to marry the MP tipped to be a future prime minister of the country!'

Corinne *Westley*, Harrie suddenly realised dazedly; Quinn's sister was *Corinne Westley*. Up till now she'd been going on the surname McBride, which had totally thrown her, but Corinne's previous marriage now explained that mistake.

Corinne Westley… Tall, beautiful, blonde, elegant, engaged to marry the MP, David Hampton. The wedding was to take place later in the summer, and her photograph, usually at some charity occasion or a political function, appeared in the tabloids nowadays almost as much as the equally elegant and beautiful Princess Diana had once done.

And a reporter working on Rome's newspaper had uncovered some sort of scandal involving the beautiful Corinne that could bring all of that particular castle tumbling to the ground…

No wonder Quinn McBride was worried! Although, in the circumstances, she didn't know what he expected Rome to do about it.

'Why don't you sit down again, Quinn?' Rome invited smoothly. 'I'll have some fresh tea sent in.' He picked up the telephone and rang down in the kitchen. 'And then you can explain all this to us quietly and calmly.'

Harrie could see by Quinn McBride's momentarily irritated expression that he was about to argue the point, that he already considered he was discussing all of this 'quietly and calmly'! And then he obviously thought better of it, sitting back in the chair he had so recently vacated, staring rigidly out of the window as Rome dealt with the ordering of the fresh pot of tea.

It gave Harrie chance to study the younger man further. At thirty-nine, he was ten years her senior, but she could see from the faint sprinkling of grey in the dark hair at his temples, the lines beside his nose and mouth, that those ten years hadn't been easy ones. And, from the sound of it, the reasons for that were understandable; Quinn McBride had had the onerous burden of responsibility thrust upon him at a very young age, both for his younger sister and, even more heavily, as chairman of a bank. His own youth had probably been put permanently on hold!

She reached out impulsively and lightly touched his arm as it rested on the side of the chair. 'I'm sure Rome will help sort this out,' she assured him softly; underneath all that money and power, she knew that Rome was really a softie at heart.

Aqua-blue eyes were turned to her glacially. 'Unfortunately, this isn't something that can be "sorted out" by the gift of a diamond bracelet, or the promise of a weekend in Paris,' Quinn answered her contemptuously.

Harrie pulled her hand away from his arm so quickly it was as if she had been burnt. She'd been right about him earlier; he *did* think she was Rome's mistress. And a very shallow one at that!

She looked at Quinn with narrowed green eyes, back in her role of lawyer now, deeply regretting her completely feminine reaction to his obvious worry concerning his sister. 'The price of happiness comes a little higher than that nowadays,' she bit out harshly.

Those aqua-blue eyes also narrowed. 'I've heard something similar to that once before today...' he murmured in a puzzled voice.

Harrie's gaze didn't waver. 'If your attitude continues to be as unyielding as it appears to be today, my guess is you're going to hear it a lot more in the future, too!' she told him scornfully.

His mouth thinned angrily. 'I—'

'Tea will be here directly,' Rome put in cheerfully. 'I don't suppose you would like to join us for dinner this evening, Quinn?' he pressed lightly.

Harrie turned to him with accusing eyes. Quinn McBride, despite his obvious genuine love and concern for his sister, was one of the rudest most arrogant men Harrie had ever met—and that was saying something! The last thing she wanted at this moment was the anticipation of having to sit down to dinner with him this evening too!

Quinn's mouth twisted ruefully. 'Perhaps you should wait and hear the rest of what I have to say before making such an invitation,' he drawled mockingly.

Rome laughed softly. 'I doubt that will make the slightest difference,' he assured, obviously enjoying the other man's company despite the gravity of the situation Quinn wanted to discuss with him.

Quinn gave an inclination of his head. 'Nevertheless, I think—'

'Ah, tea,' Rome said with satisfaction as, after the briefest of knocks, the door opened. 'Delivered by the beautiful Audrey, no less!' He smiled his thanks to the other woman as he moved to take the laden tray from her.

Audrey Archer, forty-two years of age, petite and blonde, and undoubtedly beautiful, had been Rome's secretary and assistant for the last twelve years—and her slightly exasperated glance in Rome's direction as he took the tray from her unresisting hands showed she wasn't in the least impressed by his flattery. Flannel, Audrey called it. And she was undoubtedly right!

But at least the light-hearted incident had diverted the attention for a few minutes, giving Harrie time to recover from the insult Quinn McBride had delivered to her without so much as a second's hesitation. He'd obviously summed up not only her, but also what he believed to be the situation between Rome and herself. Pompous ass! she inwardly repeated her earlier summing up of him.

She rejoined the conversation to find that Rome had introduced Audrey to Quinn McBride, but also to hear Rome inform Audrey to tell Cook there would be one more for dinner. Obviously Quinn McBride was staying whether he wanted to or not!

'Leave the number for dinner as it is, Audrey,' she told the other woman pleasantly. 'I have to go back to town in a couple of hours,' she explained at Rome's questioning look.

She noticed there was no such look from Quinn McBride, the mockery of his gaze telling her he knew exactly why she was leaving earlier than obviously expected—and that he was amused by the fact!

Whereas Rome didn't look at all pleased by her change of plan. 'You made no mention of that this morning,' he bit out, giving her a frowning look.

Harrie decided he could frown all he liked; she would not subject herself to any more of Quinn McBride's insulting company than she had to. And for the moment she'd no choice but to sit out the rest of this meeting, but this evening, she considered, was her own time, and she would spend it how she wanted to—and that most assuredly did not include being in Quinn McBride's arrogant company!

She shrugged unconcernedly. 'I'm sure you'll cope without me,' she mocked lightly.

'That's hardly the point,' Rome bit out impatiently. 'You—'

'Andie is feeling a little better now, Rome,' Audrey cut in smoothly. 'I said you would probably pop up later,' she added in parting.

'Half an hour or so,' Rome promised in a pleased voice.

From the abrupt change in Rome's mood at the mention of Andie's recovery, Harrie knew Audrey had succeeded in what she had set out to do—namely divert Rome's displeasure away from Harrie. She turned to give Audrey a grateful smile before the other woman left the room, receiving a conspiratorial one back before Audrey closed the door softly behind her.

But Harrie's smile faded as she turned back to find Quinn McBride watching her with narrowed eyes, obviously well aware of the silent exchange between the two women—and as obviously drawing his own conclusions!

Well, let him; she wasn't answerable to him or anyone else for anything she did or said! Although Rome's next comment wasn't conducive to that impression!

'Would you like to pour the tea while Quinn and I continue our discussion?' he invited distractedly, his thoughts having already returned to the matter in hand. 'You were about to tell us about your sister's "mistake",' he prompted softly.

Quinn McBride looked grim once again. 'I don't think I was about to go that far,' he bit out curtly. 'It's enough that the mistake was made, without going into the details. It's this reporter's reaction to the knowledge of it that is really the point at issue,' he added harshly. 'I—ugh!' He grimaced his distaste after distractedly taking a swallow of the tea Harrie had just poured for him.

In the absence of any preference from him as to how he

liked his tea, Harrie had added milk and two sugars before placing the cup of tea on the table in front of him.

'Too sweet?' she prompted too 'sweetly' herself!

He carefully put the delicate china cup back down onto its matching saucer before turning to look at her. 'For future reference—I do not take sugar in either tea or coffee,' he bit out grimly.

For 'future reference', she had no intention of ever pouring him either brew ever again!

Rome's narrowed gaze in her direction was sternly disapproving, bringing an end to her mental berating of the man who was fast becoming more than just an irritation. 'Please—take mine.' She held out a second, as yet untouched, cup to him. 'And for *your* future reference, I don't take sugar in tea or coffee, either,' she added pleasantly, knowing by his throaty chuckle that Rome, at least, wasn't fooled for a moment by that pleasantness.

'I'll bear that in mind,' Quinn McBride acknowledged dryly before turning back to the older man. 'Did you know that at least one reporter on your newspaper isn't averse to using blackmail in exchange for information?'

Harrie was stunned by the question, although, having come to know a little of Quinn McBride in the last fifteen minutes or so, not nearly so much so by the bluntness with which it was made!

Blackmail…? What on earth was he talking about?

And he'd said this meeting had no legal, or illegal, connotations! The last Harrie had heard, blackmail very definitely came under the heading of the latter!

She glanced at Rome, not fooled for a moment by the calmness of his expression—the angry glitter of his eyes, prompted by the other man's words, told a completely different story!

Rome placed his own cup and saucer back down on the coffee-table before meeting the younger man's accusing gaze with a frown. 'What sort of information?' he pushed hardly.

'Political, what else?' Quinn snapped harshly. 'When this man first approached Corinne with the information he had concerning her past, she believed it had to be the end of her relationship with David, that the last thing he needed to forward his political career was a wife who was going to bring disgrace to his name.' His mouth twisted contemptuously. 'But that isn't what this particular man has in mind at all...' he added grimly.

'Go on,' Rome prompted softly.

Harrie wished he would too. It wasn't too difficult to guess what Corinne Westley's 'mistake' might have been—a young widow, devastated by the premature death of her husband; she'd been prime material for a relationship she hoped might help to ease some of her pain. And, in this case, it sounded as if the partner in that relationship had probably been a married man...

As Rome said, it happened, especially when someone was that vulnerable. And also extremely beautiful.

But that was still no excuse for what seemed to be happening to Corinne Westley now...

Quinn sighed heavily. 'This man believes, as do most of us in the City, that David will eventually become Prime Minister. The price for this reporter's silence is any inside information Corinne can give him on political issues—hoping to make them political scandals!'

After what Quinn McBride had already intimated, this wasn't too difficult to guess. And in view of his closeness to his sister, it was no wonder he was angry about it.

Rome looked just as angry. 'The man's name?' he bit out in that flat, emotionless tone that showed just how angry he really was.

'I have your guarantee that nothing we have said so far

will go any further than this room?' the other man prompted again cautiously.

The guarantee was unnecessary, Harrie knew that; Rome could be determined, even ruthless if the occasion warranted it, but he had never done an underhand thing in his life. And he couldn't abide the characteristic in others. Harrie had no doubt that the reporter's days of working on any newspaper Rome owned, and possibly any others either, were numbered!

She also felt that perhaps Quinn McBride was right, and her presence at this meeting wasn't needed...

'Rome?' she quietly demanded his attention for a moment. 'Perhaps it would be better, after all, if I left you and Mr McBride to finish this conversation in private?'

'You'll stay put,' he rasped harshly, causing Harrie to look at him with puzzlement for his vehemence. 'The man's name?' he prompted Quinn again.

Harrie turned to look at the other man too, knowing there was no point in reasoning with Rome on her own behalf when he was in this mood; 'Rome's inflexible mood', she'd always called it. And it meant literally what it sounded like; generally the most affable and charming of men, Rome was implacable in this mood.

'Richard Heaton,' Quinn told him with distaste.

Harrie's breath caught in her throat, the look she gave Rome now one of silent accusation. Because she could tell by the now calm expression on his face that he wasn't in the least surprised by the name the other man had just given him—because he had already known it!

What else did he know...?

From the fact that he had told her this morning he wanted her presence at this meeting, and the way he'd told her to stay put a few minutes ago, Harrie had the feeling that he 'knew' quite a lot more than he had so far revealed to her.

Most important of all, she was sure that Rome knew of her own relationship with Richard Heaton…

CHAPTER TWO

His visual attention concentrated on Rome Summer, Quinn felt rather than saw the female lawyer's reaction to what he'd just said. She'd stiffened defensively, as if, instead of merely stating the name of the man who was hounding his sister, he had actually personally insulted her.

He turned to her, to find her gaze fixed on Rome Summer, angrily, accusingly.

Quinn shook his head as he turned away, mentally dismissing the woman, and her...relationship, with his host; it was none of his business if she chose to be the plaything of a rich and influential man. He was here to sort out the complex and potentially damaging situation Corinne was caught in the middle of.

'Richard Heaton...' Rome repeated hardly.

Quinn nodded. 'Do you know him?' With all of Rome's business interests, it wouldn't be so surprising if he didn't; efficient as he thought himself, Quinn couldn't claim to know all of his employees, either!

'Not personally, no,' Rome answered curtly. 'But I have heard of him,' he added.

Causing the woman Harrie to give the older man another sharp look, Quinn noticed irritably. Beautiful as she was, he hadn't wanted her here in the first place—and she'd done little since that time to warrant him changing that opinion!

'Really?' she prompted softly now, her emerald gaze narrowed on her employer.

Rome returned that probing gaze unflinchingly. 'Really,' he drawled mockingly. 'Surprised?' he added tauntingly.

The woman swallowed noticeably, looking slightly pale, Quinn noted curiously, giving him the definite impression that there was something going on in this conversation that he had no part of. But whatever it was, he, for one, certainly didn't have the time for their games.

'I—'

'Could we get back to the subject?' Quinn rasped his impatience over the top of what Harrie had been about to say.

'The subject being that Richard Heaton is blackmailing your sister into giving him an edge on any political stories she might have access to, both now and in the future, in exchange for not making public her own past indiscretion?' Rome stated bluntly.

This man was as forthright as he was himself, Quinn realised ruefully. But by the same token, he winced inwardly, in this case, a little softening of the truth might have been welcome. After all, it was his sister the two of them were discussing.

'That is a very strong accusation to make, Mr McBride,' Harrie put in coldly. 'Blackmail of this kind is definitely a prosecutable offence. But, by the same token, so is slander. In which case, Mr McBride, I hope that you're sure of your facts?' she asked harshly, staring at him with glittering green eyes.

Quinn realised she was Rome's legal advisor, but, nevertheless, he wished she would stop interrupting! There were only the three of them in the room, for God's sake; who, if it should emerge that what he was telling them wasn't the truth—which it most certainly was!—was going to make that claim of slander?

'I'm very sure of my facts,' he told her with dismissive contempt. 'And I'm hoping that, between the two of us—' he turned back to Rome '—we may be able to do something about it?' It was a question, but at the same time it was also a plea for the other man's help.

Which didn't sit too well on his usually capably independent shoulders, Quinn acknowledged ruefully. Although he had a feeling that Harrie would claim that independence was actually arrogance!

Oh, damn what the woman thought of him, he told himself impatiently. She was beautiful, yes, but she was also the mistress of Rome Summer—which, in his eyes, nullified her legal capabilities in this instance. Even if they should turn out to be excellent. Which was yet to be proved...

'Even if what you claim should turn out to be the truth, exactly what is it you expect Rome to do about the situation?' she persisted in claiming his attention.

Much to Quinn's increasing chagrin! In his experience, lawyers were there to advise when asked for that advice, and if not they remained silent until consulted. Rome's personal relationship with this woman had given her an arrogance of her own that was completely intrusive in this particular situation.

Quinn gave her a humourless smile. 'I think that's for Rome and myself to decide—don't you?' he prompted insultingly.

She drew in a sharp breath as that insult registered, turning to her employer. 'I strongly advise you not to become any more deeply involved in this situation until we have had chance to look into it ourselves,' she told Rome stiltedly.

'There's nothing to talk about, darling,' Rome murmured apologetically before turning to Quinn. 'And I believe I already have an idea that may be the solution to your problem.' He stood up to stroll over to the tray of drinks that stood on the dresser. 'Tea is all well and good,' he said lightly, 'but sometimes something a little stronger is required; can I get you a whisky, Quinn?' he offered, holding up the bottle of twelve-year-old malt.

Ordinarily, he would have refused, rarely indulging in the stuff, and never when he was working. But this wasn't work as such, and he *was* invited for dinner...

'Thanks,' he accepted, becoming more convinced by the moment that Rome was going to help him in this situation. 'Just a small one. No ice or water,' he added as he relaxed back in his chair. They were both more than capable men; he was sure that between the two of them—Harrie's aggravating presence excluded!—they could come up with a way to put an end to Corinne's difficulty. They had better; he'd assured his sister that they would!

'Harrie?' Rome offered smoothly.

'No—thank you,' she refused stiffly, her cheeks bright red now where minutes ago they had been unnaturally pale, her hands tightly clasped together on her primly set knees. 'Rome, I really think—'

'I already know what you think, Harrie,' Rome cut in gently, stepping forward to hand Quinn his drink before moving forward and lightly placing his free hand on one of Harrie's tensed shoulders. 'But Quinn is telling the truth, darling,' he murmured huskily. 'He—'

'I don't believe you—or him!' Harrie stood up abruptly, moving away from that restraining hand to include Quinn in her angry glare, her body rigid with fury now as she faced the two of them across the room. 'I simply do not believe Richard is capable of doing the things he has been accused of here today!' she stated coldly, her head raised haughtily.

If anything she was even more beautiful in her anger, Quinn acknowledged abstractly. Totally wrong in her summing up of the situation, of course, but extremely beautiful, her eyes flashing like emeralds, an attractive flush to her cheeks, her breasts pert beneath the tailored suit, her legs long and shapely. Beautiful, and desirable. Although Quinn had never questioned why Rome was involved with her, only the sense of mixing business with pleasure. Even with a woman as beautiful as Harrie...

And the question also remained, why was she so angry?

Although the answer to that seemed to lie in the way she'd claimed Richard wasn't capable of the things he'd been accused of today...

Quinn's eyes narrowed on her, giving her the second reassessment of the afternoon. The first had been when he'd realised she was the lawyer Rome had previously spoken of. The second was the realisation that she knew Richard Heaton. The question was, *how* well did she know him? Well enough to claim his innocence, it seemed.

He looked curiously at the older man, wondering if Rome had already known of Harrie's friendship with the young reporter. Because he certainly couldn't be in any doubt about it now!

'Then you would be wrong, Harrie,' Rome told her sadly. 'I'm afraid Richard Heaton is guilty of everything Quinn has accused him of today. And much more,' he added with distaste. 'Darling, I'm sorry you've had to hear the truth about him in this particular way, but—'

'Now that I definitely don't believe,' she cut in with a bitter laugh. 'You're enjoying every moment of this! How long have you known?' she prompted hardly, eyes narrowed accusingly on the older man.

'Harrie, I'm sure Quinn isn't in the least interested in listening to our personal business—'

'I'm not sure I believe that, either!' She turned to once again include Quinn in her furious glare, scornfully taking in his relaxed pose in the armchair, the partially drunk glass of whisky he held in his hand. 'You've drawn some pretty damning conclusions yourself here this afternoon, Mr McBride,' she told him disgustedly. 'All of which are totally wrong,' she added with satisfaction, a contemptuous twist to her red-painted lips. 'I sincerely hope—for your sake!—that the things you've said about Richard Heaton aren't as erroneous!'

Quinn stiffened in his chair, slowly sitting up straighter, his own eyes narrowed now as he sat forward in his seat. 'That sounds decidedly like a threat...?' he murmured slowly.

She was breathing deeply in her agitation. 'I—'

'Take care, Harrie,' Rome cut in gently. 'Quinn is a guest in my home,' he reminded her softly.

For a few brief moments she continued to glare at the two men, and then with an obvious visible effort, she forced herself to relax, to calm down, although the coldly angry look remained on her beautiful face.

'So he is,' she finally murmured gratingly. 'Fortunately, I'm not—so I'll take this opportunity to remove myself. That way you can continue this character assassination of Richard Heaton without fear of interruption!' she added disgustedly.

'Harrie—'

'Rome,' she came back coldly, bending to pick up the shoulder bag she'd put down earlier.

The older man sighed. 'Will you be back down tomorrow?'

Now Quinn did feel as if he were intruding. The last thing he wanted was to be witness to a man of Rome Summer's wealth and power grovelling apologetically to his mistress—especially when, as far as Quinn could see, the beautiful Harrie was the one who was in the wrong!

Quinn stood up. 'Perhaps I should leave the two of you to talk—'

'That won't be necessary, Mr McBride,' Harrie cut in derisively. 'Rome and I have said all we have to say to each other—for the moment,' she added warningly for

Rome Summer alone. 'And I have no idea when I'll be back, Rome,' she answered him.

'Are you going to Richard Heaton?' the older man demanded gratingly.

Harrie's head went up challengingly. 'And if I am?'

Rome gave an inclination of his head. 'Then I advise you to remember that you agreed the conversation we've had here today would be confidential,' he reminded softly.

Green eyes glittered like twin jewels. 'Now who's the one making threats?'

Rome shrugged. 'That's only your interpretation of what I said, darling.' He sighed. 'I was merely reminding you not to let your personal feelings cloud your professional judgement.'

Harrie gave a humourless laugh. 'Personal feelings?' she echoed scornfully. 'I didn't know I was allowed to have any of those—at least, none that don't include the Summer family! But to set your mind at rest, Rome, I am well aware of my professional obligations to you,' she assured him disgustedly before turning to Quinn. 'Just one more question, Mr McBride…?'

He met her gaze unblinkingly. 'Yes?'

'Going on a hypothetical assumption that the things you've said about Richard are true,' she bit out scornfully, leaving them in no doubt as to what she thought of those accusations, 'isn't his source of this information as much as a danger—to your sister—as you claim Richard could be?'

Bright, Quinn acknowledged appreciatively. Still furiously angry at what he had to say about Richard Heaton, but able to think logically in spite of it.

'His source,' Quinn drawled contemptuously as he thought of Andrew McDonald, the man his sister had so briefly become involved with, 'if they should choose to go to the press themselves with this story, is in a position to lose as much as Corinne.' The other man had a wife and two children who had no idea of his involvement with another woman!

'I see,' Harrie murmured, her gaze narrowed on him consideringly—giving Quinn the distinct impression she knew exactly what sort of threat had been brought to bear on that particular source! 'I won't say it's been nice meeting you, Mr McBride, because—'

'Harrie!' Rome cut in sharply.

She sighed deeply before drawing in a controlling breath, forcing the semblance of a smile onto her lips, although it came out looking more like a grimace, Quinn thought.

This meeting wasn't turning out at all as Quinn had hoped that it would: a conversation with Rome Summer, an agreement or otherwise to the other man helping him with this situation, and then he would be on his way. A personal element on the part of the other man hadn't been part of Quinn's suppositions, certainly not to the extent that the other man's girlfriend obviously had some sort of relationship herself with Richard Heaton! It changed things somewhat, although not, Quinn now had reason to believe, to the point that Rome Summer refused to help him. And Corinne...

'Well, you've had your "meeting" with the "stranger", Mr McBride,' Harrie told him tauntingly. 'Although not with the tall, dark female you obviously hoped it would be! You've also successfully maligned the reputation of a man you obviously haven't even met,' she snapped accusingly. 'I hope you're proud of yourself!' she added disgustedly before striding across the room and closing the door forcefully behind her as she left.

Quinn stared at the closed door slightly dazedly, remembering all too clearly where he'd heard Harrie's words before. At the fête earlier this afternoon... From the gypsy...

But how on earth—?

'I hope you'll excuse my eldest daughter, Quinn,' Rome told him with a heavy sigh. 'I'm afraid she's rather hurt and angry at the moment—mostly with me, I hasten to add!—and that isn't conducive to her remembering her manners!'

Quinn was still recovering from the shock of realising that the only way that Harrie could possibly have known of his teasing conversation with Gypsy Rosa earlier this afternoon was if *she* were the fortune-teller herself!

It took several stunned seconds for him to realise exactly what else Rome had just said.

Daughter…?

Harrie was Rome Summer's *daughter*?

'Your eldest daughter…?' Quinn finally prompted huskily, still blinking dazedly.

It wasn't very often he was disconcerted, but at the moment it had happened twice within a few seconds of each other. It seemed that not only was Harrie the gypsy from this afternoon's fête, but she was also Rome's *daughter*…?

Rome gave a rueful grimace. 'Harriet. But we've always called her Harrie. I had a feeling earlier when you mentioned my children that you had no idea those daughters were actually twenty-nine, twenty-seven and twenty-five respectively,' he murmured proudly.

'Or that Harrie was one of them,' Quinn confirmed distractedly, still trying to come to terms with the true relationship between Rome and the beautiful Harrie.

Father and daughter. Not lover and mistress. As he had assumed. And as Harrie, from her earlier scornful remark, had obviously known he'd assumed!

Hell!

'The eldest,' Rome confirmed again. 'Although not the most fiery, I can assure you,' he added with proud affection.

Quinn shook his head, still trying to come to terms with Harrie's true relationship to Rome. 'The redhead that's been bossing me around most of the afternoon wouldn't happen to be another of them, would she?' He grimaced in a vain hope that he could be wrong.

Rome laughed softly. 'That sounds distinctly like Danie. My middle daughter,' he explained at Quinn's blank expression. 'Andie, the youngest, is upstairs in bed with the flu,' he added with concern.

Although, according to 'the beautiful Audrey', Andie was 'feeling a little better now', Quinn recalled heavily.

Quinn could never remember feeling quite this disconcerted. Not only had the lawyer Harrie turned out to be a woman, but she was also Rome Summer's eldest daughter. No wonder she'd looked at the older man slightly askance when he had admitted his daughters had given him his fair share of headaches!

But Harrie wasn't only female and Rome Summer's daughter, she was also Gypsy Rosa...!

And she was wrong when she claimed he hadn't met his 'tall, dark, beautiful stranger'; Harrie Summer more than fitted that description herself!

She wanted to hit someone! No, not just 'someone'; her father or Quinn McBride would do just fine. More than fine!

She'd wondered at Rome's need for her presence at this meeting with Quinn McBride today; she knew that her father had made it an unwritten policy over the years never to conduct business during the weekend, that this was the time he set aside for his family. But when he'd telephoned her yesterday, to make sure she would definitely be here today, she hadn't questioned the request too deeply, just assumed that he must have had his reasons for wanting her here.

And he'd certainly had those!

Just when and how had he learnt of her relationship with Richard Heaton? That he did know couldn't be in any doubt after the things he had said to her earlier.

'What is it, Harrie?' Audrey prompted concernedly as she came out of the study further down the hallway.

The other woman's concern wasn't too difficult to understand, Harrie acknowledged self-disgustedly as she realised she was still standing outside the sitting-room, her hands clenched into fists at her sides.

She drew in a relaxing breath before replying. 'Just Rome up to his usual games,' she bit out sharply.

Audrey raised blonde brows at her vehemence. 'But I thought it was a business meeting?'

Harrie had been only seventeen when Audrey had first begun to work with Rome, nineteen when her mother had died, and so consequently it had been Audrey whom Harriet had turned to when she'd needed to talk over the usual problems teenagers had as they were growing into adulthood.

It was also no secret between the two women that Rome had been bringing home 'suitable' young men for his daughters' perusal for the last five years, in the hope that one of them might eventually settle down and present him with a grandson! 'Suitable' to Rome, of course—so far none of those men had proved in the least interesting to the three sisters.

'Not those sort of games,' Harrie told the other woman derisively; much as Rome might like to see his daughters settled, even he could never imagine Quinn McBride as a potential son-in-law.

Besides, Harrie was quite capable of picking her own husband, thank you very much. In fact, until a few minutes ago, she had thought she *had* chosen him...

'Come along to the study where we won't be disturbed,'

Audrey invited gently as she read the look of confusion on Harrie's face. 'You can tell me all about it,' she added warmly.

Much as she felt tempted to do exactly that, Harrie knew that she couldn't. For one thing she had given a promise of confidentiality to her father and Quinn McBride. And for another, the whole thing was too painful at the moment to even think of confiding in someone else, even abstractly, any of the things Quinn McBride had accused Richard of.

Not that she believed them. Not for a minute. But she needed time to gather her own thoughts. And to do that she had to get away from here!

'Not today, Audrey.' Harrie reached out and squeezed the other woman's arm in apology. 'I'm so angry with Rome at the moment that I don't even want to run the risk of seeing him again today. Or Quinn McBride,' she added as she remembered the other man was staying for dinner. 'I think it best if I keep to my decision to go back to town.' The sooner the better, as far as she was concerned!

'You know where I am if you change your mind,' Audrey told her encouragingly.

Harrie grimaced. 'Unfortunately, wherever you are, Rome tends to be too!' As her father's personal assistant, Audrey tended to travel all over the world with him. It didn't allow Audrey any personal life of her own, but, as she'd never married, Audrey didn't seem to mind that. 'But there is one thing you could possibly help me with...?' she said slowly, frowning slightly.

Audrey gave her a considering look. 'And what's that?'

She moistened dry lips. 'Has my father ever mentioned a Richard Heaton to you?' she prompted lightly.

Audrey raised blonde brows. 'In what connection?'

'In any connection!' Harrie bit out disgustedly.

The older woman gave a rueful grimace. 'Are you seriously expecting me to answer that?'

Not really, no. Close as she was to the other woman, Harrie had always known that the older woman would never betray Rome's confidence in her, either personally or professionally—just as Audrey would never betray any of the confidences Harrie had given over the years either! In fact, she was being unfair, Harrie realised, to have even asked Audrey such a question.

'Forget I ever asked.' Harrie squeezed the other woman's arm in apology a second time. 'I'll be off in a few minutes,' she added grimly. 'I hope you enjoy dinner this evening!'

Audrey laughed softly at her insincerity. 'I thought Mr McBride looked rather—interesting,' she drawled pointedly.

Harrie's eyes widened in surprise. Audrey had been involved with the Summer family for so long now that Harrie had almost forgotten that the other woman was only in her early forties, and that she was still a very beautiful and desirable woman. In fact, there were only three years' difference in Audrey's age and Quinn McBride's...!

Harrie grimaced. 'If you're partial to snakes!' she acknowledged with feeling. 'Personally, I'm not!'

Audrey chuckled again, blue eyes gleaming with laughter. 'He certainly made an impression on you, didn't he?' she teased.

'With the impact of a brick!' Harrie acknowledged disgustedly. 'I really do have to go,' she added with a pointed look towards the sitting-room; the last thing she wanted was for either man to open the door and find her still standing outside in the hallway!

'Andie will be most upset if you don't go in and see her before you leave,' Audrey warned. 'She's at the feeling-sorry-for-herself stage,' she added affectionately.

Harrie grinned at the description. 'How my little sister hates to be found looking less than her best!'

Audrey shared in the humour. 'She doesn't make the best patient in the world,' she acknowledged ruefully.

That was definitely an understatement, Harrie realised after sitting with her disgruntled youngest sister for five minutes, glad to have the excuse of returning to town as a means of making good her escape.

Although she didn't make that escape quite as she had hoped…!

Just as she reached the bottom of the wide staircase the sitting-room door opened and her father and Quinn McBride stepped out into the hallway.

Harrie gave them both a coldly dismissive glare before turning sharply on her heel and walking briskly across the wide hallway to the front door.

Was Quinn McBride now aware that she was Rome's daughter and not his mistress, as he had so obviously assumed earlier? Probably, she accepted with satisfaction. Not that she expected the other man would feel in the least uncomfortable about his erroneous assumptions; he had the look of a man who very rarely regretted any of his actions!

'Harrie!' her father called to her impatiently even as she wrenched the huge oak door open.

She froze, drawing in several controlling breaths before slowly turning back to face him. 'Yes?' She deliberately kept her attention centred on her father, patently ignoring Quinn McBride, a fact she was sure he was well aware of. And probably amused by!

Which only made her angrier than ever. There was nothing even remotely funny about this situation. Even if she could prove that the accusations Quinn McBride had made, concerning Richard, were all lies, she would still have to convince her father of that. And, as all of his daughters knew only too well, underneath that happily unconcerned persona Rome had a will of steel!

'I only wanted to ask you to drive carefully, darling,' her father told her gently.

She should have known! She'd been expecting admonition for her earlier behavior—she knew that she hadn't heard the last of that!—and instead Rome had totally thrown her by being her loving, caring parent. And he had done it on purpose. Damn him!

'I always do,' she assured him dryly, turning stiltedly to Quinn McBride. 'I hope you enjoy your weekend, Mr McBride,' she told him contemptuously.

He raised dark brows at her obvious sarcasm. 'I doubt I'll be able to do that, not when I seem to have ruined yours!'

Harrie's eye flashed deeply green at his presumption in believing anything he had to say could affect her one way or another. 'Not in the least,' she assured him scathingly, chin raised defiantly. 'What you had to say this afternoon was interesting, but, as I'm sure Rome can confirm, I stopped believing in fairly tales a long time ago!'

His mouth tightened at the intended insult. 'I'm sorry you feel that way,' he said softly. 'Maybe if you met my sister, talked to her, you would feel differently…?'

Harrie gave him an outraged glare. 'I doubt that very much,' she bit out dismissively.

Meet Corinne Westley! Tall, blonde, beautifully composed Corinne Westley? Quinn McBride's sister? That was the last thing Harrie wanted.

No…the last thing she wanted was to stand here and continue this conversation with Quinn McBride!

She turned to her father. 'I really do have to go now,' she told him abruptly. 'I'll be in the office on Monday, as usual,' she assured him dryly, knowing her father was quite capable of coming in search of her if she didn't arrive at work as usual on Monday morning.

She'd intended becoming a junior partner in a law firm

after obtaining her legal qualifications, but her father had persuaded her to work for him for a few weeks. And the weeks had turned into months, the months into years, until she was well and truly ensconced in handling all the legalities of her father's business dealings.

It had been an easy option, she realised now, and maybe it was time she moved on. Besides, she wasn't sure she could continue to work for, and with, her father after what had happened this weekend...

'Harrie...?' Her father frowned at her.

'Rome,' she returned unhelpfully, meeting his gaze challengingly.

Her father was too astute, that was his problem—because he had, she was sure, picked up on some of the thoughts that had been going haphazardly through her mind! Well, he wasn't going to know about any of them until she'd worked out in her own mind exactly what she was going to do.

His mouth tightened disapprovingly. 'We'll talk on Monday,' he muttered grimly.

'We certainly will,' she agreed lightly.

And she knew exactly what she was going to say to him too!

'Once again, I wish you both a happy weekend,' she added hardly.

'Er—actually, Harrie, Quinn has decided to take a rain check on dinner this evening,' her father told her dismissively. 'I thought you must have already left—'

'I've been up to see Andie,' Harrie told him distractedly, sure her father couldn't really be about to make the suggestion she sensed that he was!

Her father's expression brightened. 'How is she?'

Harrie shrugged. 'Improving, as Audrey told you earlier.'

He nodded his satisfaction with this news. 'I'll go up

and see her myself soon,' he murmured. 'I was actually just about to make the arrangements for Quinn to get back up to town, but as you're on your way back there, any-way—'

'You can't be serious!' Harrie interrupted him sca-thingly, absolutely horrified at the idea of spending the next hour in Quinn McBride's company. And to add insult to injury, in the confines of her own car!

'If you wouldn't mind?' Quinn McBride put in softly.

Her eyes flashed as she turned to glare at him. 'And if I do?'

'Harrie!' her father remonstrated exasperatedly.

'It's all right, Rome,' Quinn McBride assured him soothingly. 'I'm sure Harrie has her reasons for feeling the way that she does.' He turned back to her. 'The drive into London will give us an opportunity to talk. I feel that you need to hear more about my sister's—dilemma, before you get back to town,' he added as Harrie would have inter-rupted once again.

Before going back and telling Richard of his accusa-tions, was what Quinn really meant, Harrie knew. Well, she had given her word that she wouldn't do that, it was a promise she wouldn't break. But that didn't mean she couldn't leave Quinn McBride guessing. In her opinion, it was the least he deserved!

She gave him a humourless smile. 'I don't think I need to hear any more than I already have, Mr McBride,' she told him tauntingly. 'And I'm equally as sure you have no more wish to spend any more time in my company than I do in yours!' she said disgustedly.

'True,' Quinn McBride acknowledged dryly. 'However, I do believe we need to talk,' he added hardly.

And she knew exactly what they 'needed' to talk about. Well, he was going to be out of luck if he thought she would discuss Richard with him—because she most certainly would not. The man had come here and made horrendous accusations about the man she loved; there was no way anything he chose to say to her in private could change that.

She gave a deep sigh. 'You're wasting your time, Mr McBride,' she told him tightly. 'But I am leaving now—if you're ready to go?' she invited ungraciously.

His mouth quirked into a rueful smile. 'I've had politer invitations—but,' he continued firmly as she would have interrupted, 'in the circumstances, I accept.'

Harrie didn't need to be told what circumstances they were! But if he wanted to spend an unpleasant hour in her company, while she drove them both back to London, that was completely up to him.

'I'll see you on Monday, Rome,' she told her father dismissively as she opened the door to leave.

He nodded distractedly. 'I'll call you later, Quinn,' he told the other man with a frown. 'As soon as I have everything arranged,' he added grimly.

Harrie shot her father a sharp look at this enigmatic remark, but she could read nothing from his expression.

Damn him.

Damn *both* of them!

Exactly what were the two of them up to? Because she had the distinct impression Rome had told Quinn McBride his idea for a solution to his sister's problem—and received Quinn McBride's agreement to it!

She had the next hour to try and find out what that solution was!

CHAPTER THREE

QUINN wasn't so sure, when he found himself seated in Harrie Summer's car a few minutes later, that he had won this particular point!

He watched Harrie beneath lowered lids as he sat beside her in the Jaguar sports car. It was a car definitely not built for the comfort of a man six foot three inches tall; the seat had to be all the way back to accommodate the length of his legs, the back of the seat tilted back too in an effort not to have his head tilted sideways against the cabriolet roof!

Not that Harrie had the same problem, he acknowledged ruefully. She seemed perfectly comfortable in the low leather seat as she sat behind the steering wheel, and there were several inches to spare above the darkness of her hair.

He also had no doubt she was well aware of his physical discomfort as she accelerated down the gravel driveway away from the house, a smile of grim satisfaction curving those red-painted lips.

It was probably the least he deserved, he realised heavily, after the blow he had so obviously dealt her this afternoon. It might be one she might ultimately thank him for, he considered grimly, but at the moment she most certainly didn't feel that way!

To his surprise, he found he wasn't in the least worried about Harrie Summer telling her boyfriend what had been said about him this afternoon. At least…not too much; he believed he knew enough about human nature to recognise that Harrie Summer was a woman of principle, that she'd made a promise, and that she would stick to it. Even if it should cause her emotional pain to do so.

That it *had* caused her emotional pain to hear the things he had said about Richard Heaton, he didn't doubt. He'd seen the pain he had caused reflected in those expressive green eyes. And he felt a complete heel for being the one to tell her damning things concerning someone she obviously cared about. And, to his surprise, he found he didn't like that feeling at all…!

His mouth twisted at the irony of the situation. At thirty-nine, he had never even lived with a woman, let alone contemplated marrying one; he'd never cared enough one way or the other to make either commitment. Oh, there had been women in his life, sometimes for several months at a time, but they hadn't been relationships he ever thought of taking further than dinner and going to bed together. Now he found he felt more about the fact that he'd hurt Harrie Summer than he'd ever cared about the feelings of the women he'd shared relationships with.

What the hell did that mean?

Harrie Summer was beautiful, yes, and he hated the thought of being the cause of the pain in those gorgeous green eyes, but as for anything else…! Hell, the woman hated him!

Besides, he knew damn well he wouldn't be sitting beside her in this car at all—uncomfortable as it might be!— if it weren't for the fact she believed she could use this time to find out exactly what he and Rome intended doing about Richard Heaton's threats! He'd seen the shrewd look in those expressive eyes when Rome had mentioned telephoning him later, and one thing he was very quickly learning—Harrie Summer was no fool. She was, in fact, every inch her father's daughter!

He turned to her. 'I believe I owe you an apology,' he told her softly, seeing the start of surprise she quickly brought under control, instantly knowing she had misunderstood the reason for his apology. 'For the inaccurate "conclusions" I drew this afternoon,' he explained dryly.

She gave him a scathing glance. 'So Rome explained that I'm his daughter.' She shrugged dismissively.

'And not his girlfriend? Yes.' Quinn nodded self-derisively. 'Although I have the feeling *he* hadn't realised I ever thought you were anything else!' He winced.

Harrie grimaced. 'Rome just assumes everyone knows who his daughters are.'

'Whereas you aren't so naive?' Quinn turned slightly in his seat so that he might see her better, that perfume he had savoured on her earlier making him feel almost light-headed in the close confines of the car.

Gypsy Rosa's perfume...

This woman was an enigma, one moment the perfect gypsy in a fair booth, the next a super-efficient lawyer, then supposed mistress of a rich and powerful man, but in truth the daughter of that same man. No woman had ever intrigued him as much as Harrie Summer did, Quinn realised a little dazedly.

Again she turned to give him a cursory glance. 'I recognise a cynic when I meet one,' she said scornfully.

A cynic, yes; he'd been that for some years, Quinn recognised dismissively. But when faced with men like the blackmailing Richard Heaton, and the weak Andrew McDonald, was that so surprising? Although, Quinn realised, Harrie was accusing him of another type of cynicism altogether...

He shrugged. 'Rome forgot to mention the relationship between the two of you either before or after he introduced us.'

Harrie gave a scathing laugh. 'And on that basis you decided I was his mistress?'

'He did call you darling,' Quinn reminded lightly. 'Several times.'

'He called Audrey beautiful—but she isn't his mistress, either!' Harrie told him disgustedly. 'But as my mother has been dead for over ten years now, and Rome is very much a man, I have no doubt there have been and still are, women in his life.' She frowned. 'He is just very discreet about any relationships like that he might have. He certainly never brings any of those women to the family home,' she added dismissively.

Quinn smiled. 'No doubt that's because he was thinking of the moral welfare of his three daughters!'

Harrie shot him a look of intense irritation. 'Don't patronise me, Mr McBride—'

'The name is Quinn,' he interrupted softly. 'And I wasn't being patronising,' he added frowningly. 'Rome is obviously a very doting father, takes an avid interest in all of you.' And the fact that all three daughters had been present on the summer estate this weekend showed that Rome had a very good relationship with all of his daughters. A least, he *had* had. Quinn winced again…

'Yes,' she acknowledged heavily. 'Sometimes too much so,' she added hardly.

Quinn had a feeling that she considered her relationship with Richard Heaton was one of those occasions! Well if he were the father of three daughters—heaven forbid!—he had no doubt he would feel equally as protective. No matter how adult and in charge of their own lives they might feel they were!

'Harrie—'

'Quinn—'

They had both begun talking at once, breaking off at the same time too. Quinn looked enquiringly at Harrie now as he waited for her to finish what she had been about to say.

She gave a heavy sigh. 'You, like my father, have obviously realised that Richard Heaton is a personal friend of mine…?'

Of course he'd realised that. And, 'like her father', he wasn't happy about it. But for a totally different reason, he realised slowly. Rome just didn't want one of his much-loved daughters involved with a man as unscrupulous as Richard Heaton obviously was. Whereas Quinn found he didn't like the idea of Harrie being involved with any man…!

He gave her a narrow-eyed look. As he had noted several times before today, Harrie was a very beautiful woman. But she was lots of other things too…

Obviously, despite their slight argument earlier, she was a loving daughter to Rome, as well as being an efficient legal advisor to him. She also seemed to have a warm relationship with Rome's female assistant, as well as apparently having a close relationship with her sisters. Lastly, she was loyal to her friends, even when those friends—especially in the instance of Richard Heaton!—didn't deserve that loyalty. Harrie Summer, Quinn decided, was a person it was all too easy to like. And respect.

It was a pity that she couldn't stand the sight of him…!

'It has occurred to me,' he drawled lazily.

Harrie gave him an impatient glance for his inappropriate levity. 'Then it must also have occurred to you,' she bit out tauntingly, 'that I'm not going to simply stand by and see you and my father hurt him, or his career?'

That had seemed a distinct possibility, yes. 'You made a promise to your father,' Quinn reminded tightly.

Her mouth tightened stubbornly. 'That I wouldn't tell Richard any of our conversation today, yes,' she acknowledged coldly.

'But…?' Quinn prompted warily.

'But that doesn't prevent me from trying to find out for

myself if what you said is the truth,' she told him challengingly.

It was no more than he had expected. No less than he would do himself if the positions were reversed. But by the same token, he couldn't allow Harrie to upset any of the plans he and Rome had made today.

'And if it is?' Quinn did some challenging of his own.

She drew in a ragged breath, obviously not pleased at the suggestion. 'Once I know all of the facts, I'll know the answer to that question, too,' she told him determinedly.

That loyalty was indeed very strong. Or was it something much deeper than that? Could Harrie Summer actually believe herself to be in love with Richard Heaton?

'Would you have dinner with me when we get back to town?' Quinn suddenly heard himself say.

And then sat back in surprise as he considered his own invitation. That he was intrigued by this woman wasn't in doubt. That he found her attractive, both physically and mentally, also wasn't in doubt. But was this really the time for him to be suggesting the two of them had dinner together?

The answer to that question was an unequivocal no! He was leaving himself open to the biggest verbal slap in the face he had ever received in his life!

The stunned silence that followed showed him that Harrie was as surprised by his invitation as he was at having made it. Well, he mused inwardly, at least she hadn't laughed in his face!

In fact, the silence went on for so long he wondered if he had achieved the impossible—and actually struck Harrie Summer dumb! She certainly had enough to say earlier, most of it to his detriment!

'Hey, it was only an invitation to dinner, not an indecent proposal!' he finally mocked.

Her mouth twisted scathingly. 'It wouldn't have taken

me this long to answer if it had been the latter!' she scorned. 'Okay, Quinn, I'll have dinner with you,' she finally decided firmly. 'But on one condition…'

It took Quinn several seconds to take in her acceptance, but a mere split second to consider the 'conditions'. 'There is no way I'm going to agree not to discuss Richard Heaton,' he warned grimly.

'That isn't the condition,' she assured him harshly. 'I'll have dinner with you only if I'm allowed to pay my half of the bill!'

Considering his previous imaginings over 'conditions', this seemed quite mild in comparison. Although, on reflection, perhaps not… Going halves on the cost of their meal implied some sort of business arrangement—and, while Harrie might consider him to be exactly that, his own intentions towards Harrie Summer, he was quickly discovering, were not of a business nature!

'Fair enough,' he conceded lightly, deciding they could sort that sort of detail out later—once they were safely at the restaurant. 'In that case, perhaps you would like to choose where we eat?' he suggested brightly.

He didn't consider for a moment that Harrie had accepted his invitation because she had any real wish to spend time in his company. No, he'd been all too aware of the determination in her eyes when she'd assured him she wasn't about to ask for his agreement not to talk about Richard Heaton. Harrie's sole intention in having dinner with him at all *was* to talk about Richard Heaton!

'We can telephone from my home to book a table—I just need to go back there and deal with a few things before we go out,' he added as she would have protested.

Harrie's mouth firmed. 'Very well,' she finally conceded tightly. 'I could do with freshening up myself before we go on to the restaurant, anyway.'

In other words, she was only agreeing to that arrange-

ment because it suited her too, Quinn acknowledged, ruefully. Amongst the other attributes he had mentally acknowledged to her earlier, Quinn now added stubbornness.
Harrie wasn't about to concede an inch where he was concerned. And, in the circumstances, he couldn't blame her.

Oh, well, he mused as he relaxed back in the leather car
seat, 'Rome'—excuse the pun!— 'wasn't built in a day'!
and persuading Harrie to see him as a man, and not a
harbinger of bad news, was probably going to take as long
as building that city had done!

And in the meantime, he was happy enough to just sit
silently beside her now that he had her agreement to go
home with him, admiring the way she handled the powerful car. Just admiring her, actually!

But he could see that Harrie was surprised at the detached house, set in its own grounds, that he directed her
to once they reached London. No doubt she'd expected
him to live in an apartment, clinically clean and charac-
terless. But his home was nothing like that; instead it was
a gracious Victorian-style house, surrounded by beautifully
kept gardens.

It was the McBride family home, of course. It had been
his grandparents', and then parents' home, long before it
had become his. And it was a home he took pride in; he
did the majority of the gardening by himself, the hours he
spent outside usually his only form of physical exercise,
as well as allowing him to be mentally at peace with himself.

'Nice house,' Harrie murmured grudgingly as she got
out of the car to join him on the gravel driveway.

Quinn bit his bottom lip to stop himself from smiling at
the ungraciously made compliment. Instead he gave an acknowledging inclination of his head. 'I think so,' he said
dryly, taking a light hold of her arm as the two of them
strolled across to the front door.

And it was a hold he knew Harrie deeply resented as he was able to feel that resentment emanating from every pore of her stiffly held body. It was perhaps as well that she was a well-brought-up young lady, otherwise he might have found himself with his face slapped, after all, for taking even that liberty!

Although, somehow, as he unlocked the front door to allow them to enter the brightly lit hallway he had a feeling that might still be a possibility! One thing he'd learnt about Harrie this afternoon; she didn't like being manipulated into a situation, even by her father—and Quinn was about to do the same thing, major style!

He tensed as the door opened to the left of them in the entrance hall, looking at Harrie now and not at the woman who came out of what he knew to be the sitting-room, seeing the way those green eyes widened with surprise, and then recognition—seconds before she turned to look up at him accusingly...

Corinne Westley!

The woman stepping gracefully into the hallway was instantly recognisable as the fiancée of David Hampton, MP. The sister of Quinn McBride!

He had tricked her, Harrie instantly realised, the invitation to dinner all a ruse just so that Quinn could achieve his purpose. He'd said earlier that he wanted her to know more about his sister's side of things, and the problem she was facing because of Richard—a suggestion Harrie had no qualms in refusing!—only to have Quinn neatly arrange for her to actually meet his sister.

She hadn't wanted to have dinner with Quinn this evening in the first place; she'd only accepted because she'd thought she might be able to get some more information out of him. It had also occurred to her that she might be able to delay things a little if she could ensure Quinn wasn't at home to take her father's call this evening…

And instead Quinn had turned the tables on her, only bringing her here, she was sure, so that she could meet his sister.

Corinne Westley, absolutely beautiful in a fitted black dress, her blonde hair loose about her shoulders, nevertheless looked as disturbed by the encounter as Harrie felt, confusion in those aqua-blue eyes, so like her brother's, as she returned Harrie's narrowed gaze.

Damn Quinn McBride, Harrie inwardly muttered.

Corinne looked as gorgeous as she did in her photographs, but there was also a natural warmth about her, a curving generosity to her peach-coloured lips. There was also a glow of love in her eyes as she looked trustingly at her older brother, a glow that seemed to say—she didn't know who this woman was, or why he had brought her here, but she had complete confidence in the fact that Quinn would never do anything that would hurt her.

Harrie wished she could say the same where her own feelings were concerned!

'I wasn't expecting you back yet, Quinn.' Corinne Westley looked searchingly at her brother, even her voice attractive, pitched huskily low, hinting at a warm sensuality to her nature.

And the reason for her searching gaze was obvious to Harrie; the older woman knew exactly where Quinn had been this afternoon, and for what purpose—and she was anxious to know its outcome!

'Change of plans,' Quinn answered dismissively. 'Shall we all go into the sitting-room?' he suggested lightly, retaining his grip on Harrie's arm as she stiffened slightly. 'I'm sure we will all be more comfortable in there,' he added firmly.

In truth, although Harrie deeply resented Quinn's du-

plicity in getting her here to meet Corinne, she was now
wondering exactly how he was going to explain *her* presence to his sister. Obviously Corinne's problem was a very
personal one, one she definitely did not want to become
public; how was Quinn going to get around the fact that
Harrie knew about it too...?

'Please, sit down.' Quinn indicated one of several chairs
in the graciously furnished but comfortable sitting-room.
'A glass of white wine?' he offered once the two women
had sat down—in opposite chairs, almost as if Corinne
Westley already sensed Harrie was not sympathetic to her
'problem'!—moving towards the drinks cabinet, taking a
bottle of chilled wine from the refrigerator.

Harrie was aware of Corinne watching her guardedly
from across the room as Quinn poured the wine, keeping
her own expression deliberately bland, still waiting for
Quinn to explain away her presence. If he did! From the
little she had come to know about him this afternoon,
Quinn didn't appear to be a man who felt he had to explain
himself to anyone! But surely his sister was different...?

'Harrie, this is my sister, Corinne; she lives here with
me,' Quinn explained softly as he handed Harrie a glass
of white wine. 'Corinne, this is Harrie Summer; Rome
Summer's daughter—but also his legal advisor,' he told
his sister gently after her start of surprise at Harrie's identity.

Very neatly done, Harrie inwardly acknowledged with
grudging admiration. Quinn deliberately hadn't mentioned
she was also a friend of Richard Heaton's!

But, then, how could he, when his sister was sure to
have an aversion to anything and anyone involved with
Richard? Nevertheless, Harrie could still appreciate
Quinn's adeptness in overcoming a situation that had, to
Harrie, had all the indications of having disaster written
all over it.

'You may just have missed your true calling in life, Quinn,' she murmured derisively. 'I think you would have made a good lawyer yourself!' she added as he raised his brows questioningly.

He folded his length down into the chair next to her before answering. 'Strangely enough,' he drawled softly, aqua-blue gaze gently laughing at her, 'I do have a degree in law.'

She should have known! Quinn had been so sure of himself this afternoon, so definite in how far he could and couldn't go. Although Harrie also accepted that the problem Quinn was faced with at the moment, that his sister was faced with, wasn't particularly helped by his knowledge of the law…

'It's all right, Corinne,' Quinn hastened to assure his sister as she looked far from comforted by his explanation of Harrie's presence.

The other woman would have been even less comforted by Harrie's real reason for being here, Harrie decided ruefully.

'Harrie's on our side,' Quinn told his sister firmly, shooting Harrie a warning look as she gave an indignant gasp. 'Rome has agreed to help us, and, understandably, Harrie merely wants to satisfy herself that it's done legally.'

'Harrie' wanted to 'satisfy herself' of a damn sight more than that, her flashing green gaze told him warningly.

Although outwardly she said nothing. She'd taken the opportunity the last few minutes to study Corinne Westley, and it was obvious to even the casual observer—which Harrie certainly wasn't!—that the other woman was so tense she looked as if she might snap, a look of deep strain beside her eyes and mouth, her hands moving restlessly once she'd put her untouched glass of wine down on the coffee-table in front of her. Corinne Westley had the look of a woman who had come to the end of her emotional endurance, as if the least little thing could send her hurtling over the edge…

But could Harrie really bring herself to believe that Richard—tall, handsome, fun-loving Richard—with the alleged threats of blackmail, was the cause of Corinne Westley's undoubted pain…?

Harrie was no longer sure what the truth of the matter was. Quinn seemed to think that Richard was guilty. Her father believed that he was, too. Only she, it seemed, was in the minority. And couldn't that simply be because she was emotionally involved with Richard herself?

Harrie simply didn't know any more…!

Corinne swallowed hard, shaking her head. 'I've done a lot of thinking today, Quinn.' She sighed wearily. 'And perhaps the easiest thing, after all, is if I just bow quietly out of David's life—'

'No!'

To Harrie's surprise she found she was the one who had stepped in with the objection!

But even as she realised that, she realised something else too; Corinne Westley really was as lovely as her photographs, both inside and out—why else would she be suggesting giving up the man she loved just so that something she'd done in the past shouldn't endanger his future political career?

Corinne gave her a quizzical look. 'I appreciate your—concern,' she murmured, obviously puzzled by Harrie's vehemence, 'but, in the circumstances, I can't see any other way out.' She shook her head, her hair a silky blonde cloud about her shoulders. 'If I just fade out of David's life—'

'Do you really think you'll be allowed to do that?' Again Harrie was the one to interrupt her. 'If—if this man is serious in his intention of blackmailing you into colluding with him, with the threat of bringing an end to David's career—'

'Oh, he's serious!' Corinne gave a shiver of revulsion. 'He left me in no doubt about that!'

It pained Harrie to hear Richard talked of in this way. Just as it had pained her a few seconds ago to even suggest that Richard might actually be guilty of attempting to blackmail this vulnerable woman!

She drew in a controlling breath. 'Then you have to realise he could just go ahead and write the story, anyway.' Write it, because after this afternoon Harrie was in no doubt that it wouldn't be her father's newspaper that would print it. But, as she also knew, there were other, less principled newspaper owners and editors who would snap up such a scandalous story. 'Which would damage David's career whether you were still in his life or not,' she added flatly. 'After all, it's a well-known fact that the two of you are supposed to marry this summer.'

'Harrie is right, Corinne.' Quinn spoke for the first time for some minutes, having seemed content until now to sit back and let the two women continue the conversation.

Because he knew, damn him, that once Harrie had talked with his sister, seen the emotional state Corinne was obviously in, she would find it more and more difficult to believe in Richard's innocence!

Well, she *did* still believe in it, Harrie decided firmly— wouldn't stop believing in it until she had heard it from Richard's own lips that he was guilty of their accusations. Although how she was actually to achieve that she didn't have any idea. To actually ask Richard outright if it was true was tantamount to accusing him of the crime. But, by the same token, until she was absolutely sure he wasn't guilty, there was no way she could be her normal loving self with him. She was the loser, it seemed, whichever way she went…

Damn Quinn McBride, she thought vehemently—and not for the first time!

'David is going to be here in a few minutes,' Corinne choked emotionally. 'We're going out to dinner,' she explained. 'I had intended telling him then that our engagement was at an end—'

'For the wrong reason,' Harrie cut in firmly. 'I realise all of this is a strain on you,' she added gently, just how much of a strain it was on the other woman becoming more and more apparent as the minutes passed, 'but I advise you to give it a little more time.'

'I agree with Harrie,' Quinn put in softly. 'Just a few more days, Corinne,' he encouraged. 'A week at the most.'

Harrie gave him a sharp look. Just what plan had he and her father hatched between them this afternoon? The implacable expression on Quinn's face as he calmly returned her gaze told her she wouldn't get an answer to that question from him. And after the way she'd parted from her father earlier today, she didn't think he would be too forthcoming, either!

Richard, it seemed, was her only avenue of information...

She put down her untouched glass of white wine, standing up. 'Time I was going, I believe,' Harrie said lightly, deliberately avoiding Quinn's suddenly sharp gaze. 'I've already taken up enough of your evening,' she told the other woman gently. 'And I'm sure the two of you must have things you want to talk about,' she added hardly, knowing there were definitely 'things' Quinn would like to talk to his sister about—and that he couldn't do so until Harrie left! 'I hope, if we ever meet again, Corinne—' she gave a rueful grimace of a smile at the unlikelihood of that ever happening '—that it will be under more pleasant circumstances.'

'I hope so, too.' Corinne's air of fragility seemed even

more pronounced as she stood up, the skin seeming almost translucent now on the gaunt lines of her cheeks.

No wonder Quinn had been so full of anger this afternoon, Harrie accepted heavily; she would be as protectively furious herself if one of her sisters had been made this unhappy by a third party!

The problem Harrie had had earlier, and still had, was believing Richard was the cause of this woman's heartache…

'I thought the two of us were having dinner together this evening?' Quinn didn't allow her to escape that easily, standing up so that he towered dominantly over the two women.

Harrie felt the slight flush in her cheeks. 'Let's take a rain check on that, hmm? I can see you have other priorities at the moment,' she added quickly before he would have voiced his objections to her leaving a second time.

'I—' Quinn broke off as the doorbell rang. 'That will be David,' he realised grimly. 'Corinne, you are not to do anything stupid, do you hear?' he prompted forcefully even as he moved across the room to answer the door.

His sister gave a pained frown, before slowly nodding her agreement. 'It's just becoming so difficult to keep up this pretence with David,' she groaned.

'You aren't pretending with David,' Quinn told her determinedly. 'You love him. And he loves you. And for the moment that's all you have to think about. The rest of it will sort itself out in time.'

Harrie's heart ached for the other woman as they heard Quinn open the front door, the sound of male laughter, and then the two men talking easily together as they walked down the hallway towards the sitting-room.

'Quinn is right, you know,' Harrie felt compelled to reassure the other woman. 'All that really matters is that you and David love each other.'

Corinne gave her a grateful smile before turning to greet her fiancé, her face raised invitingly for his kiss.

Quinn quirked dark brows across at Harrie as the two of them were witness to the other couple's greeting, the vibrantly handsome MP obviously as in love with Corinne as she was with him, her blue eyes filled with loving pride as David looked down at her, his arm possessively about her slender shoulders as he turned to look at Harrie with politely questioning eyes.

Harrie was completely unprepared for the way Quinn stepped forward to put his arm as possessively about her shoulders, grinning across at the other man. 'You obviously need no introduction, David,' he drawled mockingly. 'And this is Harrie Summer. A good friend of mine,' he added enigmatically.

And Harrie didn't at all care for his method of introduction! Obviously, in the circumstances, it was a little difficult to introduce her as anything else, but she was neither 'a good friend', nor 'his'!

'Pleased to meet you, Harrie.' David shook her hand warmly, a self-assured man in his mid-thirties, with the natural charm of a born leader.

Harrie wasn't 'pleased' about any of this. She hadn't wanted to meet Corinne, let alone her political fiancé, certainly didn't want to witness how happy they were together. But as she glanced at Quinn she could see the satisfied smile that curved those arrogant lips.

Damn him! He had known exactly what he was doing by bringing her here, he'd known just how tenuous he would make her belief in Richard by introducing her to the other couple!

Harrie moved firmly but pointedly away from the weight of Quinn's arm about her shoulders. 'We had just agreed to take a rain check,' she reminded him lightly, avoiding meeting those compelling aqua-blue eyes as she knew they hadn't 'agreed' any such thing! 'Nice meeting you, Corinne, Mr Hampton,' she told the couple politely—if inaccurately; meeting Corinne Westley and David Hampton had been the last thing she'd wanted to do!

'I'll walk you to the door,' Quinn bit out tautly, his displeasure obvious.

To Harrie, at least; the other couple seemed totally absorbed in each other as she preceded Quinn out into the hallway. She felt an ache in her chest at Corinne and David's obvious happiness in each other, waiting only until the door had closed behind them before turning angrily on Quinn. 'You planned that!' she accused heatedly, her hands clenched at her sides.

'Yes, I did.' He gave a challenging inclination of his head.

'But why?' Harrie cried. But she already knew the answer to that! And it was working, damn him...!

Part of her so wanted to see Richard, to establish for herself what was fact and what was fiction. But another part of her was quickly becoming afraid to know that truth...

'You know why, Harrie,' Quinn told her bluntly, eyes narrowed on the paleness of her face. 'Richard Heaton is a blackmailing bastard, and the sooner you accept that—'

'You have no right!' Harrie cut in hotly.

'I have every right,' Quinn assured her grimly. 'You've seen what he's done to my sister; I'm not going to stand by while he does the same thing to you!'

She gasped. 'Richard wouldn't— He couldn't—'

'Couldn't he? You've never confided your secrets to him?' Quinn taunted, his fingers digging painfully into her upper arms as he shook her slightly. 'Pillow talk, I believe it's called. It's what lovers do after they've made love,' he derided scornfully. 'A word here, a confidence there, and before you know it someone's privacy has been compromised. In this case, probably your father's,' he added grimly.

'I never discuss other people with Richard!' Harrie defended indignantly. And there had been no 'pillow talk'! Yet… But she knew their relationship had been well on the way to that intimacy. 'In, or out, of bed,' she bit out furiously. 'And I deeply resent your inference that I would breach my client's—in this case, my father's—confidence!'

Quinn's mouth twisted tauntingly. 'You ''deeply resent'' a lot of things, Harrie—but mainly me!' His mouth twisted disgustedly. 'Could that be because I'm the one who pointed out your boyfriend's little sideline in blackmail?'

Harrie felt the remaining colour drain from her cheeks. 'You—'

'I don't think so, Harrie,' Quinn whispered grimly as he effectively prevented her hand from slapping the hardness of his cheek.

Harrie was completely unprepared for what happened next. She didn't even have time to avoid Quinn's mouth as it came down to possessively claim hers, his arms moving assuredly about her slender waist as he pulled her body in close to his.

She couldn't breathe, couldn't move, could only feel the crashing assault of Quinn's lips on hers, his hands caressing the slenderness of her back.

This is what drowning must feel like, she decided in the small part of her brain that hadn't been numbed by the demanding kiss. She felt total helplessness to a force that was much stronger than she was, her limbs having all the response of jelly, knowing she would have fallen if it weren't for the strength of Quinn's arms.

What was she *doing*?

This man was her enemy!

And yet...

Quinn slowly lifted his head, his eyes brightly blue as he looked down at her, his expression wary as his gaze moved searchingly across her face.

Harrie could only stare back at him. Quinn McBride had just kissed her, and, far from being outraged and disgusted at the unprovoked intimacy, she found that every part of her body seemed to tingle, and feel alive with—

With what?

Harrie wasn't sure. She had never felt this way before, and couldn't define it. She wasn't sure she wanted to!

She pulled firmly out of Quinn's arms, and stepped back, relieved to find her legs supported her after all, although her lips, when she ran her tongue across their moist warmth, still seemed to tingle from their contact with Quinn's.

What on earth had happened to her just now? She was twenty-nine years old, she'd certainly been kissed before, and believed herself to be in love with Richard.

Believed...?

She *was* in love with Richard!

Her eyes sparkled brightly as she glared up at Quinn. 'I wouldn't advise you to ever try doing that again,' she grated between clenched teeth. 'Not unless you want to find yourself kneed in a very vulnerable place!'

Quinn gave a humourless smile as he held up his hand defensively. 'I've never been into pain,' he drawled mockingly, seeming unmoved himself by the intimate kiss they had just shared.

Because they had 'shared' it, Harrie realised with inner mortification. She had definitely responded to the passionate demand of Quinn's lips, lips she now found her gaze lingering on as she saw his mouth was slightly swollen from the force of their kiss.

Were her lips swollen too? It felt so as she once again ran her tongue over them.

'I would advise *you* not to do that again—unless you want me to repeat the kiss!' Quinn grated harshly, his gaze fixed on the movements of her tongue.

'You know I—' Harrie broke off as the telephone on the hall table begin to ring. 'No doubt that's my father—for you!' she scorned knowingly, green gaze glittering accusingly.

Quinn's mouth twisted derisively. 'Well, it could hardly be for you, now, could it?' he mocked dryly.

Harrie gave a disgusted shake of her head. 'I'll leave you to take your call.' She turned on her heel and walked away, wrenching the front door open to close it decisively behind her.

But a part of her so wished she hadn't had to, that she could have stayed while Quinn took his call from her father…

CHAPTER FOUR

QUINN sighed frustratedly as the front door closed behind Harrie, knowing there was no point in him running after her. For one thing she was in no state of mind at the moment to listen to anything he might have to say. And for another—he had never run after a woman in his life!

And the damned telephone kept ringing incessantly, the noise seeming to jar on his nerve-endings, so that he couldn't even think straight!

He snatched up the receiver, growling a response to the unwelcome caller.

Rome Summer chuckled on the other end of the line. 'I gather you had an interesting drive back to town with my daughter?' he drawled tauntingly.

Quinn felt some of the tension leave his body at the other man's unmistakable mockery. 'That's one way of putting it,' he confirmed dryly, thinking back to the kiss he and Harrie had just shared. But even if he felt like telling Rome about that—which he most assuredly didn't!—he doubted her father would believe it had ever happened.

He had a problem believing that himself! He'd expected Harrie to pull away from him and attempt to slap his face again, but instead she had melted in his arms, not exactly responding—at least, not in the way he'd wanted her to respond!—but not fighting him, either.

Rome chuckled again. 'No one has ever accused any of my daughters of being boring!'

Quinn couldn't give an opinion about the indisposed

Andie, but the red-haired Danie certainly wasn't lacking in self-confidence, and as for Harrie—!

His mouth tightened as he pushed thoughts of Harrie from his mind. 'I hope you have some positive news for me, Rome?' he prompted harshly.

'Very.' Rome instantly sobered. 'I've set the interview up for ten o'clock tomorrow morning. Is that going to fit in with things your end?'

'I'll make sure that it does,' Quinn assured him grimly. 'I just hope that this is going to work!'

'Have a bit more faith, Quinn,' the other man advised. 'You and I both know this is the only way to go with this.'

Yes, Quinn did know that. All he had to do was convince Corinne it was the right way to go, too!

All?

His sister was falling apart in front of his eyes, he realised with a frown. His only consolation was that he knew Harrie had recognised that too. He was also aware she hadn't liked him for showing her that, but if it made her think again about Richard Heaton he could live with that.

Besides, he had every intention of seeing Harrie Summer again…

'I'm sure you're right, Rome. And thanks,' he added gruffly. 'I owe you one.'

'I don't conduct business in that way, Quinn,' the older man came back firmly. 'But thanks for the offer.'

Quinn had liked Rome Summer when he'd finally met him this afternoon, but as time passed he found himself liking and respecting the other man even more. He was rare amongst his breed: a successful man who didn't trample over other people to get where he wanted to go, a compassionate man too, who detested anyone who could threaten a woman. For whatever purpose.

Although, admittedly, in this particular case, Rome's dislike of Richard Heaton probably also stemmed from the fact that he was involved with Rome's beloved eldest daughter!

Which begged the question: would Rome feel quite so kindly towards Quinn, and be quite this helpful, if he were to realise what his own intentions were towards that same beloved daughter? Somehow Quinn doubted it!

Although, as he heard his sister and David in the sitting-room preparing to leave for dinner, he knew he had something much more pressing to deal with. 'I'm the one who's indebted to you, Rome. And somehow thanks doesn't seem enough,' he added with a frown. 'I'll be in touch,' he told the older man quickly in parting, turning to face the other couple as they came out into the hallway.

'What is it?' Corinne was instantly sensitive to his change of mood, frowning at him apprehensively. 'Who was that on the telephone?' she added worriedly.

Quinn's mouth tightened, his eyes becoming glacial as he thought of the man who had brought his sister to this state. He was going to take extreme pleasure in one day beating Richard Heaton to a pulp.

Although, even as he came to that grim decision, he knew that part of his own anger towards the other man was also because of his involvement with Harrie...

He was jealous, damn it.

And it wasn't an emotion he'd ever felt over a woman before. Over anything, he realised frowningly. His family had always been wealthy, ensuring that he and Corinne had an indulged childhood. And there had been nothing, and no one, in his adult life that he couldn't have had if he'd shown the inclination.

But the thought of Harrie going to Richard Heaton this evening, which Quinn was positive she was going to do, filled him with a rage that was also completely out of character.

'Quinn?' Corinne looked at him searchingly.

He shook his head, dismissing—for the moment!—his haphazard thoughts of Harrie. He needed time, and privacy, to try and understand the feelings she evoked in him, and that was something he didn't have at the moment.

'I told you it's going to be okay, Corinne,' he assured his sister gently. 'But before we straighten the situation out, you have to sit down and tell David what happened—'

'I can't do that!' Corinne gasped, giving her fiancé an apprehensive glance.

'Don't be silly, Corinne,' Quinn dismissed briskly. 'David is thirty-five years old, and, I'm sure, no innocent himself.' He gave his future brother-in-law a rueful grin before his face tightened into grim lines. 'And tomorrow we're going to sort out Richard Heaton, once and for all time!' he promised his sister grimly.

'Richard Heaton?' David looked puzzled by their conversation. 'I seem to know that name from somewhere…?' He frowned.

'Corinne will explain over dinner—yes, you *will*,' Quinn told his sister firmly as she would have protested once again. 'It's as well if David knows. And you did nothing wrong,' he added decisively. 'You—' he broke off as the doorbell rang, frowning slightly. 'Are you expecting anyone else this evening?' he prompted his sister even as he moved to answer the door, freezing in the doorway as he saw who stood there.

Harrie!

A bedraggled and very wet Harrie, the darkness of her hair flattened against her head, the business suit she wore damply out of shape too.

'I—'

'Don't say anything, Quinn!' she warned fiercely, her hands clenched at her sides. 'The last thing I need at the moment is one of your sarcastic comments. It must be obvious, even to an arrogant, ill-mannered—'

'I believe the two of you were just leaving?' Quinn turned to Corinne and David standing in the hallway behind him, David, at least, trying to hold back a smile at Harrie's vehement outburst, Corinne looking nonplussed at the exchange.

Exchange? So far Quinn hadn't been able to get a word in edgeways! Although, he had to admit, the fact that Harrie was still here, for whatever reason, brought a grin to his own lips.

'We were.' David was the one to quickly answer him as he saw Harrie's anger at the smile Quinn was unable to contain, and was on the point of another outburst. 'Come on, darling.' David took a firm hold on Corinne's arm. 'I believe Harrie and Quinn want to be alone,' he added dryly. 'And don't worry about a thing, Quinn.' David sobered as he reached his side. 'Corinne will always be safe with me.'

Quinn gave an acknowledging inclination of his head in the other man's direction, knowing that David had received the message in the conversation Quinn had had primarily with Corinne a few minutes ago, and that David would cooperate, no matter what the problem.

He had approved of David Hampton as a husband for his sister from the evening he'd been first introduced to him, and it felt good to know he hadn't been wrong in his judgement.

'Would you stop grinning to yourself in that self-satisfied way—and invite me in out of this damned rain?' Harrie prompted waspishly.

Corinne and David had left while Quinn had been still lost in thought and Harrie, he realised, beautifully outraged Harrie, was wetter than ever!

'Of course.' He stepped back to allow her inside out of the rain that was falling heavier than before, and he was slightly damp himself now as she brushed lightly against him.

Quinn had no idea what she was still doing here, and no clue as to the reason why she had come back to the house. It certainly wasn't so that he could kiss her again! But he was glad that she had. For one thing, it meant she wasn't with Richard Heaton...

'I'm sorry to have interrupted the rest of your evening,' she said stiffly, obviously most unhappy at being here at all. 'But I had to—'

'You have to get out of that damp jacket,' Quinn cut in firmly as he saw she was shivering in the wet clothing. 'Come back into the sitting-room and I'll put the fire on to warm you up,' he invited briskly, already walking back in that direction. 'A brandy might not go amiss, either,' he added as he saw, in the brighter lighting of the sitting-room, exactly how wet she was.

Not only was her hair flattened to her head, but she had water streaming off the silky ends, droplets of rain on her cheeks and eyelashes.

'Why the hell didn't you get into your car out of the rain?' he prompted harshly as he poured them both a glass of brandy, knowing he didn't need his because he was wet and cold, but he had a feeling he might be in need of it, for one reason or another, before this evening was over!

Harrie had bent down over the coffee-table, straightening now, a bunch of keys in her hand. 'Because I left these here earlier!' she bit out impatiently.

Quinn frowned. 'But you must have realised that as soon as you got outside...?'

'Of course I did.' Her face was flushed now, her expression flustered. 'And don't ask why I didn't come straight back and get them,' she snapped as he would have done exactly that. 'You know damn well why I had no wish to come back here!' She glared across the room at him. 'I had actually started to walk back to my apartment, with the intention of collecting my spare set of keys, and then decided that I was being ridiculous when you had a set in here,' she admitted awkwardly.

Which explained why she was so wet, Quinn acknowledged. Although he couldn't say he cared much for the fact that initially she had preferred getting wet through rather than facing him again…!

'Here.' He thrust one of the glasses of brandy out towards her. 'And take that damned jacket off—before *you* catch pneumonia and your father blames me for it!' he snapped irritably.

Harrie took the glass, sipping at the fiery liquid. 'He's more likely to think Andie gave it to me,' she assured him ruefully as she slipped the jacket off her shoulders and placed it over a chair, a little natural colour—as opposed to her earlier anger!—back in her cheeks now as the brandy began to warm her inside.

Quinn's attention was riveted on the cream blouse beneath the jacket. The rain had penetrated right through the jacket, dampening her blouse too, revealing—all too noticeably!—that she wore no bra beneath the silky material, her breasts pert, the nipples a darker pink against the creaminess of her skin.

Hell!

Quinn could never remember feeling aroused when looking at a fully dressed woman before, but the little he could see of the perfection of Harrie's body was enough to send desire surging through his body.

'Sit next to the fire and get warm,' he ordered harshly, dropping down into one of the armchairs himself before the betraying arousal of his own body totally embarrassed him.

Temper flashed briefly in Harrie's eyes as she took obvious exception to his tone, making no move to sit in the chair nearest to the fire. Making no move to sit at all...

'I only came back for my car keys,' she reminded impatiently.

'I wouldn't even send a dog back outside until the rain abates a little,' Quinn rasped insultingly, annoyed with himself for reacting to this woman like some naive schoolboy.

Harrie was beautiful, yes, but she was also opinionated and stubborn, too—too much so for comfort. And he may want her with a fierceness that was becoming stronger by the minute, but what also became more apparent, by those same minutes, was the fact that she didn't even like being in the same room as him!

'Then it's as well I'm not one, isn't it?' she bit out dismissively as she put down the still full glass of brandy before reaching for her jacket. 'Was that my father on the telephone earlier?' she questioned casually as she put the damp jacket back on.

Quinn stiffened warily. 'And if it was?' His eyes were narrowed suspiciously.

Harrie shrugged. 'The plot thickens.'

His mouth twisted mockingly. 'Wouldn't you like to know what he had to say?'

Her cheeks became flushed again, this time with irritation. 'I very much doubt you would tell me if I asked...?'

'Your assumption would be correct.' Quinn gave a mocking inclination of his head.

'Then I won't waste my breath by doing so,' she snapped dismissively. 'Once again, Quinn—'

'I know, it's not been nice knowing me,' he finished dryly, standing up. 'Which is a pity—because I've very much enjoyed knowing you,' he added throatily.

Her mouth tightened as she easily read the double edge

to his words. 'You'll never "know" me, Quinn,' she scorned.

'Pity,' he drawled again. 'But might I suggest that, instead of running straight from here to Richard Heaton's arms,' he continued tautly, 'you go home first and take a hot shower and put some dry clothes on.'

Harrie's mouth tightened resentfully. 'If I ever need your advice, Quinn—for anything!—I'll ask for it!'

He gave a rueful grimace at the deliberate snub. 'I'll come and visit you in your sickbed,' he taunted.

'Don't bother,' she flashed. 'And don't bother to see me out, either,' she snapped as he would have done exactly that. 'I know the way!'

He gave a mocking inclination of his head. 'You should do,' he murmured derisively, seeing the twin spots of angry colour in her cheeks at his deliberate mockery of the fact that she had walked out on him, not once, but twice, this evening!

Harrie gave him a disgusted look, before tossing back her rapidly drying dark hair and turning on her heel to march out of the room, with the front door closing forcefully behind her—for the second time this evening!—a few seconds later.

Quinn's breath left him in a sigh. Part of him wanted to shake her for her mistaken loyalty to a man like Richard Heaton, and another part of him just wanted to kiss her senseless!

Which, in the circumstances, probably made him as much of a fool as he considered her to be...

Rude.

Arrogant.

Opinionated.

Opportunist!

She simply couldn't think of enough expletives to describe Quinn McBride, Harrie decided on the drive home. And not just because he had kissed her... Although, she had to admit, that certainly contributed to the anger she felt towards him. So much so that she couldn't even force herself to be pleasant to him long enough to try to find out exactly what plot he and her father had hatched between them.

Which was a pity—because, despite what Quinn had said, she had every intention of speaking to Richard this evening!

A frown creased her brow as she thought of seeing Richard. Which was ridiculous. They had been going out together for several months now, and their dates had always been something she looked forward to, as she found Richard charming and intelligent. But this weekend had certainly put a shadow over the relationship.

Quinn McBride had put a shadow over the relationship!

Well, damn Quinn McBride! And damn her father too, if he had gone into collusion with the other man—which he certainly seemed to have done.

Once again she wondered exactly what it was the two men had planned. Damn it, she should have held her temper, should have— But she couldn't, Harrie acknowledged with a groan, not when Quinn kissed her in that way!

She'd thought him rather cold and calculating at the Summer Fête this afternoon, a man who rarely thought on impulse, and certainly never acted on it. But that kiss, she was sure, hadn't been planned, Quinn had seemed as taken aback by their reaction to each other as she'd been. Because, much as she disliked Quinn McBride, Harrie knew she had responded to him...

How could that be?

Admittedly, Quinn was an attractive man, tall and powerfully built, his arrogance a challenge rather than a put-

off. But she didn't like the man; she found him irritating
and presumptuous.

She had *kissed* him, damn it!

Harrie groaned low in her throat at the memory, relieved
to see she reached her apartment building, passing through
the security gate to the private car park beneath the building, hurrying up to her penthouse apartment on the tenth
floor, determined not to give herself any more time to think
of Quinn McBride and that kiss they had shared. She
picked up the telephone receiver and punched in Richard's
number from memory.

But before the number had chance to ring she slammed
the receiver back down on its cradle!

What was she going to say to him?

She slumped down into the armchair beside the telephone, putting her head into her hands. Between them, her
father and Quinn had shaken her trust in Richard.

Maybe her father, a man she'd loved and trusted all her
life, should be able to do that, but Quinn McBride too…?

No…!

Certainly not!

She snatched up the receiver again, pressing the repeat
button, her heart beating erratically as the number rang and
rang. Richard wasn't at home, she finally accepted heavily.

Of course, she'd told him she would be at her father's
estate all weekend, so she couldn't exactly complain when
Richard decided to go out for the evening rather than being
on his own. After all, he wasn't to know she would change
her plans and come back to town—

'Yes?' The receiver had finally been picked up the other
end, Richard's voice terse with irritation.

'Richard!' she returned thankfully, her pleasure at finding him at home after all reflected in her voice.

'Harrie…?' He sounded surprised now. 'I didn't expect

to hear from you until you got back to town tomorrow evening.'

As Richard was an employee of her father's, the two of them had decided it might be as well if they kept their relationship to themselves for a while, hence the fact that Harrie never called Richard when she was with her father.

Although, from her father's comments earlier today, they might just as well have saved themselves the trouble; Rome knew about the relationship anyway!

'Change of plan,' she told Richard lightly. 'I'm back in town now, and wondered if you would like to have dinner?'

It was an invitation she had made a dozen or so times before; their free time, because of work commitments, was often limited. But for some reason Harrie felt uncomfortable making the invitation this time, and she wasn't sure whether the hesitant pause on the other end of the line was real or imagined.

Damn, damn, damn!

She didn't even feel her customary ease with Richard now. She seemed to be looking for—looking for what? Guilt?

'Where did you have in mind?' Richard returned huskily.

She *had* imagined that pause! This was Richard, damn it, the man who could make her laugh, who talked to her as an intellectual equal, the two of them sharing many heated debates about the law and politics—

Politics…?

Richard had been very anti David Hampton's political party during one of those conversations, Harrie remembered with a sick feeling in the pit of her stomach, and not too complimentary about the man himself either, now she thought about it.

She gave an inward sigh. It seemed she was questioning

Richard's integrity herself now, which was something she had never thought she would do. She'd always admired his dedication to his work, and believed his articles to be informative and well written.

And nothing had really happened to change that! Okay, so Quinn McBride had come to her father with some wild tale of blackmail, and her father, disliking Richard as he disliked many of the men she chose to go out with, had been easily swayed into believing it. But that didn't mean she had to fall into the same trap!

'I'm sure we'll be able to get a table at Bradleys,' she named a favourite restaurant of theirs, determined to put Quinn McBride's accusations out of her mind. To put the man himself completely from her mind!

'Great,' Richard enthused. 'I'll meet you there in half— no, better make that an hour,' he corrected lightly. 'I need to shower and change first.'

So did she, Harrie accepted as she began to shiver once they had ended their call, peeling off the damp clothing before going into the bathroom to run a steaming-hot shower.

Her father and Quinn were wrong, she decided determinedly as she soaped herself beneath the hot water. Richard was warm and caring, as well as being handsome and intelligent. And it would take a lot to convince her otherwise.

It would take more than Quinn McBride to convince her otherwise!

Although she felt her resolve shaken a little when she was shown to the table at Bradley's shortly before nine o'clock, only to spot Corinne Westley and David Hampton seated at another table across the room!

Not that the other couple were aware of her entrance as they were deeply engrossed in each other, and their conversation. About Richard, no doubt, Harrie decided scornfully.

Oh, God, Richard! He would be arriving here himself in the next few minutes. And even if Harrie didn't believe the things that had been said about Richard, Corinne Westley certainly did; how was the beautiful Corinne going to react to seeing him here?

And with Harrie, of all people!

Well, she was going to find out the answer to that soon enough, she realised with a sickening jolt of her stomach, as Richard had just arrived at the restaurant and was even now being shown to their table…!

'It's great to see you!' Richard bent down to kiss Harrie lightly on the lips before sitting down opposite her at the table, neither of them into great displays of emotion in public. 'And so unexpectedly, too,' he added warmly.

Harrie found herself studying him in a way she never had before, admiring his blonde, boyish good looks, his body lithe and fit, despite his thirty-four years. He was looking relaxed and comfortable in a lightweight dark blue suit and lighter blue shirt, the latter matching the sky-blue colour of his eyes.

And not the greenish-blue, aqua colour of Quinn McBride's eyes…

Quinn McBride again! *He* was the reason she was looking at Richard so critically in the first place!

Well, she needn't have worried; Richard hadn't turned into a two-headed monster since she'd last seen him two evenings ago. In fact, he looked just as relaxed and charming as usual.

But that didn't stop Harrie giving Corinne and David a surreptitious glance across the restaurant, heaving an inward sigh of relief as she saw they were still totally engrossed in each other, and had no idea Richard was in the room. Or Harrie, either, for that matter…

'You seem a little—preoccupied, this evening?' Richard prompted lightly as he noticed her distraction.

Harrie turned back with a guilty start. The last thing she wanted was for him to see the direction of that 'preoccupation'! 'I think I'm catching a cold,' she excused awkwardly, thinking no such thing, having just said the first thing that came into her head. But also having noted, thankfully, that Corinne and David were already at the coffee stage of their meal; hopefully they would be leaving soon. It couldn't be soon enough as far as Harrie was concerned!

Richard reached out and lightly touched her hand. 'Are you sure you feel up to dinner?' He frowned. 'You're looking very pale,' he explained at her questioning look.

'I'll be fine.' She gave him a bright smile. 'And you're right, this is unexpected,' she answered his initial comment. 'I haven't disrupted your own evening, though, have I?'

Richard grimaced, sitting back in his seat. 'The story I'm working on at the moment just isn't coming together; I was glad of the chance to walk away from it for a while!'

'Oh?' Harrie prompted lightly. 'Anything you can talk to me about?'

What was she doing? Richard never discussed his work with her until it was actually in print, so why was she asking him to do so now? She knew why, damn it, and once again she cursed Quinn McBride for being the one to put these suspicions concerning Richard into her mind.

Richard gave a regretful shake of his head. 'You know how it is, Harrie,' he excused ruefully.

'Yes, I know how it is,' she echoed flatly. 'I—' She broke off as she saw that it was Richard's attention that was diverted this time, and, following the line of his narrowed gaze, she could clearly see the reason for it...

Corinne Westley and David Hampton were leaving the restaurant!

Harrie turned sharply back to Richard, her breath catching in her throat as she saw the tension in his body, the calculated hardness of his gaze as he still watched the other couple, the slightly scornful twist to his mouth at the obvious warm intimacy between the two of them.

She was imagining Richard's response to seeing Corinne and David! Looking for signs of recognition!

No, she wasn't, Harrie realised with an inward groan...

There was something about Richard at this moment that reminded her of a satisfied cat that had just lapped up the cream, that same self-satisfied smugness.

A certain knowledge of Corinne that gave him that smugness?

Now Harrie really did feel ill. And it had nothing to do with an imaginary cold!

She swallowed hard once Corinne and David had left the restaurant—thankfully without having seen either her or Richard! 'Do you know them?' she prompted Richard lightly.

The hardness was gone from his gaze now as he turned back to Harrie, giving a dismissive shrug of his shoulders. 'Doesn't everyone?' he drawled derisively. 'The Beautiful Corinne, and the Handsome David!' The scorn could be heard in his voice now. 'But, no, I can't say I know either of them personally.' Richard shook his head.

Harrie didn't believe him. And it had nothing at all to do with the things Quinn McBride had said about Richard, or what her father had intimated, either. She had come to know Richard rather well herself in the last few months, and she also had a lawyer's eye and ear for the truth—and at this moment she knew Richard was lying to her.

Could Quinn's story of blackmail be true, after all? *Was* Richard really capable of that?

Harrie didn't really know. From watching Richard's own reaction on seeing Corinne and David, she felt uncertain enough about it right now not to feel like spending the rest of this particular evening in his company!

She gave a shaky smile. 'I think perhaps you're right about dinner this evening,' she murmured huskily, standing up unsteadily, unable to actually meet Richard's gaze now, needing time—and space—to assimilate her thoughts. 'Suddenly, I don't feel very well at all.' And if she didn't get out of here in a minute, she was actually going to be physically ill!

Richard stood up too. 'I'll drive you home—'

'No! Er, no,' she refused less sharply. 'I can get a taxi—'

'You most certainly won't,' he told her firmly, taking a grip of her arm, making their excuses to the *maitre d'* as they left.

Harrie huddled miserably on her side of the car on the short drive to her apartment. This had been a terrible day, the worst day of her life—and she had no doubt Quinn McBride was to blame for that!

'Shall I come up with you?' Richard offered solicitously once he had parked outside her apartment building.

She swallowed hard, shaking her head. 'I'm really sorry about this, Richard, but I—I think it would be best if I just went straight to bed.' And buried her head under the covers until this nightmare went away!

'I'll call you tomorrow,' Richard called after her, obviously still dazed by the abrupt end to their evening.

Harrie didn't answer him, hurrying up to her apartment as if a pack of wolves were at her heels. Or just one wolf, she realised sickly once she had reached her apartment and locked her door behind her.

Had she been wrong in her defence of Richard to her father and Quinn? Or had she just imagined the look on

Richard's face as he'd watched Corinne and David leave the restaurant, as if he were studying specimens under a microscope?

She had been so adamant, so sure in her defence of Richard—what was she going to do if her father and Quinn had been right about him all along?

If that turned out to be the case—and she so hoped that it wouldn't!—one thing she did know for certain; she would never give Quinn McBride the satisfaction of knowing how stupid she had been.

But, with any luck, she would never see him again, anyway!

CHAPTER FIVE

NERVOUS.

He was nervous, damn it. And it wasn't an emotion Quinn was either familiar or comfortable with!

He should be angry with Harrie for being the cause of his uncertainty, at the unaccustomed way his heart was pounding in his chest as he waited the long, interminable minutes it was taking for her to answer his ring of the security bell to her apartment. But somehow anger was the last thing he felt…!

With any luck, in a few minutes, he was going to see Harrie again. And the forty-eight hours since he'd last seen her somehow seemed much longer than that. No doubt she would be spitting fire and brimstone at him again, but he probably wouldn't recognise her if she were any other way. In fact, he grinned just at the thought of seeing those flashing green eyes again!

'Yes?' her tense response finally came over the intercom.

Some of Quinn's nervousness abated; at least she was at home! 'I told you I would visit you in your sickbed,' he drawled mockingly, instantly rewarded by what he guessed to be a stunned silence on the other end of the intercom.

She had recognised his reference, if not his voice, and she wasn't pleased to know he was her caller! Not that he had expected a warm welcome, he acknowledged ruefully. Harrie was not a woman who shielded her real emotions behind a polite façade. Thank goodness.

'Sorry to disappoint you, Quinn,' she finally snapped back, 'but I'm not in my sickbed!'

'And I'm not disappointed,' he returned dryly. 'Can I come up?'

'No,' came her instant response.

Quinn grinned again. 'That isn't very polite, Harrie,' he chided mockingly.

'If it's politeness you want, I suggest you find someone else to talk to!' she snapped sarcastically.

He couldn't stop grinning, damn it! Even defensive and rude, Harrie made him smile. He shook his head; if she thought she was putting him off, she was mistaken!

'I would rather talk to you,' he murmured softly.

'If you've come to gloat—'

'I haven't.' He sobered, knowing exactly what she was referring to. And it didn't please him that he had hurt her. It was the last thing he wanted to do!

'I don't believe you,' Harrie told him wearily. 'And who told you where I live?' she added suspiciously.

'Guess,' he said dryly.

She gave a heavy sigh. 'I'll talk to my father later!'

'Press the button and let me come up, Harrie,' he instructed firmly. 'And then you'll be able to see for yourself that I've come in peace.'

Quinn looked down at the flowers he carried, having bought them on impulse from a vendor down the street. He grimaced slightly now. Maybe they were a little over the top—they certainly looked like some sort of peace-offering!

He looked around for somewhere to dump them, dropping them over the metal railing in front of the building. 'Fear the Greeks bearing gifts' came to mind. Not that he was Greek, and the flowers weren't exactly a gift to hide his real reason for being here, but he knew Harrie well enough by now to realise exactly how she would see them!

It seemed an age before the buzzer sounded on the door to let him know he could go in, after all. He stepped quickly inside—before she could change her mind! Harrie obviously felt no friendlier towards him now than she had on Saturday. And, as he knew only too well, with good reason!

She was nowhere to be seen when the lift deposited him straight in her penthouse apartment on the top floor, giving him chance to look around. Warmth and comfort were the two things that struck him about her choice of decor; the wooden furniture was obviously golden antique oak, the cream sofa and chairs were large and comfortable, and there were cream and yellow flowers adorning the dining-table.

A woman of discerning taste, Quinn decided—except in one particular subject. Richard Heaton! His mouth tightened just at the thought of the other man, and Quinn knew it was no longer just because of his attempts to blackmail Corinne…!

'Quinn,' Harrie greeted him tightly at that moment as she came through from what he assumed was her bedroom. 'You've called at a bad time, I'm afraid, I'm just on my way out,' she told him dismissively, fixing the clasp on the gold bracelet she wore as she walked towards him.

Quinn had realised on Saturday that she was beautiful, but with her dark hair in loose curls over her shoulders and down her back, the short emerald-coloured dress she wore clinging lovingly to the perfection of her body, her legs long and slender, three-inch heels on the matching emerald-coloured shoes she wore, Harrie looked absolutely stunning. So much so that she took Quinn's breath away!

'Quinn?' she prompted impatiently at his lack of a response.

Except he wasn't without a response, the stirrings of his

body telling him that. As it would tell Harrie if he didn't soon sit down!

'Sorry,' he grimaced ruefully. 'I was just thinking that you're right—you don't look sick enough to be in bed, either!'

Harrie frowned at him. 'I'm not sure—'

'As well as giving me your address, Rome also informed me that you didn't feel well enough to be at work today.' He quirked mocking brows at her more than healthy-looking appearance.

Resentful colour highlighted her cheeks. 'He was right—I didn't!' she finally snapped.

'In that case…you've made a miraculous recovery!' Quinn drawled derisively. 'And do stop fidgeting, Harrie; surely you have time to share a drink with me before you have to leave?' he challenged mockingly—even as he moved to fold his long length gratefully in one of the comfortable armchairs!

She looked at him coldly. 'Celebrating, Quinn?' she bit out pointedly.

'Perhaps,' he drawled easily. 'What do you think?' He quirked one dark brow at her.

Angry colour now highlighted her cheeks as she glared at him. 'I think you and my father did rather a good job today of painting your sister as whiter than white, and— I'm sorry—' she sighed, holding up an apologetic hand '—that was uncalled for.' She swallowed hard. 'Jane Freeman's article in today's newspaper, on your sister, was very warm and human,' she conceded tautly.

Rome's solution to Corinne's problem had been so very simple, so simple Quinn could have kicked himself for not thinking of it first. The public would know the truth of Corinne's marriage, and the mistake she had made afterwards, but it would be done in such a way that there was no sensationalism involved in the revelation, more a tribute to the strength and courage of the woman who was to be the wife of the probable next prime minister.

And it had worked, Quinn acknowledged with inner satisfaction. Jane Freeman had interviewed Corinne as planned on Sunday morning at ten o'clock, and the story had appeared on the women's page of Rome's newspaper this morning—and so far the response to Corinne's frankness had all been positive. Several other newspapers, and a prominent television interviewer, were now interested in following up on the story, but as a tribute to Corinne, not the character assassination Richard Heaton had hinted at. Quinn just hoped it continued to be that way…

But, in the meantime, he realised it had totally upset Richard Heaton's plans for Corinne, something the other man would not be pleased about…

Quinn nodded. 'I believe so,' he conceded guardedly. 'I don't suppose your friend Richard is too happy about it, though,' he added with satisfaction.

Harrie gave a rueful shrug. 'Why don't you ask him?' She looked down at the slender watch on her wrist. 'He should be arriving in a few minutes,' she added with satisfaction.

Quinn sat forward in the armchair, his eyes narrowed. 'Are you telling me that you're dressed—like that—to go out on a date with Richard Heaton?' he rasped with rapidly rising anger.

Harrie gave an acknowledging inclination of her head. 'We're off to a literary dinner,' she told him challengingly, that air of satisfaction having deepened at the disclosure.

Quinn's scowl deepened, too. Richard Heaton was going to arrive here in a few minutes, with the intention of taking Harrie out for the evening. The former was bad enough, the latter was totally unacceptable!

His mouth twisted contemptuously. 'Your taste in friends is appalling!'

She met his furious gaze unblinkingly. 'Fortunately, my taste in enemies is much worse!'

Him. She meant *him*, damn it. And he didn't want her to think of him as her enemy. He wanted to be something much closer to her than that!

'Harrie—'

'You mentioned a drink,' she cut in smoothly, moving gracefully to the tray of drinks on the sideboard. 'What would you like? I can offer you red or white wine, and I have most of the spirits, too.' She looked across at him with polite query.

With the knowledge that Richard Heaton was to arrive here at any minute, with the intention of whisking Harrie away for the evening, a stiff brandy wouldn't go amiss!

'I'll have whatever you're having,' he muttered grimly, totally disgusted a few minutes later when he found himself in possession of a glass of orange juice!

'I may not look sick, Quinn, or have actually taken to my bed,' Harrie drawled in amusement at the grimace of distaste on his face, 'but as it happens I do have a throat infection, and the doctor recommended I not take any alcohol with the antibiotics he prescribed!'

Orange juice! Not that he didn't like juice; it was usually his first drink of the day. But it certainly wasn't what he'd had in mind for just now!

He scowled up at Harrie as she stood beside the unlit marble fireplace. 'I'm sure he also "recommended" you stay away from other people until you're free of infection,' he bit out tersely, placing the untouched glass of juice down on the coffee-table.

She arched dark brows. 'Frightened you might catch something, Quinn?' she taunted.

Thinking of a way to stop her going out with Richard Heaton was more like it! But, considering the other man was due here in a matter of minutes, he was probably wasting his time.

His mouth twisted. 'I was thinking more of your date for the evening,' he rasped harshly.

She shrugged. 'I've already explained the situation to Richard—and he's prepared to take the risk.'

Quinn would just bet he was! The thought of Harrie spending the evening with Richard Heaton was driving him crazy!

'I'm sure he is,' Quinn said disgustedly. 'Harrie—' He broke off as the buzzer for the door sounded on the wall beside the lift, glaring across at the offending intercom—almost as if it were Richard Heaton himself already standing there!

Harrie made no effort to move. 'I'm sure you must have somewhere else to go, Quinn…?' she prompted tautly.

She didn't want him to meet Richard Heaton any more than he thought it prudent at this particular moment to come face to face with the other man—which was more than enough reason for Quinn not to move!

He settled more comfortably into the armchair. 'Not that I can think of, no,' he returned mildly.

Her mouth tightened with impatience. 'Quinn—'

'Harrie,' he drawled unconcernedly.

She gave an irritated sigh. 'You know you have no wish to meet Richard—'

'Don't I?' he challenged softly. 'Are you sure that isn't your own wish? Your caller seems to be becoming a little anxious,' he drawled as the buzzer sounded a second time.

Her mouth set angrily. 'Just don't cause a scene in my apartment, Quinn,' she warned him irritatedly as she marched over to speak on the security intercom.

Quinn smiled grimly to himself as he listened unashamedly to her side of the intercom conversation, her voice light and friendly, but not, he noted with satisfaction, in the least breathlessly loving. Although that, he realised with less satisfaction, might just be because Harrie was all too aware of his listening presence!

Richard Heaton. In a few minutes Quinn was going to meet the man he had come to despise over the last few weeks, a man he didn't believe good enough to be in the same room as Harrie, let alone—

Let alone, what...?

Were Harrie and the other man lovers? Quinn felt nauseous just at the thought of it. But in a few minutes he was going to know the answer to that question. He knew he would be able to tell by the way Harrie and Richard reacted to each other just how intimate their relationship was.

That realisation made him angrier than ever!

And that anger wasn't in the less lessened when the other man stepped from the lift into the apartment a minute or so later, bending to kiss Harrie lightly on the lips— before calmly handing her the bouquet of flowers Quinn had minutes ago dropped over the railing outside!

Harrie accepted Richard's kiss, and the flowers, distractedly, all too aware of Quinn seated in the room behind her.

She'd spent the most miserable day on her own yesterday, her thoughts alternating between an unwanted belief in Quinn and her father's accusations concerning Richard, and then instantly contradicting those thoughts by recalling Richard's warmth and charm when the two of them were together, sure that her companion of the last few months couldn't possibly be guilty of the things he was accused of.

And that certainly had been endorsed by Richard himself when he'd telephoned her in the afternoon to see if she was feeling any better, his concern as to her well-being obviously genuine as he'd told her not to give this evening's literary dinner another thought, just to get herself well. But Harrie had assured him she was only feeling slightly under the weather, that she was sure she would be well enough to go to the dinner with him the following evening.

It had served her right when she'd woken this morning with a raging headache, and a sore throat to go with it, but at least the call in sick she had made to her father had been completely genuine!

She hadn't even seen the newspaper until her return from the chemist after picking up her prescription, but the article on Corinne Westley had done nothing to improve the way she felt.

Although looking at Richard now, his smile warm with concern as he gazed down at her, Harrie couldn't see that he had been in the least affected by that same article.

Well, of course he wasn't, she instantly berated herself; Quinn was mistaken in his accusations towards Richard, and her father was just going along with them because Richard wasn't a man of his own choosing for his eldest daughter!

'They're beautiful, Richard, thank you.' She buried her face in the fragrant blooms he had just given her—the first flowers he'd ever given her, in fact.

'You're more than welcome,' he assured her huskily. 'But I have to say their beauty can in no way compare to yours,' he added warmly.

Harrie's smile of pleasure was arrested on her lips as she heard the strangulated sound coming from the room behind her. Quinn! And the noise he'd made sounded distinctly like a muffled laugh to her!

'I have a visitor, Richard,' she told him stiltedly—before they gave Quinn anything else to laugh at! 'He was just about to leave,' she added for Quinn's benefit. 'But come and be introduced, anyway.' She linked her hand lightly with his as she led the way back into the sitting-room.

Quinn had stood up since she'd left the room, his expression guarded as he looked across at the man at her side. Given the circumstances of how Quinn had told her he felt towards Richard, Harrie supposed she should feel grateful for the fact that he hadn't immediately crossed the room and punched Richard in the face!

But, of course, they were all civilised people—weren't they…?

Lord, she hoped so!

Although the look on Quinn's face as he looked at her hand linked with Richard's didn't augur well for that hope!

'Richard Heaton, Quinn McBride.' She made the introductions as briefly as possible. A bit like lighting the blue touch-paper—and waiting to see if the rocket would go up or not!

Quinn, of course, made no reaction to the identity of the other man—why should he? He had been forewarned.

But Harrie found herself watching Richard closely to see how he reacted to knowing who Quinn was. If he did know. After all, she hadn't made any connection herself between Quinn and his sister, Corinne Westley…

Richard's smile was coolly polite as he released Harrie's hand to hold his own hand out to the other man. 'A little late in the day to be working, isn't it, Harrie?' he remarked lightly, obviously wondering at the other man's reasons for being here.

Quinn barely touched the other man's hand, his aqua-blue eyes having taken on a flinty quality. 'Actually, I'm a friend of the family,' he bit out harshly. 'Harrie tells me the two of you are off to a literary dinner this evening…'

Harrie was recoiling from having Quinn describe himself as a 'family friend'; he and her father might have become friends during the last few days, but she certainly didn't consider herself any sort of friend of Quinn McBride's!

'It's a bit of a bore, but, yes,' Richard answered the older man, dressed for the part in his black evening suit and snowy-white shirt.

'I'm sure with Harrie at your side it won't be in the least boring,' Quinn came back smoothly.

Challengingly, it seemed to Harrie. Exactly what was he trying to do now?

Richard looked blank for several seconds, and then he gave a rueful smile. 'I wasn't including Harrie in that remark, of course.' His eyes were narrowed as he looked at the older man. 'Quinn McBride...' he repeated slowly. 'Now why does that name sound familiar?'

Harrie felt herself tense. Was this going to be it, the showdown between these two men, here in her apartment? She closed her eyes as she waited for the explosion.

'I have no idea,' Quinn answered Richard dismissively before turning to Harrie. 'You're looking a little pale still,' he told her huskily. 'Are you sure you feel up to going out this evening?'

She would begin to feel a whole lot better—probably recover some of her colour, too—if he would only leave! Because she knew, the longer Quinn stayed, the more chance there was he would cease to hold on to that civilised veneer she was so depending on!

'I told you earlier, I feel perfectly well again now,' she said tautly. 'And we really mustn't keep you any longer,' she encouraged lightly, the determined look in her eyes telling him just how much she wanted him to leave.

Quinn looked for a moment as if he were about to argue the point, and then he gave a stiff inclination of his head. 'I'll give you a call tomorrow. To see how you are,' he added harshly after Harrie gave him a sharply questioning look.

'There's really no need, Quinn,' she assured him dryly. 'I'm sure I shall be fully recovered by tomorrow.'

He nodded abruptly. 'I'll call you anyway. Walk me to the lift, hmm?' he prompted harshly.

Harrie gave him a startled look. Walk him to the lift…? From anyone else that would have sounded almost lover-like—from Quinn McBride it sounded like the order Harrie was sure it actually was!

'Of course,' she agreed with cool politeness. 'Help yourself to a drink, Richard.' She indicated the tray of drinks on the sideboard.

Neither man made any effort to say a polite goodbye to the other, and the tension emanating from Quinn as Harrie walked beside him to the lift was so heavy she felt she could almost reach out and touch it. Which made her realise, for the first time, just how much control Quinn must have exerted over himself the last ten minutes not to have hit Richard for the distress he felt he'd caused his beloved sister…

She reached out and touched his arm once they stood outside the lift. 'Quinn—' She broke off with a gasp as he turned to look at her, a look of such savage anger on his face it literally took her breath away. 'Quinn…?' she choked concernedly, her hand still on his rigidly tensed arm.

He glanced coldly back into the room where Richard now had his back towards them as he poured himself a glass of red wine. 'If I had met him under any other cir-cumstances…!' he grated softly between clenched teeth, shaking his head disgustedly. 'Nice flowers,' he added sca-thingly.

The last few minutes had been filled with such tension she hadn't even realised she still held Richard's flowers in her hand, glancing down at them now as if she were seeing them for the first time. 'Very,' she confirmed stiltedly, frowning at the unexpectedness of the remark.

Quinn's mouth twisted derisively. 'Almost as lovely as when I purchased them half an hour ago!'

When *he*—! What—? How—? Why—?

Her thoughts were going round and round like a scratched record, damn it, Harrie realised crossly. What did Quinn mean, *he* had purchased the flowers…? And if he had, how had it ended up with Richard giving them to her?

'Remember the adage about Greeks and gifts, Harrie?' Quinn warned scornfully even as his fingers dug into her arms as he suddenly reached out to grasp hold of her. 'Especially when they happen to be someone else's gifts!' he drawled with a disgusted look in Richard's direction.

She swallowed hard. 'I don't understand—'

'Oh, I think you understand very well, Harrie,' Quinn murmured softly, his eyes hard aqua-blue as he once again glanced across at the younger man. 'It's only your stubborn pride that is making you hold on to an illusion.'

Her own eyes glittered with anger at his daring to tell her what she did or didn't understand. 'Is this the part in the conversation where you remind me of another old adage? That of pride coming before a fall?' she pointed out disgustedly at his enquiring look.

Quinn's mouth twisted mockingly. 'Oh, you're nowhere near falling yet, Harrie,' he assured her tauntingly. 'And even if you were, I would be there to pick you up,' he added grimly.

She blinked up at him, looking away as she found herself unable to meet the intensity of his gaze. 'I have no idea what you're talking about,' she muttered hardly—not sure that she wanted to know, either!

Quinn released her as abruptly as he'd reached out to

hold her. 'Get rid of him, Harrie,' he warned harshly. 'Before I do it for you,' he added with grim determination.

Harrie gasped at his arrogance. But before she could think of a suitable reply, he had stepped into the waiting lift and pressed the button for the ground floor, the doors closing quietly before it—and Quinn!—began their descent.

Now that he had actually gone, Harrie couldn't seem to move. What had Quinn meant about the flowers? If he had bought them for her, then why hadn't he given them to her? And how was it they'd come to be in Richard's possession?

But more to the point, what had he mean by that last remark…?

'Harrie…?'

She turned to find Richard lounging against the wall as he watched her intently. Forcing those questions to the back of her mind, she gave him a bright, meaningless smile. 'Sorry.' She grimaced. 'Quinn can be a little—overpowering,' she understated.

Quinn wasn't just overpowering—he was all-consuming! And, she acknowledged with a troubled frown as she looked at Richard, Quinn made the younger man fade into insignificance by comparison.

What was happening to her? Quinn McBride wasn't actually getting to her, was he? Surely not—he was even more unsuitable for her than he claimed Richard to be!

'So I believe,' Richard answered her remark, straightening away from the wall, his eyes narrowed as he looked across at her. 'And now that he's gone, perhaps you would like to tell me just what the hell is going on,' he added in a silkily soft voice.

'With Quinn?' She gave a lightly dismissing laugh as she walked over to join Richard. 'Why, nothing—'

'No, not just ''with Quinn'',' Richard cut in gratingly,

his face distorted with anger now. 'Until a short time ago I believed that what happened today was just bad luck as far as I was concerned, a case of bad timing on Jane's part, or, at worst, a lack of communication between colleagues. But then I arrive here and find you cosily ensconced with none other than Quinn McBride. So I'll ask you again, Harrie,' he bit out harshly. 'What the hell is going on?'

Harrie looked at him wordlessly, shaken by the sudden change that had come over him. He was no more the charmingly attentive man she was used to, but one consumed by fiercely burning anger.

Jane. He had mentioned a colleague called Jane. Jane Freeman…? The woman who had written today's article on Corinne Westley…

My God, Harrie realised as she looked at Richard dazedly; *he* had also known exactly who *Quinn* was all along…!

CHAPTER SIX

IT TOOK all of the couple of minutes that passed as the lift made its descent to the ground floor for Quinn to realise there was no way he could just calmly walk away.

For one thing, he detested the idea of leaving Harrie alone with Richard Heaton. And for another, the man may have seemed charmingly vague when Quinn had been introduced to him, but surely a man with Richard Heaton's hard-hitting reputation, especially where his work was concerned, would have made himself aware of all of Corinne Westley's background, but especially the fact that the only family she had was an older brother—and *his* name was Quinn McBride!

The man had been putting on an act!

The more Quinn thought about it, the more sure he became, pressing the button for the recall of the lift, stepping agitatedly inside once the doors had opened, his movements restless as he waited for the lift to reach the penthouse floor.

At which time the doors didn't open!

And wouldn't be opened, Quinn realised frustratedly, until Harrie released the security button inside her apartment!

Trust Harrie, Quinn muttered to himself agitatedly, to live in an apartment that kept the 'bad guy' in and the 'good guy' out!

Then he realised he was being unfair to her. And probably making an idiot of himself too. What real reason did he have, apart from his own aversion to Richard Heaton, for coming back up to Harrie's apartment? And exactly what was he going to say when and if he did get back inside her apartment: 'unhand that woman'? It sounded like something out of a Victorian novel, and a cheap one at that!

Better to just go back downstairs, return home, and do as he had said he would—telephone Harrie in the morning. Early. Very early.

Harrie!

He could hear Harrie's voice from inside the apartment now, slightly raised, Richard Heaton's reply a soft murmur, inaudibly so. Either the two of them were nearing the door as they prepared to leave for their dinner—or they were arguing!

Quinn knew which he hoped it was, although if it were the latter, with his own recent departure, the probability was the argument was about him—or Corinne...!

He banged loudly on the lift door. 'Harrie? Harrie! Open the door, damn it,' he swore as impatience took over from prudence.

So he made a fool of himself—so what? He had a feeling he was going to do that some time in the future over Harrie Summer, anyway, so why not make a start now?

'Harrie, I said—' He broke off abruptly as the lift doors swooshed open, a dishevelled Harrie standing on the other side of them, her beautiful dark hair tousled and untidy, her scarlet-coloured lip-gloss ever so slightly smudged on puffy lips.

Quinn's heart sank at the sight of her. He had seen her looking this wantonly beautiful only once before. When *he* had kissed her. And the thought of having interrupted Richard Heaton doing the same thing made him feel—

'Quinn!' Harrie cried thankfully, grabbing hold of his arm and pulling him into the apartment. 'Richard was just leaving. Weren't you?' she added pointedly, her hand tucked snugly into the crook of Quinn's arm as she glared angrily across at Richard Heaton—murderously! Because if Harrie had been kissed in the last few minutes it certainly wasn't something she had enjoyed!

Richard Heaton had adopted a slightly scornful pose as he looked across at them unconcernedly. 'Was I?' he sneered. 'I thought we were going out,' he reminded Harrie dryly.

'Then you thought wrong!' Her eyes flashed deeply emerald. 'I would prefer it if you just left,' she added tautly, her hand gripping Quinn's arm so tightly now her nails were digging into his flesh through the material of his jacket.

Exactly what had transpired in the few minutes since his departure, Quinn wondered savagely, to have created this total aversion to the other man inside Harrie? As if, Quinn decided after another glance at her dishevelled appearance, he really needed to ask himself that!

'You heard her, Heaton,' Quinn rasped, squeezing Harrie's hand reassuringly before releasing himself from her grasp and walking over to stand mere inches away from the other man. 'And I would advise you to make it sooner rather than later.' His voice was dangerously soft now.

Richard Heaton gave an unabashed shrug. 'Oh, don't worry, I'll leave peacefully,' he drawled mockingly, a humourless smile curving his lips. 'But this isn't over yet,' he added assuredly. 'The first round may have gone to you, but it certainly wasn't a knockout!'

The gloves were most assuredly off, Quinn acknowledged grimly. 'It isn't just me you've—offended, Heaton,' he told the other man contemptuously. 'And I can assure you that it's a mistake—on your part—to have made an adversary of Rome Summer, too,' he added warningly.

Blond brows were raised over mocking blue eyes. 'I was just doing my job—'

'I don't think any of us see it that way,' Quinn ground out savagely.

Richard Heaton shrugged. 'Perhaps we'll just let the general public decide that, hmm?'

Quinn's mouth tightened. 'I think that, after this evening, you may just find yourself without a newspaper to print anything you have to say!' His eyes glittered threateningly.

'Fortunately, Rome Summer doesn't own all the newspapers,' the other man scored.

'Maybe he doesn't,' Quinn conceded shortly. 'But no reputable newspaper would touch anything you want to write about Corinne after the publication of today's article about her!' But unfortunately, as Quinn was sure Heaton knew only too well, one of the more lurid tabloids probably would! 'So unless you want to find yourself completely out in the cold in the newspaper world, I would advise you to proceed with extreme caution,' he added warmly.

'Now who's issuing threats?' Richard Heaton taunted, but less confidently, Quinn thought.

Or, rather, hoped! Corinne had looked so much better when Quinn had left the house earlier this evening, happier and more confident than Quinn had seen her look for a very long time. Of course David's love and support, on being told of Corinne's unhappy love affair after the death of her husband, had gone a long way to achieving that effect, but Quinn knew it was also due to the fact that his sister believed the nightmare of being blackmailed was over. But, as Quinn was all too aware, Richard Heaton still had the means to shatter that fragile happiness if he should choose to do so…!

Nevertheless, Quinn's smile was completely confident. 'I think I should warn you—' his voice was silkily soft

'—you will find me a much more formidable adversary than Corinne could ever have been!'

'No doubt.' The younger man gave an acknowledging inclination of his head. 'Just how close a ''friend'' of the Summer family are you?' he added speculatively after an insulting glance at the silent Harrie.

Quinn's mouth tightened into a thin line. 'Very,' he bit out tautly.

Richard Heaton gave a scathing laugh. 'That's what I thought,' he murmured, walking past Quinn to stop in front of Harrie.

To give Harrie her due, Quinn noted with admiration, she met the other man's scornful gaze unflinchingly. In that moment she had the look of a sleek black jaguar, green eyes blazing with challenge. And Quinn knew that to him she'd never looked more beautiful!

'No hard feelings, Harrie?' Richard Heaton prompted softly.

For a brief moment she looked nonplussed by the comment, and then her expression turned to disgust. 'As I don't intend even so much as thinking of you again—the answer to that is a definite no!' she bit out forcefully.

The other man laughed softly. 'It's a pity you feel that way, Harrie,' Richard drawled. 'Because, after all that we've shared together these last few months—I'm going to find great difficulty in forgetting you!'

Quinn felt the fury rising within him as he took in the full implication of the other man's words. Richard Heaton and Harrie *had* been lovers, after all…!

Something very like a physical pain ripped through his chest, to be quickly quelled again. Harrie was twenty-nine years old, for goodness' sake, and not an inexperienced child. He wouldn't want her himself if she were!

But, nevertheless, the thought of her and Richard Heaton

together, intimately entwined in each other's arms, made him feel ill…

'Get out, Richard,' Harrie told him dully. 'And take your flowers with you!' She picked the blooms up from the side-table where she had placed them earlier, thrusting them towards him.

Richard Heaton made no effort to take them from her. 'Keep them.' He pressed the lift button. 'As a reminder of me!' he added tauntingly.

'How can they be—when it appears you didn't even buy them for me?' Harrie spat the words at him.

Richard Heaton gave Quinn a speculative look before stepping inside the waiting lift and closing the doors behind him.

Silence followed the other man's departure. Harrie seemed unable to move away from her position near the lift, and Quinn's head was still full of visions of Harrie in the other man's arms. And worse! The more he tried to push those visions from his mind, the more determined they seemed to be to want to stay, vividly graphic—and achingly painful!

At last Harrie's breath released in a shaky sigh as she turned slowly to face Quinn. And she knew the disgust she could see in his expression wasn't all directed at Richard!

Well, Quinn couldn't possibly feel any more disgusted with her than she did with herself! She had been so wrong about Richard, the full extent of his deception becoming apparent after Quinn's departure; the insults he'd levelled at her, as the spoilt, gullible daughter of Rome Summer, had been only the beginning!

She swallowed down the nausea as she thought of the way Richard had pulled her roughly into his arms and tried to force her to— The bruises she was sure she would have on her arms by morning were as nothing compared to the ones in her heart!

Quinn and her father had been right about Richard's duplicity all the time!

She closed her eyes as she remembered the hurtful words Richard had so deliberately thrown at her. He was angry at losing his hold over Corinne Westley, she knew, furious at the way he'd been duped by her father and Quinn—but that didn't take the sting out of the string of insults he had launched at her.

Whoever had quoted that adage about 'sticks and stones may break my bones, but words can never hurt me', had been so wrong; the bruises to her flesh would heal within a day or two, whereas the personal insults Richard had verbally lashed her with would never be forgotten...

She let out a shaky sigh. 'So you were right after all,' she said dully.

Quinn scowled. 'I can assure you, it gives me no pleasure to have been so,' he rasped harshly.

Harrie swallowed hard, not altogether sure she believed him. 'If you will excuse me—I'll just get rid of these!' She held up the much detested flowers, no longer caring which man they came from; they were a reminder of this evening, and they were going in the bin—where they belonged!

She staggered once in the privacy of her kitchen, leaning against one of the work units, her legs feeling weak and shaky. Richard was everything—and more!—that her father and Quinn had claimed him to be. And, after her fierce defence of him, she didn't know what to do next.

That she would have to go out of here and face Quinn again she knew for certain; there was no way he would just quietly leave and give her time to lick her wounds. If only she didn't feel so stupid!

Well, she *was* stupid, she muttered with self-recrimination, her despair starting to be replaced by anger. Stupid, and arrogant, in believing that she knew best where Richard was concerned.

But, stupid or not, that did not mean she was going to give Quinn the satisfaction of seeing just how shaken she was by all of this…

She thrust the flowers in the bin before turning and walking determinedly back out to the sitting-room. 'I think a glass of wine is called for, don't you?' she announced brightly, knowing an inner pleasure when Quinn turned from the bookcase he had been looking through, dark brows raised in surprise at her cheerful tone.

Well—like Richard—she might be 'down', but she wasn't 'out'!

'Red or white?' she offered lightly.

'White—thank you,' Quinn accepted slowly, his lids narrowed as he watched her warily.

If he was expecting her to collapse in an emotional heap, he was in for a disappointment, Harrie determined firmly. She would wait until Quinn had left before she did that!

The half-full glass of red wine that stood near the drinks tray was a sharp reminder of Richard's abrupt departure minutes earlier. Harrie carefully avoiding so much as looking at it as she poured the two glasses of wine from the cooled bottle of Chablis.

'Here we are.' She handed Quinn one of the glasses of wine before taking a grateful sip from her own glass. Not exactly nectar, but it was welcome nonetheless!

Quinn made no attempt to drink his own wine. 'What are we drinking to?' he prompted hardly.

'Absent friends?' Harrie returned sharply.

Quinn drew in a harsh breath. 'Harrie—'

'Or perhaps you would like to make a toast to your sister?' she cut in tautly over his protest. 'I'm sure she must be feeling relieved that all of this is over.' Whereas Harrie felt that, for her, it was only just beginning!

How on earth was she going to face her father again after the things she had said to him during her defence of Richard?

The same way she was facing Quinn again, she told herself firmly; with a mask of indifference very firmly over her inner emotions!

'But is it?' Quinn came back softly. 'Over, I mean,' he explained at Harrie's frowning look.

'But of course it is,' she scorned, moving away to stand over near the window that looked down over the beauty that was London on an early summer's evening. 'Richard was just blustering at the end,' she dismissed with distaste. 'I'm sure your remark about the possibility of finding himself unemployable, if he continued with this, hit home.' If it hadn't, then Richard was more of a fool than she had given him credit for—because her father was not an adversary who pulled his punches!

'Maybe.' Quinn shrugged. 'And how about you? How do you feel about him now?' he clarified as Harrie gave him a blank look.

Did this man have no tact, no sense of where he could and couldn't venture? Obviously not, she decided irritably as Quinn continued to look at her questioningly.

She drew in a deep breath. 'I've obviously—seen another side of Richard this evening,' she began guardedly. 'I can't say it's a side I particularly care for.'

'And?' Quinn prompted harshly.

Harrie frowned. 'And what?'

His glass landed with a loud crash on the coffee-table. 'Will you be seeing Heaton again, damn it?' he bit out savagely.

She blinked at his vehemence. 'I'm sure you heard me tell him I wouldn't be,' she answered dazedly.

Quinn's mouth twisted. 'You've said the same to me, several times—and here I still am!'

Ah. 'It's hardly the same thing, is it, Quinn?' she dismissed hardly. 'You aren't here by invitation,' she added pointedly.

Those aqua-blue eyes became as stormy as a wind-tossed sea. 'Forgive me if I'm wrong,' he bit out coldly, 'but I could have sworn you invited me in—actually, dragged me in is probably a better description!—the second time I arrived this evening!'

Harrie drew in a sharp breath at his deliberate cruelty. 'You're enjoying this, aren't you, Quinn?' she scorned. 'You—' The rest of her words were cut off as Quinn's mouth came down possessively on hers!

Not again! It was just too much. It had been bad enough that Richard believed he could treat her exactly how he pleased now that he had no further need to hide behind that charming façade—because façade it most certainly had been; Harrie had seen a completely different side to him as he'd forced his kisses and caresses on her.

But there was no way she was going to take the same insulting behavior from Quinn McBride. Especially when he claimed to have saved her from the other man's unwanted attentions!

But as savagely as the kiss had begun, it now gentled to questing passion, Quinn's mouth moving searchingly over hers, sipping and tasting, his tongue running over the sensitivity of her inner lips.

Harrie could feel herself melting in a way she'd never known before. There was not a thought in her head now other than the sensation of Quinn's possession of her mouth, clinging to the broad width of his shoulders as one of his hands sought and found the pointed tip of her breast, the nipple instantly responding to the warm caress.

Heated desire coursed through her body like molten

flame, her legs becoming entwined with his as she could feel the pulsing hardness of his own arousal.

His lips left hers to trail a path down to the pointed hunger of her breast, her fingers becoming entwined in the thick darkness of the hair at his nape as she held him closer to her, wanting, needing, so much more!

She desperately wanted Quinn to make love to her!

Even as she acknowledged that aching need she wrenched her mouth away from his, stunned at her own admission. 'No, Quinn!' she gasped, breathing hard as she pushed ineffectually against the hardness of his chest. Ineffectually, because Quinn was much stronger than her, and he didn't want to release her.

He looked down at her with those stormy aqua-coloured eyes. 'No?' he grated.

'No!' She shook her head firmly, looking up at him pleadingly. 'Quinn, we can't do this!' She grimaced protestingly, giving up all effort of trying to release herself, knowing she was just wasting her energy. And from the purposeful look in Quinn's eyes, she might still have need of that!

'Can't we?' he grated. 'Strange, I thought we already were.'

'Not like this, Quinn,' she groaned. 'You'll only regret it,' she added warningly—knowing that if he wouldn't, she certainly would!

'Why?' he scorned. 'Because you'll set your father on me?' he taunted.

Colour warmed her cheeks as he misunderstood her words of caution for a threat. 'I can fight my own battles, thank you!'

'Then could it be because you'll hate me "after-wards"?' He gave a derisive snort at his own suggestion. 'You've already made it more than clear that's how you feel about me, so what have I got to lose?' he added dismissively.

Harrie swallowed hard. 'I don't hate you, Quinn—'

'Dislike me, then,' he cut in scathingly. 'What's the difference?' He shrugged scornfully.

'I don't dislike you, either,' she said huskily.

She had thought she did dislike Quinn. For his arrogance in his initial assumption that she was the mistress of Rome Summer. For his scorn and derision towards the man she had thought she loved. Thought—because she no longer felt anything but loathing towards Richard! But just now, when Quinn had thought—correctly!—that Richard would turn on her once the two of them were alone, Quinn had come back to see if she'd needed any help. There was no way she could hate or dislike the man who had done that...

Or deny that seconds ago she'd been as desperate for him to make love to her as he appeared to want to do so!

Good grief—did that mean she actually *liked* Quinn McBride?

Ridiculous!

She was grateful to him, that was all, and that gratitude had raged completely out of control.

Quinn was looking down at her uncertainly, obviously trying to read her thoughts from her expression. Well, there was no way she was going to allow him to read those particular thoughts!

Especially as she hadn't had the time herself to sit down and think them through logically!

'Let me go, Quinn,' she requested again quietly. 'Let's drink our wine and—'

'And then I can leave!' he finished derisively, releasing her as abruptly as he had taken her into his arms, turning away disgustedly.

Harrie sighed, feeling suddenly cold without the protective warmth of his arms. And unsure whether that disgust was directed at her or at himself! 'This has not been a particularly—pleasant evening for me, Quinn—'

'And I've done nothing to improve it,' he acknowledged harshly, turning to pick up his previously untouched glass of wine, throwing the contents to the back of his throat. 'You're right, Harrie, this is not a good idea,' he rasped harshly. 'I'll leave you to—well, to enjoy the rest of your evening—'

'That's hardly likely!' she put in self-derisively.

'Unmolested,' he finished grimly, turning away to walk stiffly towards the lift.

'Quinn…?' Harrie called after him uncertainly.

He glanced back briefly. 'Yes?' he prompted coldly.

She moistened dry lips before replying, not quite able to meet his gaze. 'I would like to thank you—'

'Thank me?' he repeated incredulously.

She nodded, shuddering slightly. 'If you hadn't come back, when you did—'

'You would have handled the situation, Harrie,' he assured her firmly. 'After all,' he added tauntingly, 'you *are* Rome Summer's eldest daughter!'

She couldn't help smiling at his attempt at mocking himself for his initial assumptions concerning herself and Rome. 'So I am,' she acknowledged huskily.

Quinn gave a brief nod. 'Don't let anything Richard Heaton said or did get to you, Harrie,' he advised harshly. 'You are Rome's daughter, but you're also yourself. And Harrie Summer is a pretty formidable person in her own right—as I know to my cost!' he added self-derisively.

Harrie watched him leave, standing unmoving as he stepped into the lift, the doors closing behind him, the light overhead telling of the lift's descent to the ground floor.

Quinn had gone, Harrie acknowledged dully…

And now that he had she wished he were still here.

If only to save her from her own thoughts, she acknowledged shakily. Because, as she already knew only too well, they weren't all going to be recriminations against Richard!

Because if she hadn't called a halt to the situation when she did, Quinn would still be here now, and the two of them would be making love...

And Quinn McBride was an enigma to her. So cool and detached that first day, so scornful of what he thought she was, even more so once he realised it was Richard she was involved with and not Rome.

But Quinn had been anything but cool this evening, either before or after Richard's arrival. Her skin still burned from his kisses and caresses, her breasts, swollen and aroused, aching with that unfulfilled need.

How could that be? she asked herself self-recriminatingly. Until a few hours ago she'd believed herself in love with Richard. Now just the thought of ever seeing him again made her feel ill.

Whereas the thought of never seeing Quinn again—more than just a possibility—made her feel just as ill...!

What on earth was wrong with her?

But was there actually anything wrong with her? Wasn't it perfectly natural that she would have strong feelings towards the person who had, effectively, just saved her from another man's forced attentions?

Then why, she asked herself seconds later, after dropping down weakly into one of her armchairs, were there hot tears falling down her cheeks? And not because of Richard's betrayal, but because Quinn had gone, and she didn't know when or if she would ever see him again...?

CHAPTER SEVEN

'SO TELL me, Quinn,' Rome drawled, a teasing glint in his eyes as he lounged across from Quinn in a chair in the sitting-room of his estate home, 'just how much longer did you think you could stay away from my daughter?'

He had tried, Quinn groaned inwardly, really tried, to keep out of Harrie's way, to give her time to lick the wounds Richard Heaton's betrayal had undoubtedly left her with. But in the end a week had been as long as he could stand, Quinn acknowledged.

'You invited me here for the weekend,' Quinn reminded the other man dryly—although he was aware, as Rome was, that the invitation had been at his own instigation.

He had telephoned the older man on Friday afternoon, with the excuse that the two of them needed to discuss the events—or, rather, non-events!—of the week, knowing from past experience that the other man wouldn't have had any free time that afternoon in which they could have had a general chat. Rome's invitation for Quinn to spend the weekend at the Summer estate had been exactly what Quinn had been hoping for; at least here he stood some chance of accidentally bumping into Harrie!

Rome quirked blond brows. 'Would you rather I hadn't?' he teased.

That all depended...on whether or not Harrie intended coming down here this weekend too!

Quinn shrugged. 'The Richard Heaton situation seems to have gone very quiet.' He deliberately misunderstood the other man.

'On both fronts, so I understand,' Rome acknowledged

dryly. 'Don't pretend to look so mystified, Quinn; Harrie has told me what took place on Monday evening,' he added grimly.

Not all of it, Quinn would wager! He still had difficulty himself in coming to terms with the way his own emotions had raged out of control once Richard Heaton had left Harrie's apartment on Monday evening, let alone that briefly—too briefly!—Harrie had responded as heatedly. There was no way Harrie would have told her father about that!

Although, from Rome's earlier comment, he seemed to realise *something* had happened between Quinn and Harrie...

'Then you know that Richard Heaton has finally shown Harrie his real self, too,' Quinn said harshly, remembering exactly in what way he had shown that side of himself to Harrie.

'Mmm,' Rome acknowledged abruptly. 'And, believe me, it wasn't easy for Harrie to admit to me,' he added grimly.

Quinn could imagine that all too easily; Harrie's pride had been damaged on Monday as much as anything else. It was to her credit that she had swallowed that pride and admitted her mistake to her father...

'Needless to say,' Rome rasped harshly, 'Heaton no longer works for my newspaper.'

Or anyone else yet, if Quinn's information was correct. And he had no reason to believe it wasn't. But, surely, there lay the danger; at the moment they had no idea what the other man was doing...

'I've heard on good authority that Heaton has decided to look for employment in the States.' Rome seemed to read some of his thoughts. 'I have it on even better authority,' he continued, 'that he's going to be successful!'

Quinn frowned across at Rome. How could he possibly know—?

'I have business interests in several publications over there, Quinn,' Rome told him ruefully. 'And, believe me, Heaton's employment contract is going to be bound up so tight he won't be able to sneeze without asking permission first!' he added grimly.

Quinn looked at the older man admiringly. But, then, he had known there had to be a harder side to Rome than he'd previously seen; the man couldn't have been as successful in business as he was if there hadn't been.

'Don't worry, Quinn, Heaton is well taken care of,' Rome said assuredly. 'And your sister looked extremely happy in the photographs I saw of her in the newspapers this last week,' he added with satisfaction.

'She is,' Quinn confirmed.

Now that the threat to her happiness with David had been removed, Corinne had ceased to look worried and drawn, throwing herself into her role as David's partner with new vigour and enjoyment, and their wedding plans were moving along briskly too.

'So how about answering my earlier question?' Rome prompted teasingly. 'Harrie,' he reminded as Quinn gave him a blank look.

Quinn had known exactly which question the other man had meant—he simply wasn't sure how to answer it. Because he wasn't sure of anything where Harrie was concerned, let alone how he felt about seeing her again!

Part of him very badly wanted to see her again, but the other side of him, that cautious, detached side of him, questioned what he was going to do with her when he did see her. That he wanted her, he didn't doubt, but actually becoming involved in an affair with her was something else entirely.

Harrie was nothing like the women he usually became

involved with. She certainly didn't give off any clear signals that a brief, uncomplicated affair was what she wanted. Besides, Quinn had never known—and liked—the father of any of the other women he'd been involved with, either!

This desire he had for Harrie was a complication he hadn't really had time to work out yet…

Just walking away and never seeing Harrie again was unacceptable to him, but the alternative—! Even if Harrie were willing, he did not want to get seriously involved with her—with any woman!

One thing he was very sure of: marriage—to any woman—did not figure in his immediate plans.

Quinn gave a dismissive shrug. 'I don't know what you want, or expect, me to say to that, Rome. Of course I'm concerned about Harrie; she was very upset on Monday evening.' He frowned grimly at the memory.

'Only concerned?' Rome taunted, blue eyes gleaming speculatively. 'You know, Quinn,' he continued softly, 'you're going to have enough of a battle on your hands convincing Harrie into a relationship—without fighting your own feelings too!'

Quinn sat up defensively in his armchair, his expression guarded as he looked across at the older man. 'I think you've misconstrued the situation, Rome,' he began coldly.

'I don't think so,' the other man drawled confidently. 'Remind me to tell you some time of the battle I had trying to woo the girls' mother,' he murmured fondly. 'Harrie is very like her,' he added pointedly. 'And not just in looks.'

'I—'

'Believe me, Quinn,' Rome continued firmly. 'The ones you have to fight for are the ones worth having!'

Quinn felt as if he were becoming more and more entangled in a web he was going to have trouble getting out of. Maybe it would be better if he left now.

He turned sharply towards the door as someone entered after the briefest of knocks, breathing a sigh of relief when he saw it was Audrey Archer, Rome's personal assistant. As long as it wasn't Harrie!

Idiot! he instantly chided himself. As Rome had already guessed, it was Harrie that Quinn had come here to see…!

Audrey Archer gave him a polite smile before turning to her employer. 'You asked me to let you know as soon as we heard from Andie,' she reminded economically. 'She rang through on her mobile a few minutes ago. She and Harrie will be here in about fifteen minutes.' Having delivered her message, Audrey didn't linger in the room, obviously busy with other things.

Not only Harrie, but the youngest Summer sister too, Quinn realised with an inward groan. Hell!

He stood up abruptly. 'I think I had better be on my way—'

'You were invited for the weekend, Quinn,' Rome reminded softly.

He nodded. 'I don't want to interrupt what looks like being a family time—'

'You won't be,' Rome instantly assured him. 'I have several other guests arriving later this afternoon.'

Cornered. And it was his own doing, Quinn acknowledged self-disgustedly. But would it really be so bad? He had wanted to see Harrie again, and it looked as if he was very shortly going to do that. And if there were other guests, then his being here wouldn't look too contrived. Would it…?

Oh, damn it; he wanted to see Harrie again, to look at her, to just drink her in. And if he had to do that surrounded by a lot of other people, it was probably for the best. Perhaps he wouldn't make such an idiot of himself then!

Although Rome's interest in his attraction to Harrie was a little unnerving...

A matchmaking father in the background hadn't entered into his thoughts about Harrie, let alone any relationship he'd had in mind.

A note for future reference, Quinn, he told himself ruefully; never get even close to the woman's father, let alone make a friend out of him!

Although all of those thoughts went out of his head fifteen minutes later when he heard the arrival of a car outside on the driveway, remembering all too vividly how Harrie had looked the last time he had seen her, her dark hair tousled, her lips swollen from the passionate kisses they had just shared, those green eyes mistily sleepy in her arousal.

And how much he had longed, in the last five days, to see her looking like that again!

But the look of intense dislike that washed over her face, when she entered the room a few minutes later and saw him sitting there with her father, did not give him too much hope of that happening in the near future. If ever!

Her father and Quinn McBride!

And sitting here so cosily together, as if the two of them had known each other years, instead of just the week that Harrie actually knew it to be.

What could the two of them be plotting together now? was her next thought as she studied the two of them with narrowed eyes. Someone's downfall, she didn't doubt.

'Rome,' she greeted abruptly, bending to give him a perfunctory kiss on the cheek, still vaguely resentful of the part he'd played in Richard's downfall. Oh, she accepted that Richard had been everything her father and Quinn had claimed him to be, but that didn't mean her own pride hadn't suffered as a result of it. 'Quinn.' She straightened to greet him tensely, her eyes narrowed with suspicion now.

Quinn stood up, and for a moment—a brief, panicked moment!—Harrie thought he was going to step forward and greet her as familiarly as she had her father.

But he merely gave an abrupt inclination of his head. 'Harrie,' he rasped as economically.

She turned back to her father. 'Andie still seems to be suffering from that flu she had last weekend; she's gone to lie down for a while before dinner.'

Rome scowled at this news. 'Damn it, this has gone on long enough; I've a good mind to get a doctor in to her.'

Harrie smiled, shaking her head. 'You know how Andie feels about doctors.'

'She's twenty-five now, not five!' their father rasped impatiently as he stood up.

Her sister Andie had acquired a dislike of doctors, and hospitals, since the age of five, when she'd had to have her tonsils removed. It had become something of a family joke as, over the years, Andie had flatly refused to consult a doctor over anything, preferring to just take to her bed until she felt better.

Not that Harrie felt disposed into explaining that to the obviously puzzled Quinn! Nothing about her family was any of this man's business.

'You can try telling her that, if you like.' Harrie shrugged at her father. 'But I doubt she will listen,' she added from experience. The mildest tempered of the three sisters, Andie could nevertheless become a spitting virago if pushed into a corner. And Harrie didn't doubt that Andie would put suggesting calling in a doctor under that heading.

'I'm going to try anyway,' Rome said grimly, heading towards the door.

Great, Harrie muttered crossly; within two minutes of her arrival she was left alone with Quinn McBride. The last person she wanted to be alone with. Ever.

It hadn't been the easiest of weeks, having to come to terms with Richard's duplicity, her response to Quinn's kisses and caresses, and then finally having to admit to her father that he'd been right about Richard all along.

Although, of the three, she knew which had been the hardest to live with!

And being alone with the cause of this major discomfort was not what she wanted right now.

'How is your sister?' she enquired politely, her gaze not quite making contact with Quinn's as he stood across the room.

'Very well. Thank you for asking,' he added abruptly.

Very polite, weren't they? Harrie thought. But, then, in the circumstances, what else could they be...?

Her father hadn't mentioned that Quinn McBride would be here too this weekend. Deliberately so? Probably, she inwardly acknowledged. Her father was a grand manipulator—and he had known damn well she wouldn't have come within fifty miles of the estate if she'd known Quinn was here!

Every time she thought of that time in Quinn's arms, of the intimacies they'd shared, she cringed with embarrassment. And God knew what Quinn thought of her behaviour!

'No Danie this weekend?'

Harrie looked across at him blankly for several seconds, and then his question penetrated her tortured thoughts. 'She'll be along later,' she answered lightly. 'My father has several other weekend guests arriving this afternoon.'

It was just a pity he hadn't told her that Quinn was to be amongst their number.

His mouth twisted ruefully. 'So he's just informed me.'

'There will be even more arriving for champagne brunch tomorrow.' She grimaced—the 'surprise' her father had presented *her* with took on more the form of a nightmare.

On Monday night she had initially been devastated at the thought of never seeing Quinn again, but as the days had passed she'd been grateful for the fact; how could she ever face him again after her wanton behaviour!

Well, she was facing Quinn now—and it was just as awkward and uncomfortable as she had known it would be!

'Don't be too hard on your father,' Quinn drawled now. 'He only invited me here late yesterday afternoon,' he explained at Harrie's frowning look.

Still time enough for her father to have warned her. If he'd wanted to. Which he obviously hadn't.

'Harrie—'

'Quinn—'

They both began talking at once, only to break off as abruptly, looking at each other warily now.

'You first,' Quinn invited ruefully.

She twisted her hands together in front of her. 'I just wanted to say that—' she drew in a ragged breath, still unable to look at him directly '—Monday evening. What happened.' She could feel the hot colour entering her cheeks as she spoke of that embarrassing incident. 'I was—very—emotional.' She swallowed hard. 'After what had happened with Richard. And I had drunk some wine, too, after the doctor warned me not to with the antibiotics—'

'You know, Harrie,' Quinn cut in softly, 'this way you have of meeting things head on is only one of the things I like about you.'

Now she did look at him, her heart pounding in her chest as she took in his appearance for the first time, the casual black denims and pale blue shirt adding to his ruggedness, the relaxed handsomeness of his face only making her heart beat faster.

She'd never just looked at a man before and known that she physically wanted him. But with Quinn…!

'Only one of the things?' she challenged mockingly, defensive in her feelings of weakness towards this man.

Quinn's mouth quirked with amusement. 'Fishing, Harrie?' he taunted.

'No! Certainly not,' she corrected mildly. 'If you will excuse me, Quinn,' she added abruptly, 'I think I'll just go up and check on Andie.'

'It seems to me that there are already enough people 'checking' on Andie,' he drawled derisively. 'And wouldn't it be very rude to leave one of your father's guests here alone?' He quirked dark brows.

Harrie gave a dismissive shrug. 'I would say that's my father's problem, not mine,' she bit out sharply. 'I didn't invite you here, Quinn, so don't attempt to monopolise my attention,' she added cuttingly.

He drew in a hissing breath, his expression coldly arrogant now. 'You're excused, Harrie,' he snapped icily.

Her eyes flashed deeply green as she looked across at him. 'Don't start ordering me about, Quinn,' she rasped. 'I'm not one of your minions!'

His mouth quirked in a humourless smile. 'Harrie, I wouldn't employ you if you were the last lawyer left in the world!'

She gasped. 'Why, you—'

'And I have to say, Harrie,' he continued mildly, 'that although there are a lot of things I *do* like about you— your temper isn't one of them! Apart from the fact that it makes you look more beautiful than ever, that lack of con-

trol also hints at a recklessness in your nature that would
be totally unacceptable in the banking world. You—'

'I think you've already made yourself more than clear,'
Harrie burst out angrily, the colour in her cheeks from
anger now rather than her embarrassment of earlier.

And this last week she had fought against what she'd
believed was her attraction towards this man…! But not
any more! He was arrogant, condescending, totally lacking
in humour—

She was being unfair now, and she knew that she was.
But Quinn seemed to have the power to hurt or annoy her
with just a few misplaced words. If they were misplaced…?

'I'm sure we will meet again at dinner, Quinn,' she said
stiltedly. 'But other than that I'm sure we can manage to
stay out of each other's way for the rest of the weekend!'
She turned on her heel and marched briskly out of the
room, closing the door firmly behind her.

Only to lean weakly back against it, her vision becoming
blurred as the hot tears flooded her eyes.

But what had she expected? That after Monday evening
the two of them would fall into each other's arms when
they saw each other again? She didn't want that anyway—
so why did she feel so hurt and upset that Quinn had
shown himself to be so emotionally detached?

Because *she* wasn't, damn it. She only wished that she
were!

But somehow—and she had no idea how, when she and
Quinn seemed to do nothing but argue every time they
met!—Quinn McBride had stepped into her life and refused to leave.

And her heart…?

CHAPTER EIGHT

QUINN watched Harrie with a jaundiced eye as she circulated unhurriedly about the room, stopping to chat to each of the guests gathered in the sitting-room for a pre-dinner drink, her occasional husky laugh grating on his already ragged nerve-endings.

She reminded him of a butterfly, flitting from flower to flower, never stopping for long, but moving steadfastly on before she could be drawn into a lengthy conversation.

She looked like a butterfly too, Quinn thought dourly, a red admiral, her hair looking almost black against the blazing red of the short dress that clung so lovingly to the willowy curves of her body.

And not once, he acknowledged frustratedly, had her gaze so much as rested on him as he'd stood alone near the window, that flitting she was doing from group to group of people never including him.

'Dear, dear, dear, Mr McBride, what have you done to annoy my big sister?' an amused voice drawled mockingly at his side.

Quinn turned sharply to find Danie Summer, the middle daughter, had quietly come to stand beside him, looking the exact opposite of Harrie, her long hair blazing fiery-red down her spine, her short black dress clinging no less lovingly to her own slender curves.

More surprising, she was actually smiling at him! Last weekend she'd been decidedly unfriendly, Quinn remembered with an inward grimace, and in the circumstances— that of being totally ignored by Harrie!—he found the change in Danie more than welcome. Even if her opening remark had been about Harrie!

'Nothing—as far as I'm aware,' he answered dryly.

Danie shook her head mockingly. 'Our daddy told us it was very naughty to tell a lie!' She quirked mocking auburn brows.

Quinn chuckled huskily at this completely unexpected sense of humour from a woman he had hitherto thought bossy to the point of rudeness. 'And your father was quite right to do so,' Quinn happily joined in the slightly flirtatious conversation.

Anything was better than standing here on his own glowering across the room at Harrie! A Harrie who now seemed to have stopped flitting, and was deep in conversation with a tall, rather distinguished-looking, silver-blond-haired man. Damn it, she seemed to be attracted to blond-haired men!

And his inattentiveness was unfair to Danie, who, in truth, didn't have to talk to him at all if she didn't want to. Despite 'her daddy's' efforts to teach his daughters good manners!

'The truth of the matter is, Danie—' he sighed, dragging his attention away from Harrie and the man she was animatedly talking to '—your "big sister" just doesn't like me!' He grimaced.

She took a thoughtful sip of her champagne. 'No?'

Quinn shrugged. 'Afraid not.'

'And, of course—' Danie gave a derisive smile '—you have no idea why that is?'

Oh, he knew exactly why that was; Harrie hadn't liked him before Monday evening, but she had even less reason to do so after that! Not only had his actions shown Harrie what an utter bastard Richard Heaton was, but he had as quickly shown her he was no better by attempting to make love to her himself. Rather a lot for Harrie to forgive him for, he acknowledged heavily. And she obviously hadn't succeeded!

If she had even tried…!

'I could take a pretty accurate guess as to why,' he answered Danie ruefully. 'But I'm not about to bore you with the details,' he added dryly as he saw the speculative glint in her eyes. Eyes, he noticed for the first time, the same colour emerald as her older sister…

Quinn wondered vaguely whether the youngest sister, Andie, would have those same drowning green eyes… He obviously wasn't about to find out tonight; Rome had grimly made his youngest daughter's excuses for dinner when he'd entered the room five minutes ago. But as Rome had very blue eyes, the sisters' emerald green must have come from their mother. If they had also inherited their mother's beauty, as Rome claimed they had, then it was no wonder Rome had been so determined to win her all those years ago!

'But, I can assure you, I wouldn't be bored,' Danie teased.

He gave a humourless smile. 'Nevertheless…'

'I could take a guess myself on it having something to do with the treacherous Richard Heaton,' Danie said disgustedly.

Quinn raised dark brows. 'You know about him?'

Danie smiled, green eyes laughing at his surprise. 'Sisters, especially ones who have been without their mother for ten years—' she sobered slightly '—tend to rely on—confide in—each other more than they would normally. I knew weeks ago that Harrie was seeing Richard Heaton,' she added scathingly. 'Not exactly my type. Too smoothly charming.' She grimaced. 'But he seemed okay.' She shrugged. 'It hurt Harrie pretty badly that he turned out to be such a rat,' she added dismissively.

Quinn wasn't sure he wanted to hear this. In fact, he

knew he didn't. The last thing he needed to know was how much Harrie was still hurting from Richard Heaton's betrayal.

But if the sisters were as close as Danie claimed they were...he couldn't help wondering whether Harrie had also 'confided' anything concerning him to Danie...?

Danie smiled as she astutely read his thoughts. 'As a matter of fact, no,' she murmured slowly, looking at him speculatively over the rim of her glass as she took another sip of her champagne. 'Which, in itself, is very interesting,' she added enigmatically.

'It is?' Quinn attempted to prompt casually—and failed miserably, he knew as he saw Danie's smile widen. The trouble was, there was nothing in the least 'casual' about his feelings towards Harrie.

'Oh, yes,' Danie confirmed lightly. 'I don't— My big sister is about to join us,' she muttered warningly under her breath. 'Why don't you try looking as if you find me wildly interesting—and see what happens?' she suggested wickedly.

Quinn couldn't help laughing at the impishly taunting smile she threw his way before turning to warmly greet her sister. There was obviously much more to Danie Summer than he had first realised!

Although he didn't give that realisation another thought as he also turned to look at Harrie, his own expression defensively wary. Which was probably as well, Harrie returning that gaze with cold disdain!

'Still here, Quinn?' she said sharply.

He drew in a harsh breath at her deliberate rudeness. 'As I'm sure you're well aware, I'm your father's guest, not yours!' he snapped pointedly.

And then wished he had held on to his temper. How could he ever hope to get close to Harrie again if they argued every time they met...?

'I'm sorry,' he bit out abruptly. 'That was uncalled for.'

'I believe that's your cue to apologise for your own rudeness...?' Danie told her sister pointedly.

'Shut up, Danie,' Harrie snapped irritably, looking relieved when Audrey chose that moment to announce it was time for them all to go in to dinner.

'In that case—' Danie linked her arm with Quinn's '—you won't mind if Quinn takes me in to dinner, will you?' She quirked auburn brows at her older sister.

'Why on earth should I mind?' Harrie scorned. 'I've already promised Adam that I shall go in to dinner with him,' she announced with satisfaction, leaving them, to bestow a glowing smile on the distinguished-looking man she'd been talking to a few minutes ago.

Quinn scowled as, having returned to the other man's side, Harrie linked her arm as intimately with his as Danie was now doing with his own.

'Careful, Quinn,' Danie drawled softly at his side, 'your jealousy is starting to show!'

'Jealousy!' he snapped angrily. 'I would like to tan her backside!'

Danie laughed softly as the two of them strolled through to the dining-room. 'I wouldn't give her being with Adam another thought; we've all known him for years,' she added dismissively.

Quinn still thought Harrie could have stood a little further away from the other man, and she certainly didn't have to pull her chair that intimately close to his as the two of them sat across and slightly down the table from Danie and himself in the dining-room!

Damn it, his jealousy wasn't just showing; it was eating him alive!

'You've probably heard of him,' Danie continued conversationally as she saw he was still distracted by the other couple. 'Adam Munroe,' she supplied at Quinn's frowning look.

Adam Munroe! The Adam Munroe?

'The film producer?' he prompted as lightly as he felt able—which came out more as a grating of teeth!

'The one and only,' Danie confirmed brightly.

Quinn looked across at the other man with new eyes. There was no doubting that the other man would be attractive to women, with that blond hair shot through with silver, an aristocratically handsome face, and possessed of an air of cynicism that probably owed nothing to his late thirties in age but more to the world of film-making where he had made his fortune.

A film producer or a banker! Could the two men really be further apart, in career as well as in looks?

And there was no doubting which of the two Harrie found the more exciting as her husky laugh rang out once again!

Quinn sighed. 'I suppose it's too much to hope that he's already married?'

'A bachelor through and through.' Danie laughed at Quinn's expense. 'He's a friend of Daddy's, Quinn,' she added in a bored voice, obviously not impressed herself, either by the other man's looks or profession. 'Oh, for goodness' sake, Quinn, Adam has known us all since we had pigtails and braces on our teeth!' she assured him impatiently.

Quinn looked at her with raised brows as her smile showed him a row of even white teeth. 'I commend your orthodontist,' he murmured dryly, having a problem associating either Harrie or Danie with pigtails let alone braces on their teeth; they were both such beautiful women, in a totally individual way, it was difficult to imagine either of them any other way!

'Forget the orthodontist,' Danie snapped with some of

her old sharpness. 'The point I'm trying to make, Quinn, is that Adam no more has a romantic interest in Harrie than she does in him. The two of them are just playing the socially polite game of flirtation!' she added exasperatedly as he continued to look less than convinced.

Quinn understood her exasperation with him, wished he could believe what she was saying. But as dinner progressed, and he watched the couple on the other side of the table seeming completely engrossed in each other, he found it very hard to accept.

Not that Danie wasn't an entertaining dining companion herself, telling him several funny anecdotes, edged, of course, with that sarcastic asperity that seemed such a part of her nature. She even made him laugh a couple of times—which was a feat in itself when he felt so little like laughing.

But all the time he listened or spoke to Danie he was aware of Harrie sitting further down the table. And, from her complete preoccupation with Adam Munroe, she was no longer even aware of Quinn's presence in the room!

Quinn and Danie, Harrie silently accused inside—even as she appeared to listen attentively to what Adam was saying.

She wouldn't have believed it if she hadn't witnessed it with her own eyes. Oh, not that she thought Danie was serious in the flirtation; she knew her sister's views on meaningless relationships too well to believe that. But the same couldn't be said for Quinn; Harrie had no doubts that he had meaningless relationships off to a fine art!

What was he trying to do? she fumed inwardly. Work his way through the Summer sisters, until one of them actually fell into his arms? Well, as far as she was concerned he was going to have a long wait, and Andie was in no fit state to be charmed by anyone. Which brought her back to Danie…

But her younger sister certainly seemed to be enjoying herself, Harrie noticed with a frown…

'Your father was telling me earlier that Andie isn't well again?'

It took tremendous effort on Harrie's part to drag her attention back to what Adam had just said, her head full of visions of one day having to welcome Quinn into the family—as her brother-in-law!

'Harrie…?' Adam prompted gently.

Pull yourself together, Harrie, she instructed herself firmly. Quinn and Danie were only talking together—not making wedding plans!

'She has the flu,' she answered Adam distractedly.

He made a face. 'I thought Rome said that was what was wrong with her last weekend, which was the reason she was unable to be at the Summer Fête…?'

The Summer Fête… The scene of her first meeting with Quinn McBride. Was that really only a week ago…?

'It was,' Harrie confirmed inattentively, having noticed now that Danie and Quinn had both refused coffee, excusing themselves from the table to stroll out of the dining-room together.

To go where? she frowned.

Despite the fact that Quinn was—as he'd reminded her all too forcefully earlier!—her father's guest, Harrie had secretly believed—hoped?—Quinn had really come here to see her again.

Idiot! she chided herself disgustedly. So Quinn had kissed her on Monday. Maybe more than kissed her, she allowed grudgingly. That didn't mean it had meant anything to him.

As it had to her…?

She shied away from such a thought. Just because Quinn

had now turned his attention to Danie was no reason for her to feel—to feel what? Hurt? Betrayed? *Jealous?*

'Actually, Harrie, you don't look too well yourself,' Adam said concernedly as he looked at her closely.

'Really, Adam,' she replied teasingly. 'That is hardly gallant! But as it happens—' she sobered, taking pity on him as he looked a little sheepish at the rebuke '—I'm still recovering from a throat infection.'

And a bruised heart?

But who'd done the bruising?

There was no doubting the fact that she had felt a fool over her mistake concerning Richard, but she'd reasoned that out over this last week, and had realised, from the hurtful things Richard had said to her on Monday evening, that he'd just been using her, that as Rome Summer's daughter she had opened doors for him that might otherwise have been closed. Harrie had also realised that the man she'd thought herself in love with simply didn't exist.

But there was still an unexplainable ache in her heart—which had nothing whatsoever to do with Richard.

And everything to do with Quinn McBride...?

A lot of good that was going to do her, when he now seemed to have transferred his interest to Danie!

What was *wrong* with her? She couldn't be in love with Quinn—could she...?

Of course not, she told herself firmly. Love happened slowly, between two people who liked each other, who enjoyed each other's company—it didn't come bursting into your life riding roughshod over everything, and everyone, else in your life. Certainly not in the guise of Quinn McBride!

That decided, she turned attentively to Adam. 'Would you like to take a stroll outside in the garden?'

He raised blond brows. 'This is all very sudden, Miss Summer.' He pretended to be shocked by her invitation.

Harrie gave him a playful punch on the shoulder. 'Don't be ridiculous, Adam,' she dismissed easily. 'I'm not one of your impressionable actresses; my invitation for a walk in the garden meant exactly that!'

'I know.' Adam sighed his disappointment, standing up to pull back her chair for her, and the two of them strolled over to make their excuses to Harrie's father. 'If I'm ever in need of having my feet planted firmly back on the ground, I just pay the Summer sisters a visit; you never hesitate to let me know just how unimpressed you all are!'

Harrie laughed huskily. 'I'm glad we're useful for something!' Having reached her father, she bent down to kiss him lightly on the cheek. 'Adam is taking me outside for a romantic stroll in the garden,' she excused with a teasing grin in Adam's direction.

Her father looked slightly perplexed. 'I've given up even trying to keep up with you girls.' He shook his head. 'Just make sure you tell me when any of you decide to get married—and to whom!' he added disgustedly.

Adam kept a light hold on her elbow as they walked outside. 'What was all that about?' he prompted, frowning.

Harrie gave a dismissive shrug, having no intention of explaining any of the circumstances of this last week to this friend of the family. Although she was in no doubt herself as to what her father was alluding to: Danie, and not herself, was the daughter who'd left the room with Quinn, and now Harrie was going outside with Adam. No wonder Rome was confused!

But it was not conducive, to a stroll or anything else, when the two of them walked out onto the patio to find Danie and Quinn sitting there together in the semi-darkness!

Harrie stiffened at the sight of her sister sitting so close beside Quinn on one of the wicker sofas. But at least they were only sitting together, she reasoned a few seconds later; it could have been much worse!

Quinn stood up abruptly at their approach, his eyes glittering brightly in the semi-darkness of the summer evening, although he made no effort to speak.

Harrie didn't know what to say, either. Which was odd in itself; she usually had plenty to say to Quinn!

'You're looking particularly handsome this evening, Adam,' Danie drawled as she stood up beside Quinn to kiss the other man lightly on the cheek.

Harrie frowned; was that a mocking glance Danie also shot in Quinn's direction? And if it were, for what reason?

'Let's take it as said that we all look wonderful this evening,' Adam derided dismissively, looking curiously at Quinn.

Of course, the two men probably hadn't been introduced, Harrie realised belatedly. Well, that was easily rectified.

'Adam Munroe. Quinn McBride.' Her voice hardened slightly over the second name, giving a slight shiver as Quinn turned to look at her with arctic-blue eyes.

What was wrong with him? She was the one who'd made a fool of herself earlier in the week, not him, so why should he be looking at her so accusingly? Besides, it hadn't taken him long to find someone else to flirt with!

'Cold, love?' Adam noticed her shiver concernedly, putting an altogether wrong interpretation on it. 'Here, take my jacket—'

'No!' Harrie protested as he began to shrug out of the pristine black evening jacket. 'I'm not cold. Really,' she assured him hastily as she could see he wasn't convinced. There was a dangerous glitter in Quinn's gaze as he watched the exchange—a gaze she was unable to meet!

'Perhaps we should go back inside, anyway.' Adam still

frowned. 'There's a slight chill in the air, and we don't want your throat infection to flare up again.'

Her five-day course of antibiotics had already taken care of that. But the suggestion they go back inside, in view of the fact that Danie and Quinn were out here too, sounded like a good one to Harrie...

'No, we certainly wouldn't want that, would we?' Quinn rasped harshly before she could answer Adam.

Harrie gave him a sharp look. Why on earth was he so angry? Okay, so she hadn't exactly been polite to him earlier, but they weren't exactly polite to each other most of the time, were they?

'It is getting a little chilly; why don't we all go back inside to the library and have a nightcap together?' Danie put in lightly.

Harrie shot her sister an accusing look. What was Danie playing at? Her sister knew exactly what had happened between Richard and herself earlier this week, and the part Quinn had played in it—which meant Danie also had to know that a cosy nightcap with Quinn, a witness to her humiliation, was the last thing she wanted!

'An excellent idea.' Adam instantly accepted the suggestion. 'The beauties of nature have never been high on my list of "have-to-sees"!' he explained dryly.

Adam had never made any secret of the fact that he found the removal of his friend Rome, along with his wife and three daughters, to this country estate bizarre in the extreme. He was a townie to his fingertips, and the last twenty years of visiting them at Summer Manor hadn't changed Adam's opinion of the countryside one iota!

Danie laughed at his obvious aversion, moving to link her arm with his. 'Come along, my poor pet,' she drawled tauntingly, 'I'll take you back inside, away from the horrible moths and flies!'

Harrie watched disbelievingly as her sister strolled back

into the house with Adam—leaving her alone outside with Quinn!

She looked up at him beneath lowered lashes, stiffening resentfully as she saw he was looking at her warily. What did he think she was going to do now that the two of them were alone in the moonlight: pounce on him?

'Come along, Quinn,' she snapped, turning away. 'It seems we're about to have a nightcap together!' But before she'd managed to walk two steps she found her arm grasped as she was turned roughly back to face him.

'You certainly haven't wasted any time, have you?' Quinn grated scornfully. 'You've given "off with the old, on with the new" a completely new meaning as far as I'm concerned!'

'What on earth—?' she gasped as Quinn's fingers dug painfully into her arms that were still covered in the bruises inflicted by Richard.

'Munroe!' Quinn bit out with distaste.

Her eyes widened at the unmistakable accusation. 'Are you saying—? Implying—?'

'Both of those things,' he confirmed disgustedly. 'And I've been feeling like a heel this last week because I kissed you on Monday evening!' He shook his head. 'I should have pressed home my advantage when I had the chance!'

Harrie could feel herself pale, staring up at him with dark green eyes. 'You're fooling yourself if you believe you ever *had* the advantage, Quinn,' she told him dully.

'Am I?' he scorned, his aqua-blue eyes glittering down at her with dislike. 'Maybe. But maybe not. As the experience will never be repeated, we'll never know the answer to that, will we?' He thrust her away from him. 'I'll wish you a pleasant night, Harrie,' he added. 'Make my excuses to your sister concerning the nightcap, will you? If I have to be with you a minute longer I think it would choke me!'

He turned sharply on his heel and strode forcefully back into the house.

Harrie dropped down weakly into one of the wicker patio chairs, her face buried in her hands.

Quinn despised her. It had been there in his expression, in his eyes, in his words and the tone of his voice.

Quinn despised her—and she—she *loved* him!

She'd been wrong, so very wrong. Liking didn't always come first. Love didn't always grow between two people who were already friends.

Because she loved Quinn, ached with loving him. And he'd just made it quite clear that he despised her...!

CHAPTER NINE

HE HAD slept badly, Quinn acknowledged with a groan as he opened one eye to look at the bedside clock, and saw it was only seven-thirty. The time he usually woke up at home to go to work!

Except he wasn't at home, was still at the Summer estate. Although he wished himself a hundred miles away from here…!

It had been barely ten o'clock when he'd retired to his room the evening before, and, after pacing those confines for well over an hour, he'd finally given up, making his way quietly down the wide staircase, in the hope of being unobserved by any of the guests who'd still been downstairs, before leaving the house completely to go for a walk in the chilly evening air.

It had done little to improve his chances of sleeping, his mind consumed with thoughts of Harrie. As she had last looked.

As if he had just hit her…!

And in a way, he had, he'd realised as he'd walked away from the house. His last words to her had been chosen deliberately to hurt.

As he'd been hurting all evening as he'd watched her with Adam Munroe…?

Damn it, yes!

He couldn't bear the thought of any other man being near her, talking to her, let alone hearing her laughing with them. Because—as he'd acknowledged somewhere around one o'clock this morning, as he'd walked back through the neighbouring wood trying to find his way back to the house—he wanted all of that for himself. He wanted *Harrie* for himself!

He sat up in the bed with a groan, swinging his legs to the floor, his expression despondent. What was he going to do about these feelings he had for Harrie? What could he do? Because there was no doubting that, after last night, he had totally alienated her. He would be lucky if she ever spoke to him again, let alone anything else!

Even one of her insults would be welcome at the moment, Quinn decided ruefully.

He stood up abruptly as he heard the sound of voices down on the driveway outside through his partly open window, arriving at that window just in time to see Danie standing on the gravel below, watching Harrie as she rode away on the back of a huge black horse.

Quinn watched Harrie too, admiring the way she sat on the huge animal as if she were a part of it, bent low over the horse's neck, her long dark hair streaming out behind her.

He hadn't realised she could ride. But, then, there were still a lot of things he didn't know about Harrie! Or was ever likely to find out now…?

'Why don't you come down and join me for coffee?'

Quinn turned sharply from where he'd just watched Harrie, sitting confidently astride the horse, as she disappeared amongst the trees he'd been temporarily lost in last night. Obviously she wasn't going to have the same problem…

Danie grinned up at him as he looked down at her, her hand over her eyes to shield them from the dazzling bright sunshine. 'Come down and have some coffee with me,' she invited again lightly. 'But put some clothes on first, hmm?' she added derisively.

Quinn became instantly aware of the fact that he was standing at the window, in full view of anyone who cared to look up, wearing only a pair of black underpants! And that Danie, with a display of her usual wicked sense of humour, was now laughing at his obvious discomfort at that fact!

He held up an acknowledging hand. 'I'll be down in a few minutes,' he agreed dryly.

Danie nodded. 'I'll keep the coffee warm!'

One thing he was quickly learning to do, when around the acerbic Danie Summer, was to laugh at himself, Quinn acknowledged as he went through to the adjoining bathroom to take a shower. If he didn't, she would do it for him!

'I would offer you more than coffee—' Danie shrugged when Quinn joined her in the otherwise deserted breakfast-room fifteen minutes later '—but it's Sunday, and we all have to wait until everyone else is up, and the other guests arrive, before we can have brunch.' Her grimace of disgust showed exactly what she thought of that arrangement.

'Coffee will be fine,' Quinn accepted as he sat down opposite her; after his lack of sleep last night he couldn't even bear the thought of food at the moment!

'In case you were worried earlier,' Danie drawled, holding out a steaming cup of coffee to him, 'Harrie has been riding almost since she could walk.'

Quinn kept his expression deliberately bland; this young lady was far too astute to allow his barriers to slip! 'I wasn't worried,' he told Danie truthfully; it was obvious, even to a novice like himself, that Harrie was a first-class horsewoman.

Danie arched auburn brows. 'No?'

'No,' Quinn informed dryly. 'Danie, exactly why do you think that I would be in the least worried about Harrie riding that huge black monster?' he derided.

'His name is Ebony,' Danie corrected firmly. 'And the

reason I thought you might be worried about Harrie is because you're in love with her.'

Quinn almost choked over the sip of hot coffee he had been in the process of taking. He swallowed it down as he stared disbelievingly at Danie, stunned by the boldness of the statement she had just made.

In love with Harrie!

He was?

'Correct me if I'm wrong,' Danie commenced slowly, 'but—'

'You're wrong!' Quinn cut in firmly before she could say anything else to shake him. Although that last remark must rate a ten on the Richter scale!

Because there was no doubting Danie had shaken him with that casually made statement. Because he'd never been in love with any woman. And he certainly wasn't in love with the prickly Harrie Summer now!

He wanted her. Desired her. To the point where he didn't want any other man near her, he admitted... But that didn't mean he was *in love with her*, damn it!

'What conclusions did you just come to?' Danie asked him interestedly, obviously having watched him as he'd digested the possibility of being in love with Harrie—and as quickly dismissed it as being ridiculous! 'It doesn't matter.' She sighed dismissively. 'I thought I was stubborn.' Danie shook her head disgustedly. 'But you two are much worse.'

'Two?' Quinn prompted as lightly as he was able.

'Two,' Danie confirmed scathingly. 'Harrie won't admit—to me, at any rate!—that she's in love with you, either!'

Quinn swallowed hard, carefully putting his cup back down on its saucer before answering. 'Maybe that's because she isn't.' He shrugged.

'Rubbish,' Danie scorned.

Quinn couldn't help grinning at her disgusted expression. 'I wouldn't change your profession and take up matchmaking, if I were you,' he teased. 'You would make a complete hash of it!'

'Very funny!' Danie wrinkled her nose at him. 'You—'

'This looks very cosy,' rasped a harsh voice. 'Would it be too much of an interruption if I joined you for a cup of coffee?'

Quinn had looked up sharply at the sound of Harrie's voice, a shutter coming down over his inner thoughts as he took in how beautiful she looked after her early morning ride. Her hair was loose and tangled down her back, her eyes sparkled, and there was a healthy glow in her cheeks. A little like how she would look when making love, he thought achingly.

'Of course you can join us,' Danie assured her sister warmly. 'I don't think anyone else is awake yet,' she dismissed, pouring out the third cup of coffee and pushing it across the table to the place next to where Quinn sat.

He looked with narrowed eyes at the mischief-making redhead, knowing she had deliberately put the coffee there so that Harrie had to sit next to him. But he should have realised, as should Danie—with Harrie there was no 'had to' about anything!

'Thanks.' Harrie leant forward and moved the coffee-cup to the end of the table—as far away from Quinn as it was possible for her to sit! 'I'm a bit hot and sticky after my morning ride,' she gruffly excused the reason for her distance, before burying her face in the coffee-cup.

Danie grinned across at Quinn knowingly. 'Of course you are,' she acknowledged dryly before standing up. 'I hope you'll both excuse me; I have a few things to do for Rome before brunch.'

Quinn watched frustratedly as Danie turned and left the room. Damn it, she had done it again: manoeuvred him into a situation—as she had outside in the garden last night—and then just walked off and left him alone with Harrie. A Harrie, he was sure, who certainly didn't want to be alone with him!

Harrie lowered her coffee-cup slowly, her expression wary as she looked across at him with apprehensive green eyes.

An apprehension he had put there last night, Quinn realised, when he'd been so insulting to her. Damn it, Harrie was the last person he wanted to hurt—and the one person that he constantly seemed to be doing so!

Neither of them spoke after Danie's departure, the seconds slowly slipping past, the silence stretching awkwardly between them, the atmosphere becoming more and more tense.

This was ridiculous, Quinn finally decided. But the reason for the tension was mainly his own doing, he also acknowledged...

He gave a deep sigh. 'I believe I owe you yet another apology,' he bit out tautly.

Harrie raised dark brows uninterestedly. 'You do?' She frowned.

'Yes,' he rasped. 'I said some pretty—damning things, to you last night. And—'

'Actually, I would say they were more insulting than damning,' Harrie interrupted softly, slowly putting down her coffee-cup. 'But there was probably a lot of truth in what you said, too,' she added dryly.

Quinn frowned. 'You mean you are involved with Munroe?' Surely Danie hadn't been wrong about that situation, after all...? His chest tightened, and his hands clenched under the table just at the thought of it!

Harrie gave a softly humourless laugh. 'No, I don't mean that at all,' she dismissed. 'I'm no more Adam's type than he is mine. Adam likes his women small, fluffy, and dependent. I think you would agree, Quinn—' she quirked dark brows at him mockingly '—that I'm out on all three counts!'

As she was five feet eight inches tall in her bare feet, with a very determined nature, and an independence that bordered on arrogance, Quinn would have to say he did agree! But, then, up until a week ago, Harrie wouldn't have been his type, either! Things, and people, changed...

Because Harrie was certainly 'his type' now—in fact, she made every other woman seem insipid and uninteresting in comparison!

'What I meant, Quinn,' Harrie continued heavily at his silence, 'was that, in retrospect, it must have looked as if I were flirting with Adam yesterday evening.' She grimaced. 'The truth of the matter is I've been feeling a little...raw, since—well, since Richard, and maybe I did overreact with Adam last night.' She avoided his gaze. 'To put it in Danie's words, I was "all over the man"!'

Danie again. He'd actually come to like the other woman over the last twelve hours or so—but that didn't alter the fact that she had a way of saying things that would be better left unsaid!

And if Harrie had needed to 'overreact' with some man, why couldn't it have been him?

He shook his head, smiling ruefully. 'I shouldn't take too much notice of what Danie says, if I were you,' he drawled. 'She's great fun to be with, but her powers of observation aren't very accurate!' On two counts that he knew of: he wasn't in love with Harrie—and she most definitely wasn't in love with him! '"All over the man" sounds like an exaggeration to me,' he added dismissively.

Over-friendly more adequately described it, he decided. Although last night, before he'd had time to calm down, he would probably have agreed with Danie's summing up of the situation...! In fact, he had!

'It does?' Harrie said hopefully.

'Yes.' Quinn smiled reassuringly.

'Thank heavens for that!' Harrie gave a relieved sigh. 'After what Danie said earlier, I was beginning to wonder how I would ever be able to face Adam again,' she added ruefully.

Face *Adam*…! What about him? Obviously he didn't even come into the equation, Quinn realised angrily.

'Thanks for the coffee and conversation,' Harrie said lightly, standing up. 'I had better go up to my room now; I need to shower and change before the others start to come down.'

Before Adam came down, Quinn muttered to himself once Harrie had left the breakfast-room!

Damn it, on top of everything else, he was talking to himself now!

Since meeting Harrie Summer he'd found himself doing lots of things he'd never done before, such as insulting a woman, kissing her against her will, and, worst of all— chasing after her!

And Harrie Summer was that woman!

As quickly as it had risen, his anger abated. There had to be a reason he was acting so out of character. But the only reason he could come up with was so unbelievable that it left him paralysed with shock.

Could Danie be right…? Could he be in love with Harrie…?

Harrie breathed a sigh of relief once she was outside in the hallway. But she didn't linger there, hurrying up to the privacy of her bedroom, closing the door thankfully behind her.

Her first instinct, on arriving back in the house after her ride and hearing the sound of Danie and Quinn's voices coming from the breakfast-room, had been to go quietly up to her bedroom before they realised she was there.

Her second instinct had told her not to be such a coward, that she would have to face Quinn again some time today, and maybe it would be better if it were done now, with only Danie as a witness.

She'd received a jolt to her confidence when she'd seen how relaxed Danie and Quinn looked in each other's company, the two of them laughing together over something as she'd entered the breakfast-room. And why shouldn't they enjoy each other's company? Before leaving for her ride, Harrie had very firmly told Danie that she had absolutely no romantic interest in Quinn.

Leaving the way clear for Danie with Quinn if that was what her sister decided she wanted…?

And hadn't Quinn just told her that he found Danie 'fun to be with'…?

Something Harrie was sure he didn't find her. But, then, there hadn't been that much for her to laugh about since she'd first met Quinn! Not that that was Quinn's fault; he wasn't responsible for the fact that Richard had turned out to be such a swine. It just meant that she and Quinn had started off badly—and it had deteriorated from there, she acknowledged with a groan.

Quinn found Danie 'fun to be with'…

Those words kept going round and round in her head until she could have screamed. Danie was fun, the two of them the best of friends as well as sisters—but that didn't mean Harrie could ever sit back and watch Danie and Quinn together.

But what choice would she have if that was the way things turned out?

None, she realised achingly.

Her tears mingled with the shower water as she stood under the punishing spray. She couldn't—wouldn't—compete with her own sister for the man she loved. Besides, Quinn himself had shown a decided preference for her beautiful and witty sister.

She would have to get through today as best she could, Harrie finally decided. The future—especially one that might include Danie and Quinn being together!—would have to wait.

But it didn't help in that decision that the first people she saw, when she came outside onto the sun-warm patio to greet their guests before brunch, were David Hampton and Corinne Westley—Quinn's sister!

Rome hadn't mentioned that he'd invited the other couple here today—but, then, he hadn't told her he had invited Quinn for the weekend, either!

'Harrie!' Corinne greeted her warmly, obviously relaxed and happy now the tension of the last few weeks was at last over, looking glowingly beautiful in a sun-dress the exact colour of her aqua-blue eyes.

Quinn's eyes...

Harrie mentally shook herself, returning the other woman's smile as she tried to push thoughts of Quinn from her mind. Which wasn't very easy when confronted with his sister!

'It's lovely to see you both again,' she murmured politely as David bent to kiss her lightly on the cheek.

'And under such different circumstances.' Corinne squeezed her hands warmly in recognition of the part she believed Harrie had played in that change of circumstances.

'Quinn is around somewhere,' Harrie told the other woman noncommittally, feeling rather guilty at the other woman's obvious gratitude. Corinne still had no idea that until five days ago Richard Heaton had been a friend of hers—and Harrie would rather it remained that way!

The fewer people that knew of that particular stupidity on her part, the better!

There were already a dozen or so guests sitting down in the wicker chairs, or standing around on the patio, chatting easily together. But a quick look round showed Harrie that neither Danie or Quinn were here yet. Because they were somewhere together...?

'Have you said hello to Rome yet?' she prompted forcefully, having spotted her father a short distance away as he chatted easily with Adam.

'When we arrived,' David confirmed easily.

Now what did she do with them? Harrie frowned. Not that she didn't think the smoothly confident politician and the beautiful Corinne couldn't very well take care of themselves in any social situation; it was just that as their host's daughter she felt an obligation not to just walk away and leave them to it! But, in actual fact, Quinn's sister was the last person she wanted to talk to.

'Come and meet Adam Munroe,' she suggested lightly, not feeling she was being too unfair to Adam; he always liked to be introduced to a beautiful woman, and Corinne was certainly that!

The five of them were chatting comfortably together when Harrie saw Quinn's arrival onto the patio. Actually, she had felt him there before she saw him, experiencing a tingling sensation down the length of her spine that made her turn and look in Quinn's direction.

Just Quinn. There was no Danie at his side.

She smiled her relief, turning back to make her excuses to the others before strolling over to greet Quinn. 'Corinne and David have arrived,' she told him unnecessarily, sure he must have seen his sister and her fiancé standing beside her father and Adam when he'd glanced across at their group a few seconds ago.

But she had to find something to say to him; she was

determined he should never guess at this second—even more devastating!—folly of hers. And loving a man as detached as she knew Quinn McBride to be had to be her biggest folly of all!

'Really?' He scowled, looking around irritatedly until he saw Corinne and David talking to Rome. 'I had no idea they were going to be here,' he muttered grimly.

And that he wasn't pleased by the fact was obvious. But why wasn't he? Harrie wondered. Her father was exactly the sort of wealthy and influential man David Hampton should cultivate if he were intent on getting to the top in politics. Besides, after the way her father had helped Corinne last weekend, it was only natural that the three of them should meet up at some time...

She turned to look at Quinn searchingly. Only to find him looking down at her as intently, those aqua-blue eyes narrowed, and as unfathomable as the sea they resembled.

'Quinn, what is it?' she burst out when she could stand the rapidly building tension between them no longer.

A nerve pulsed in his rigidly clenched jaw. 'I need to talk to you,' he finally rasped.

Her frown deepened as she searched the hard planes of his face for some sign of what he needed to talk to her about. But she was wasting her time; his eyes were icy as an arctic sky, and his expression was as coldly unreadable.

'What about?' she prompted agitatedly.

He looked about them restlessly at the socially relaxed people milling about the patio. 'Not here,' he finally ground out. 'Could we go somewhere else? Somewhere where we won't be disturbed?' he added harshly.

'What is it?' Her agitation increased, her hand moving to the hardness of his arm.

It couldn't be anything to do with her father; he was obviously his normal charming self as he talked with Corinne and David. And it couldn't be Andie, because she was still in bed suffering from the after-effects of her illness. Which only left Danie...

Or Richard...?

'What's he done now?' she gasped, feeling her face pale.

'Who?' Quinn frowned his irritation. 'What are you talking about, Harrie? I said I wanted to talk to you; it doesn't involve anyone else.'

Danie, then, she accepted heavily.

Did the fact that he'd kissed her a couple of times give Quinn the impression he owed her some sort of explanation now that his interest had transferred to her sister? Because there was no way she was going 'somewhere where they wouldn't be disturbed' just so that she could listen to Quinn telling her how he now felt about Danie!

'Do stop looking so grim, Quinn.' She made her tone deliberately taunting. 'I hope you don't think that I imagine what happened between the two of us—if anything *did* happen,' she added with a dismissive laugh, 'meant anything?' She arched mocking brows.

His arm tensed beneath her touch. 'It didn't?'

'Of course not,' she assured him scornfully, her lips feeling frozen into position as she continued to smile up at him. 'We're both grown-up people, Quinn. And one day, I'm sure, we'll both look back on this little episode and remember it with affection,' she assured him lightly.

He continued to frown down at her, and it took every ounce of self-determination Harrie possessed to continue to meet that piercing gaze. But she would not let Quinn see how this was hurting her. She couldn't. She wasn't going to be left with a lot once he had gone, but the self-respect that had only recently returned to her, was something she was determined to hang on to. It was all she had!

Although she wished Quinn would just finish this conversation and let her quietly slip away—because she wasn't sure just how much longer she could keep up this act!

'I'm glad you feel that way,' Quinn finally rasped. 'Although, the same can't be said for—' He broke off, his gaze suddenly fixed on something over Harrie's shoulder.

Harrie turned sharply to look at the reason for his sudden distraction. Danie stood in the doorway, silently beckoning Quinn over to her, her expression anxious.

'Excuse me, won't you?' Quinn murmured vaguely to Harrie even as he moved towards Danie.

Leaving Harrie with the knowledge that she was never going to learn who or what 'the same couldn't be said for'!

She stood transfixed as Quinn and Danie talked softly together in the doorway for a few seconds. Then Quinn turned abruptly on his heel to stride back into the house. And, after one last anxious glance in Harrie's direction, Danie quickly followed him.

Let them go, Harrie told herself. Obviously Quinn had made his choice. She would only make matters worse if she were to follow them.

And yet…

Something hadn't been quite right about that last lingering glance Danie had given her. Her sister hadn't just looked anguished, she had seemed angry too.

What was going on…?

She found the answer to that almost as soon as she re-entered the house, as she followed the sound of raised voices coming from the sitting-room. Voices she recognised.

Quinn's.

And Richard's…!

CHAPTER TEN

QUINN looked at the younger man with unmistakable dislike. That Heaton had the gall to just turn up here—!

Quinn hadn't been able to believe it when Danie had told him a few minutes ago that Richard Heaton was here, and had marched angrily back inside the house to see for himself.

The younger man looked as confident as ever as he stood at the side of a woman Quinn realised he also recognised.

'I don't need to ask how you wormed your way in here,' Quinn scorned at the other man, his gaze sweeping pointedly over the woman at Heaton's side.

'Mr McBride…?' The woman looked at him dazedly. 'I don't understand what the problem is.' She shook her head. 'Mr Summer invited me down here for Sunday brunch. And, of course, I was thrilled to come.' She shook her head. 'But this young lady seems to feel there's some problem—'

'This "young lady" is Danie Summer,' Danie informed the other woman tautly. 'Rome's daughter.'

'One of them,' Richard Heaton interjected.

'And you aren't the problem—*he* is!' Danie looked vehemently at Richard Heaton.

'Richard is…?' Jane Freeman frowned in confusion. 'But Mr Summer assured me it would be perfectly all right with him if I brought a friend with me. I simply don't understand,' she repeated dazedly as Danie continued to glare at Richard, and Quinn looked ready to hit him!

In fact, Quinn felt quite sorry for the female reporter.

The two of them had first met last Sunday when Jane had come to interview his sister, and Quinn had found her intelligent as well as empathetic. Unfortunately, Jane had had no idea of the real reason she was being asked to write the article on Corinne. Which meant she also had no idea of Richard Heaton's part in any of that, either!

But Richard Heaton knew! As he also knew the havoc he would wreak by his coming here today!

Quinn turned his attention back to the other man, angered anew by the look of challenging insolence on the younger man's face. 'I thought I warned you about making an enemy of Rome Summer…?' he murmured softly.

Richard Heaton shrugged unconcernedly. 'I'm here as Jane's partner for brunch—'

'You're here to make trouble!' Quinn cut in forcefully. 'We both know that. So why don't you—?' He broke off, having become aware of someone else having come to stand in the doorway behind him, turning slowly, dismayed to see Harrie standing there.

She looked as if someone had just slapped her in the face!

Her face was very pale as she stared across the room at Richard Heaton, her eyes looking huge and dark as emeralds in stark contrast.

Damn Heaton, Quinn thought, and far from the first time. Damn the other man to hell!

'Harrie—'

She pushed Quinn's hand away as he would have reached out to her, walking past him, going to stand directly in front of Richard Heaton. 'Get out,' she told him coldly.

If anything the other man's expression became even more insolent. 'I was invited,' he drawled. 'Or, at least, Jane was.' He reached out and slid a possessive arm about the female reporter's shoulders. 'I'm sure I've mentioned

Jane Freeman to you before, Harrie,' he drawled mockingly. 'And Quinn already knows her very well, don't you?' He looked across at Quinn tauntingly.

'Jane Freeman...' Harrie repeated softly, anger flashing in her eyes as she obviously remembered where she had heard that name before. 'You are so low, Richard,' she told him with contempt, shaking her head. 'I can't believe I was ever taken in by you!'

'Richard, you're here as a colleague, nothing else.' Jane Freeman impatiently shook off the heavy weight of his arm about her shoulders. 'Although it seems I've missed something here...' she added.

Richard Heaton raised blond brows. 'Shall I tell her—or would one of you like to?' he taunted.

Quinn felt his hands tighten into fists at his sides. He knew this was Rome's home, that there were a couple of dozen guests not twenty yards away, too—but if this meeting didn't soon come to an end he knew he was going to be unable to stop himself from administering the punch he had wanted to give Richard Heaton for so long. And Quinn knew it was no longer just for what he had done to his sister...

'I don't think any of us need to tell Jane anything.' Surprisingly it was Harrie who answered the other man. 'You've had your fun, Richard,' she continued firmly, 'now I think it's time you just left. Quietly. Don't you...?' she challenged softly.

Quinn had to admire her in that moment. Not only did she sound completely in control of the situation, but she looked magnificent too!

Richard Heaton looked momentarily shaken by her confident calmness too. 'Now, why should I want to do that...?' he murmured slowly, frowning in puzzlement.

Harrie shrugged. 'Because of a contract you've agreed to sign with Leeward Publications on Monday...?' she returned coolly, glancing calmly down at her wrist-watch. 'Tomorrow, in fact.'

Quinn watched as the other man paled. And with good reason. There had been a definite threat behind Harrie's words.

Richard Heaton moistened his lips. 'How do you know about that?' he asked suspiciously.

Harrie raised mocking brows. 'Because I drew up the contract,' she informed him coldly.

Now the younger man looked more than shaken. As well he might, Quinn acknowledged ruefully. He'd just been informed that he had been manoeuvred into a corner—by the very people he had believed he was besting by coming here today!

Quinn looked at Harrie with admiration. He should have known, should have guessed, from the little Rome had been willing to tell him yesterday, that Harrie would also be in on his legal dealings with Richard Heaton. After all, she was Rome's lawyer...

And for Harrie, it would have meant so much more than carrying out her legal duties; Heaton had used her, made a fool of her. God, she was magnificent, Quinn decided.

He only hoped she hadn't overplayed her hand by telling Heaton as much as she had...?

'The contract isn't signed yet,' Richard Heaton reminded with harsh defiance, his top lip turned back in scorn.

'True,' Harrie accepted mildly. 'But I think we both know you will be a fool if you don't sign—don't we?' She quirked mocking brows at him.

Quinn had never admired—loved?—Harrie as much as he did in that moment. She was amazing, unlike any other woman he had ever known. An undoubtedly loving sister and daughter—but a most formidable enemy. And he wanted her for his own!

Richard Heaton's breath left him in a vehement hiss. 'I could still break the real story about the snow-white Corinne,' he sneered.

Quinn tensed, taking a step forward, only to be held in check by Harrie as she turned to give him a briefly reassuring smile.

She turned back to Richard Heaton, giving a humourless laugh. 'Following Jane's article on Monday, you would only make a complete idiot of yourself. You'd come over as a vindictive man harassing a vulnerable woman. Why don't you just grow up, Richard?' Her voice hardened. 'Take the new start you've been offered. Take the job in America.'

'Or else what?' Richard Heaton growled, obviously realising—at last!—that this situation was well out of his control.

Harrie shrugged. 'I think you may find it's the only decent offer you're going to get. Until a few months ago,' she added less forcefully, 'I believe you were a reporter with scruples.' She looked at the other man challengingly.

She still cared, Quinn realised achingly. And he—he 'cared' for Harrie! He could no longer fight or deny it, to himself at least; he was totally under her spell… And after what Harrie had said to him earlier, about how they would eventually look back on the circumstances of their acquaintance with affection, what good would that do him?

'Jane—' Danie was the one to speak lightly into the telling silence that had followed Harrie's statement '—why don't I take you outside and introduce you to some of the other guests?'

It was made as a polite suggestion, but there was no doubt in anyone's mind—Quinn was sure—that it was nothing of the kind.

'Yes,' the female reporter accepted huskily, obviously intelligent enough to have realised now exactly what was going on. 'Enjoy America, Richard,' came her parting shot as she followed Danie out of the room.

Leaving the three of them, a proudly challenging Harrie, a deeply resentful Richard Heaton, and a tense and angry Quinn, to put an end to this unacceptable situation.

Quinn only hoped Harrie was up to this…

She could do this, Harrie told herself firmly.

It had been a tremendous shock to realise that Richard was actually here at the house, and she had instinctively wondered why he was here. But she needn't have worried; he hadn't come to the house with the intention of expressing undying love for her! Not that she had any feelings of love left towards him, but to think that he might actually have cared for her, after all, might have taken away some of the sting of humiliation she still felt whenever Richard was mentioned.

And he had been mentioned several times by her father in the last few days. Rome had been determined that Richard should be removed from causing any further harm, either to Corinne or herself. And he had acted accordingly…!

But what an idiot she was to have even thought, however briefly, that Richard might actually feel contrite over his actions this last week! One look at his face when she'd entered the sitting-room, seeing him with the blonde-haired woman who had obviously accompanied him, and she had known that Richard had only come here to make more trouble.

She could look at him now quite objectively, and see him for the opportunist he obviously was. He had used Jane Freeman to get himself in here today, in the same way that he had used her in the past.

Yes, she could do this!

'I think that's your cue to leave, Richard,' she told him pointedly once Danie had taken Jane outside.

His expression remained scornfully defiant for several seconds. And then he gave a shrug, his smile rueful. 'I don't suppose it would do any good now to say that I did— do—genuinely care for you?' He raised blond brows.

Harrie heard Quinn's angrily indrawn breath behind her, although she made no effort to turn and look at him. Just what kind of idiot did Quinn think she was? That she would be drawn back in by Richard's charm, that she wouldn't see this was a last-ditch effort on Richard's part to try and retrieve something from the mess he had created? Quinn hadn't come to know her at all this last week if he thought that!

'No, Richard,' she drawled mockingly, even managing a self-derisive smile, 'I don't suppose it would!'

He nodded. 'I don't suppose we'll see each other again, either?'

She quirked her dark eyebrows. 'Not much chance of that once you're based in America.'

It was Richard's turn to smile self-derisively now, shaking his head. 'You know, Harrie, I think I may have underestimated you these last few months,' he said without rancour.

'I think that's a clear possibility,' Harrie nodded, her smile much more genuine now.

'No hard feelings?' Richard prompted softly.

'Eventually…probably not,' she conceded dryly. 'At this particular moment…?' She grinned pointedly.

He gave an acknowledging nod before turning to look at Quinn, who, Harrie realised, had been very quiet the last five minutes or so. Although she doubted that would remain the case for very long!

'I never forget, Heaton. Or forgive,' Quinn told the other man raspingly. 'My advice to you is to stay in America.

An ocean between us may—just may—be enough for me not to have to trouble myself with you again!

And Harrie could see he meant every word of his threat. Luckily, it was obvious that so could Richard!

Although that didn't stop Richard from taking the two steps that separated them, bending down to kiss her lightly on the cheek. 'You're quite a woman, Harrie,' Richard told her admiringly. 'Far too good for me.'

'Well, at least we're in agreement about one thing!' Quinn put in harshly.

Richard turned to the other man with mocking blue eyes. 'I wouldn't look so damn self-satisfied if I were you,' he bit out scornfully. 'Because she's too good for you, too!'

Exactly what did Richard mean by that? Harrie inwardly gasped, avoiding looking directly at Quinn. It was bad enough that she knew she was in love with Quinn, without having a third party allude to the possibility of a relationship between them!

'I think you can safely say that's something else we're in agreement about,' Quinn answered the other man coldly.

Harrie turned to him with widely startled eyes. What on earth did he mean— And then she knew. For Harrie, a relationship that involved her loving someone would ultimately lead to permanence, marriage. To have a husband. But, at thirty-nine, Quinn had obviously never felt the need, so far in his relationships, to legalise anything…! She wasn't 'too good' for Quinn at all, he just had no intention of putting himself in a position where something permanent might be asked of him. Besides, there was Danie…

She straightened proudly. 'Well, at least we now know where we all stand,' she snapped dismissively. 'Now, I really think—'

'Heaton!' her father bit out with dislike as he came rushing into the room, obviously having been informed by

Danie, probably when neither Harrie nor Quinn had come back out onto the patio, that Richard Heaton was in the house. 'If you know what's good for you—'

'He does, Daddy,' Harrie cut in gently, resting a hand lightly on her father's arm.

Rome turned sharply to look at her, and Harrie knew why he did: none of his daughters ever called him 'Daddy' to his face any more. But what he read in Harrie's face seemed to reassure him as Harrie felt some of the tension leaving his body where she still rested her hand on his arm.

'Richard was just leaving—weren't you?' She turned pointedly to the younger man.

Richard gave her a rueful smile. 'I believe I was. But perhaps I'll see you both tomorrow?' he obviously couldn't resist adding mischievously.

'Not me, I'm afraid.' Harrie shook her head. 'I only drew up the contract, someone else will deal with witnessing the signature of it.' There was only so far she was willing to go with this situation—and she had drawn the line at having to see Richard again.

Although this morning rather nullified that decision…!

'I have assistants to deal with such trivialities,' Rome added caustically as Richard looked at him enquiringly.

'In that case…' Richard gave an acknowledging inclination of his head before turning on his heel and walking out of the room, the quiet closing of the front door a few seconds later telling of his departure.

And the tension that filled the room after that departure was not caused by Rome, Harrie freely acknowledged! But the atmosphere that now existed between Quinn and herself was so intense it was impossible for any of them not to be aware of it. Rome looked at the two of them now through narrowed lids.

'I think it's time I was leaving,' Quinn finally rasped.

'But we haven't had brunch yet.' Harrie was aghast as
she heard herself make the inconsequential protest. After
all, Quinn's departure concerned Danie more now than it
did her…

Quinn gave her a scathing glance. 'Somehow I seem to
have lost my appetite,' he bit out with distaste.

She swallowed hard. 'In that case, maybe you could
offer Richard a lift back into town!' she scorned.

Quinn's eyes became glacial. 'He can crawl the whole
damn fifty miles for all I care!' he retorted with disgust
before turning to her father. 'I really think it would be
better if I left now,' he told the older man flatly.

'Better for whom?' Rome snapped impatiently.

Quinn drew in a harsh breath. 'Me, actually,' he admitted evenly. 'I suddenly find that the country air is too much
for me,' he added hardly.

Rome raised blond brows. 'Only the air?' he challenged
softly.

'As it happens—no,' Quinn confirmed tautly.

'Quinn—'

'Rome,' Quinn firmly interrupted the other man, his
aqua-blue gaze hardening in warning. 'Distance and time
are what's needed at the moment, I think.'

'Don't believe that saying about "absence making the
heart grow fonder",' Rome rasped harshly. 'It's usually a
case of "out of sight, out of mind"!' he added knowingly.

Harrie had been bewildered by their conversation to start
with, but now she realised they had to be talking about
Danie… God, did everyone know of Quinn's interest in
Danie? Rome obviously did—and he approved!

She swallowed hard as the tears came unbidden to her
eyes. 'I'll go and tell Danie you're leaving,' she muttered
abruptly before hurrying from the room.

When those tears began to fall in earnest.

Quinn and Danie…!

How was she going to bear it?

CHAPTER ELEVEN

'DON'T say a word,' Quinn warned Rome gratingly as he could see the other man was about to do just that.

'But—'

'Not a word, Rome!' Quinn rasped harshly, his eyes glittering a warning too now.

He needed to think. Needed time to work out what to do next. If there was anything he could do next!

Because he loved Harrie Summer. And the thought of leaving here—leaving Harrie!—without at least making her aware of how he felt was beyond all comprehension to him now.

Was this what it was like to be in love with someone? This aching need deep inside him? The knowing that to walk away, to leave her, would be to leave a part of himself—the part of himself that mattered!—behind?

He dropped down heavily into one of the armchairs, staring sightlessly in front of him. He had never known—never realised—that, to love, and not be loved in return, was the most painful thing in the world!

How did people survive this totally helpless feeling? How did they carry on with their normal lives? *If* they did…!

Because at the moment nothing mattered to him but Harrie. Not his sister. Not the bank. Nothing. Certainly not his freedom! And those things, the fabric of his life up to this point in time, the things he'd believed important in his life, had become so much excess baggage since he'd discovered how much he was in love with Harrie…!

He turned dazedly to Rome. 'Is it always like this?'

Rome gave him a sympathetic smile. 'Always,' he confirmed gently. 'Until things are settled. One way or another,' he added softly.

'Hell,' Quinn muttered.

Hell, indeed—to be without that one person who could make those other things mean anything ever again.

Quinn shook his head. 'How on earth did you get through it?' he groaned.

Rome gave a rueful smile. 'It had its compensations!'

'Because yours obviously worked out,' Quinn muttered. 'You married the woman you loved, and had three beautiful daughters with her. But this—this is a damned mess!' he added achingly.

'Only because you've made it so,' Rome told him patiently. 'Oh, not just you,' he conceded as Quinn looked up at him, frowning. 'The two of you—' He broke off as a rather puzzled-looking Danie came back into the room.

'Harrie tells me you're leaving,' she murmured politely.

Quinn gave her a humourless smile. 'Is she outside celebrating?'

'Not that I noticed.' Danie grimaced. 'She was heading off in the direction of the stables as I came in here.'

He frowned. 'What the hell for?'

'She's going out on Ebony, I expect.' Danie shrugged. 'She always does when she has something on her mind.'

Heaton… It had to be seeing Heaton again that had upset Harrie, Quinn realised heavily.

'Rome, exactly what is going on?' It was the blunt Danie who pushed the issue.

Her father shook his head impatiently. 'I've given up even trying to understand,' he muttered.

Danie turned on Quinn, green eyes flashing. 'Have you said or done something to upset Harrie?'

'Me?' he echoed indignantly. 'Has it not occurred to

either of you that Heaton coming here today was more than enough to upset Harrie?'

'Heaton?' Rome repeated in a vaguely dismissive voice.

'Why should that have upset Harrie?' Blunt Danie was once again the one to demand an answer.

Quinn stood up impatiently. 'Are the two of you completely insensitive to—? No, of course you aren't.' He shook his head self-disgustedly; one thing he had learnt this last week, the Summer family were a very close-knit bunch. 'Sorry,' he muttered uncomfortably. 'But of course seeing Heaton again would upset Harrie—'

'Why?' Rome grimaced his puzzlement.

'Because she's in love with the man!' Quinn burst out impatiently, surprised he had to put it into so many words. Both Rome and Danie had to know how hurt Harrie had been by Heaton's behaviour.

'Not that again.' Danie grimaced scornfully. 'Of course Harrie isn't in love with Richard Heaton. How could she be? The man is a total nerd!'

Quinn couldn't help smiling at this apt, if less than grammatical, description of the other man. 'Unfortunately that doesn't preclude someone falling in love with him!'

'It does if that someone is Harrie,' Danie assured him stubbornly.

'If you think of Heaton as a—nerd, what do you think of me?' He looked teasingly at Danie.

'You?' She grinned at him mischievously. 'It's difficult to tell, because at the moment you're so blinded by how you feel about Harrie that you can't see straight,' she told him bluntly. 'But I have a feeling you might just be okay.'

He shook his head, chuckling softly at what he knew, coming from Danie, was a compliment. 'You know, Danie, if I hadn't met Harrie first…!'

She smiled back at him. 'Sorry, Quinn, but you aren't my type.'

'Oh, and just what—?' Quinn broke off abruptly as he saw Rome watching the two of them and frowning. 'We're only joking, Rome,' he told the other man.

'Hmm,' Rome murmured thoughtfully.

'What?' Quinn snapped irritably.

'I know you're joking,' Rome said slowly. 'And the two of you know you are. But it doesn't naturally follow that Harrie knows it too.'

Quinn frowned at the older man. Of course Harrie knew that there was nothing between himself and Danie. It was Harrie that he had kissed. Harrie that he had come here to see. For goodness' sake, Danie spending time with him yesterday evening had just been her taking pity on him.

He had assured Harrie that he hadn't come here to see her! After which he had spent the evening with Danie. And he had been having coffee alone with Danie this morning too when Harrie had returned from her ride.

Could Rome have actually hit upon something...?

Quinn swallowed hard. 'What if you're wrong?'

'What have you got to lose?' Rome challenged.

What had he got to lose?

Yes...what had he got to lose? Hadn't he just realised that he didn't have anything if he couldn't have Harrie?

He drew in a ragged breath. 'Point me in the general direction of the stables?' he requested huskily of Danie.

'I'll do better than that.' She grinned. 'I'll take you as far as the back of the house; you can see the stables from there. And if Harrie won't have you—' she linked her arm lightly through the crook of his as she grinned at him '—come back and we'll go off and have some lunch together somewhere.'

'And to think that until the last couple of days I've been thinking of you as "that bossy redhead"!' he returned mockingly.

'You weren't wrong,' Rome assured him ruefully as he

gave his daughter an affectionate smile. 'The man that takes on Danie will have a fight on his hands as to "who wears the trousers"!'

'The "man who takes me on" had better think himself damned lucky to have me!' Danie came back with an arrogant wrinkling of her nose.

'Or else!' Rome smiled conspiratorially at Quinn.

He liked this family, Quinn decided as he walked through the house at Danie's side.

But he loved Harrie...!

His smile faded as he thought of the task ahead of him. What if Harrie rejected him? Worse, laughed in his face...! No, he knew her well enough to realise she wouldn't do that. If she turned him down at all, it would be gently.

But, however, it was done, it would still be a turndown...!

'Have you ever accepted defeat, Quinn?' Danie questioned softly at his side as they reached the courtyard at the back of the house, the stables, as she had said earlier, in view now. 'In business? In anything?'

'This is different—'

'No, it isn't,' she assured him. 'The only difference with this is that you're emotionally involved—'

'That's a hell of a difference, Danie!' he protested laughingly.

She shrugged. 'My mother always said, "If something's worth having"...'

'"It's worth fighting for",' he finished, knowing that to have Harrie permanently in his life was worth everything. 'You're right, Danie.' He straightened determinedly. 'Watch out, Harrie Summer, I'm about to start fighting!'

'But gently,' came Danie's laughing parting shot as he strode forcefully towards the tables.

Gently, she said, Quinn muttered to himself as he entered the gloom of the stables. He wasn't even sure if

Harrie was still here; she might already have gone out on Ebony.

'Lost your way, Quinn?'

He turned to find Harrie looking at him over the top of a stall, the horse snorting beside her easily recognisable as Ebony. Brought up in the city, Quinn had admired horses from afar, but never been this close to one before. He didn't find the experience any more reassuring than he had as he'd stood at his bedroom window watching as Harrie had ridden away on the back of this monster this morning!

'I was looking for you,' he answered Harrie's opening comment, all the time keeping a wary eye on the snorting Ebony.

Harrie raised dark brows. 'You've found me.' She shrugged.

Quinn frowned. 'I would like to talk to you. But not here,' he added quickly as Ebony stretched his head over the top of his stall to move that snorting nose dangerously close to Quinn. 'I don't think your horse likes me.'

'Of course he does,' Harrie assured him briskly as she let herself out of the stall. 'He would have tried to bite you by now if he didn't!'

Somehow Quinn didn't find that reassuring. But as they moved away from Ebony's stall, it wasn't something he had to worry about.

But what he said to Harrie, now that he was face to face with her, was definitely something to worry about!

'I'm sorry about what happened this morning,' he told her gruffly, noticing that, for all Harrie's outward calm, there was a trace of tears down the paleness of her cheeks. The bastard had made her cry! he realised angrily.

'You mean Richard?' She frowned. 'But that wasn't your fault.'

'No. But—' he grimaced '—I don't like to see you being hurt.'

'No?' Harrie looked at him steadily.

'No!' he confirmed tautly.

'You're missing out on brunch,' she told him huskily.

'So are you,' he pointed out harshly.

She shrugged narrow shoulders. 'I'm not hungry.'

'Neither am I,' he bit out abruptly.

'But your sister and David—'

'I'll see them later,' he dismissed impatiently. 'Harrie, I tried to talk to you earlier this morning—'

'We did talk, Quinn,' she cut in lightly.

'No, we didn't,' he rebuked evenly. 'At least not about anything that matters.'

And he was going to have his say now, if it killed him!

As he had already been told once today—what did he have to lose?

Harrie could feel the tension inside her rising. She didn't want to hear the things Quinn had to say, especially when it involved telling her he now found himself attracted to Danie! Hadn't she made that more than obvious earlier this morning?

'You certainly know how to pick your moments, Quinn,' she taunted lightly, their surroundings far from conducive to any confidences he might want to make concerning Danie.

Although, maybe not... The stables were shadowed, meaning Quinn probably couldn't see her as well as he would be able to if they were outside in the bright sunshine. And there was the added advantage of her being able to escape on Ebony once their conversation was at an end.

'Step into my office, Mr McBride,' she mocked, indicating they should sit down on the bales of hay that were piled in a corner of one of the empty stalls.

Quinn looked far from enamoured at the suggestion,

Harrie noted with amusement as the two of them moved to sit down. He probably didn't want to get hay on his black tailored trousers and blue silk shirt, she acknowledged ruefully. Come to think of it, Quinn had probably never been inside a stable in his life!

The stables were kept meticulously clean, but there was still an aroma of horses and the smells that went along with them. Poor Quinn, she acknowledged ruefully.

'Some office,' he grimaced, looking around them pointedly.

Harrie shrugged. 'I'm a country girl. Maybe not born here, but certainly brought up here. And I love life in the country. One day I intend having a home and stables like this of my own,' she added decidedly.

It had always been her dream. She didn't want to live and work in the city for ever; she'd always hoped that once she married, had children of her own, they would be brought up in the country as she had been. Although, she realised self-derisively, that dream would never have come true if she and Richard had ever decided to make their relationship a permanent one; Richard was definitely a townie, and the work he did would never allow for him living in the country.

Not that Quinn would have been much better, she also acknowledged wistfully. He was as much a town person as Richard had been.

Maybe it was a dream she would have to realise on her own...

'Now what did you want to say?' she prompted Quinn briskly.

He was looking at her searchingly. Although what he hoped to find, Harrie had no idea. She had been upset earlier when she'd left the house, couldn't bear the thought of Quinn and Danie being involved together, but hopefully none of that showed in her face now...?

'Does he really still matter to you that much?' Quinn rasped, letting Harrie know that something certainly did still show on her face.

She frowned. 'Who?'

'Heaton!' Quinn bit out impatiently.

She relaxed slightly. But only slightly. Feeling about Quinn as she did, it wouldn't do to relax too much in his company!

'He doesn't "matter" to me at all,' she dismissed easily.

Quinn shook his head. 'You were upset after he left. And you've been crying,' he added harshly.

Damn, *that* was what showed!

She raised her hands instinctively and smoothed her fingers across the dampness of her cheeks. Those tears certainly hadn't been for Richard!

'I had something in my eye earlier,' she excused.

'Both of them?' Quinn challenged harshly.

She gave an impatient sigh. 'Exactly what is you want from me, Quinn?' she asked, standing up restlessly. 'I've told you I don't care for Richard. I'm not sure that I ever did in the way that you seem to think I did,' she added dismissively; she loved Quinn, damn it—and it was a feeling like nothing else she had ever known before!

Or would ever feel again with anyone else…?

'I've also assured you that you owe me no explanations or apologies yourself just because you've kissed me a couple of times.' She paced up and down the small confines of the stall now. 'What else is it you want?' She rounded on him angrily. 'A blessing on your relationship with Danie? Okay, Quinn, you have it. Now get out of here and let me get on with—' The rest of what she had been going to say was swallowed up as Quinn stood up suddenly, pulling her determinedly into his arms, his mouth coming crashingly down on hers.

Heaven… Oh, God, heaven…!

She'd told herself that she would have to accept that this would never happen again, that she would never again feel the strength of Quinn's arms about her, never know the fierce possession of his mouth against hers.

Never know the hard response of his body as it curved perfectly against hers...?

She wrenched her mouth away from his, looking up at him with glitteringly tear-wet eyes. 'I don't understand...!' she gasped her confusion. How could he respond to her in this way if it were Danie he wanted...?

'We're going to start again, Harrie,' Quinn told her determinedly. 'I'm going to ask you out. You're going to accept,' he bit out firmly. 'We're going to do all those things that other people do when they go out together. And, eventually, in time, you'll forget all about Heaton, and realise that not every man is like him, that some of us—*one* of us,' he added decisively, 'wants you for yourself!'

Now it was Harrie's turn to look searchingly at Quinn. And what she saw there made her breath catch in her throat, her heart leap in her chest. It was true; it was her that Quinn wanted!

'But I thought—you and Danie—'

'I like your sister very much, Harrie,' Quinn cut in dismissively. 'She's blunt, and funny, and—'

'Beautiful,' Harrie put in uncertainly.

'Not as beautiful as you.' Quinn shook his head. 'But even if she were, it would make no difference to how I feel. Can't you see—feel!—that it's you I want?' he groaned impatiently. 'Damn it, not just want, Harrie! I—I—'

She looked at him wonderingly. Because she could see, could feel— 'Quinn...?' she gasped, still not able to believe the emotion she could see in his face.

'I love you, Harrie Summer!' he burst out gratingly.

'Every damned stubborn inch of you! And I wasn't going to tell you that yet, don't want to frighten you off,' he muttered impatiently. 'But it makes no difference,' he added determinedly. 'I am going to ask you out. And you are going to accept!' His arms tightened about her warningly.

Quinn loved her...! Nothing else he had said mattered. Quinn loved her!

She rested her forehead weakly against him. 'I thought it was Danie you were interested in, were going to give "distance and time" to.' She shook he head. 'I couldn't bear it, Quinn. That's the reason I was crying!' She raised her head to look at him. 'You see, Quinn McBride,' she said chokingly, 'I love you, too!'

He looked thunderstruck, holding her at arm's length as he studied her intently.

Harrie looked back at him glowingly. It didn't matter what they had both thought about Richard and Danie. Because they loved each other!

'Say something, Quinn,' she finally laughed chokingly. 'Before I collapse from the tension!'

'I told you once before that if you fall I'll be there to pick you up,' he reminded huskily as he pulled her back against him, his cheek resting against the silkiness of her hair. 'I may not have been willing to admit it, even to myself,' he added self-derisively, 'but I loved you even then. I think I fell in love with you that first day!' he said ruefully.

'You didn't like me very much that day,' she chided lovingly. 'You believed I was Rome's mistress.'

'I was an idiot,' Quinn scorned. 'A jealous one at that. Harrie...' he raised his head to look at her intently '...will you marry me?'

Marry...? Quinn wanted to marry her?

'We'll still go out together,' he told her quickly as she

didn't answer, 'still do all those things other people do when they're getting to know each other. I just—'

'Yes, Quinn,' she burst out breathlessly.

'You'll go out with me?' He looked down at her uncertainly.

She shook her head, smiling glowingly, dark hair tousled down her back. 'I'll marry you,' she corrected huskily. 'Today. Tomorrow. Whenever you want!' she added with certainty. 'I just want to be with you, Quinn. Always,' she told him firmly.

He swallowed hard. 'A banker isn't going to be too boring for you?'

'In comparison with what?' She frowned her puzzlement.

Quinn shrugged. 'A film producer sounds rather more exciting—' He broke off as Harrie put her fingers firmly over his lips. 'No?' he prompted uncertainly.

'Most definitely not,' she assured him laughingly, knowing he had to be talking about Adam. How stupid they had been, jealous of other people in their uncertainty of loving each other! 'I doubt Adam will ever settle down with one woman,' she dismissed. 'And even if he does, it most certainly won't be me! I'm ashamed to say I used Adam as a shield last night. In the same way I now believe you used Danie…?'

'Guilty, I'm afraid.' Quinn sighed. 'Although Danie mischievously went along with it,' he added ruefully. 'I think she wanted to see what your reaction would be.'

'She would,' Harrie acknowledged affectionately. 'She didn't like the fact that I was less than honest with her about my being in love with you.'

Quinn nodded. 'She thinks we're both stubbornly uncooperative on that score,' he confirmed ruefully.

'I think what my sister needs is a man of her own. But it won't be you!' Harrie added with a possessiveness of her own. 'You're the man *I* love, Quinn,' she added seriously. 'The man I want to spend the rest of my life with,' she told him shyly. 'And I don't want to spend weeks or months "going out together",' she assured him determinedly. 'I want us to be together now. In fact...' She groaned her physical as well as emotional need of him as the two of them sank to the hay-strewn floor.

Quinn's arms tightened about her as they lay together. 'You don't think Ebony will be too jealous?' he teased emotionally.

'I don't care how anyone else feels about us being together, Quinn,' she assured him confidently. 'Although I have a feeling Rome approves of you...!' she added affectionately. If her father hadn't liked and respected Quinn, then she knew the younger man would never have been invited back here.

Quinn laughed huskily. 'He may not feel quite so approving if I bring his beloved eldest daughter back to the house with bits of straw sticking out of her hair from where I've obviously ravished her in the stables!'

Harrie curved her arm up about his neck as she slowly pulled him down to her. 'Then we had better make sure we dispose of the straw before we go back,' she murmured longingly. 'Hadn't we...?'

Quinn looked down at her intently. 'I do love you, Harrie. So very much.'

And it obviously wasn't an emotion he found it easy to admit to. But then, neither did she. The joy of it all was, despite what they might have thought otherwise, that the love they felt was for each other...!

'And I love you, Quinn McBride,' she told him huskily before their mouths fused together.

Harrie McBride. Yes, she liked the sound of that.

But not as much as she loved Quinn McBride...

EPILOGUE

'So TELL me,' drawled the husky voice of Gypsy Rosa as she gazed down into the palm of his hand, 'what happened after you met your tall, dark, beautiful stranger?'

Quinn grinned as he lay beside her in the bed. 'I married her, of course!'

Of course... They both knew there had been no 'of course' about their brief and tempestuous courtship. It still brought him out in a cold sweat every time he thought about how nearly he and Harrie had walked away from each other, each believing the other was in love with someone else.

'Hey, I was only joking!' Harrie snuggled down against him. 'Of course you married her—I would have been very disappointed if you hadn't!'

Quinn's arms remained firmly about her as he held her close to him. The two of them had been married for three weeks now—three weeks of pure heaven as far as he was concerned—and he still found it hard to believe Harrie returned his love as fiercely as he loved her.

They had been married by special licence only five days after realising they were in love with each other, and the following three weeks had been the happiest Quinn had ever known. Looking back on his life before Harrie, it seemed bleak and empty; in fact, he wondered why he'd ever fought against his love for her. It was like a tidal wave, washing him off his feet—and he didn't care if he never went back on dry land ever again!

'We'll have to get up soon, my darling.' Harrie stretched sensually beside him. 'Danie is coming for lunch today.'

Quinn laughed huskily. 'It won't be the first time she's arrived here and found us still in bed!' On one memorable occasion, it had been five o'clock in the afternoon!

Being part of the Summer family was as warm with belonging as he had thought it would be. Rome had been obviously more than pleased to see his eldest daughter married to someone he liked and respected, and Danie and Andie—he had finally met her at the wedding!—treated him much like the big brother he was to Corinne.

Life was good, he realised. More than good. With Harrie at his side, as his wife, it was perfect…!

Harrie moved to look down lovingly at her husband. 'I thought we might make an effort today,' she said indulgently. 'Danie is going to think we're always in bed together!'

Quinn quirked one dark brow. 'And aren't we?'

She laughed softly. 'Yes,' she conceded ruefully.

Having Quinn as her husband was like nothing she could ever have imagined, their love for each other all-consuming, meaning they resented anything, or anyone, that took them away from each other.

In fact, after making what she had taken at the time to be a disparaging remark about 'never having her work for him'—a remark he had since explained really meant he couldn't see himself getting any work done if she were that close to him!—she now spent a considerable amount of time at the bank assisting Quinn on legal matters. Much to her father's irritation!

'Do you think—?' She broke off as the telephone beside the bed began to ring.

'With any luck, that's Danie calling to say she can't make it,' Quinn murmured hopefully.

'Naughty!' Harrie chided lovingly even as she reached over and picked up the receiver.

She listened patiently as Danie spoke economically on the other end of the line. 'That's okay, Danie,' she assured once her sister had finished talking. 'We'll see you later in the week,' she told Danie warmly before ringing off.

'There is a God, after all!' Quinn unashamedly showed his approval of Danie's obvious inability to make it here for lunch.

Harrie laughed huskily even as she snuggled back down into his arms. 'She has to go somewhere for Rome,' she dismissed lightly. 'Now, Mr McBride, what were you saying about staying in bed...?' She looked up at him mischievously.

'I was saying—Mrs McBride—' he rolled over in the bed, curving her body into his '—now that Danie won't be here for lunch, that I see absolutely no reason to get out of bed at all today!'

'We could starve.' Harrie chuckled.

'What a way to go!' Quinn murmured even as his mouth came down possessively on hers.

What a way, indeed...!

To Become
a Bride

CAROLE MORTIMER

PROLOGUE

'MR NOBLE?'

He slowly opened one sleepy eyelid above an even sleepier, bloodshot eye. Only to raise the other eyelid, above an equally bloodshot eye, and find himself looking into the most amazing green eyes he had ever seen.

They weren't the green he usually associated with eye colour, that faded colour that could look a hazelly grey, but the deep, deep green of a clear-cut emerald. High cheekbones sided a pert nose, the skin was clear and smooth, the mouth had a mischievous quirk to it even though it was unsmiling at this moment, and the chin pointed and raised determinedly.

The rest of the woman was harder to distinguish, Jonas realised a little irritably. A black baseball cap was pulled low over those amazing green eyes, her hair tucked neatly inside it, although the lashes that surrounded her eyes were dark and long. Black combat trousers were worn beneath a black fleece top, the latter zipped up to her creamy throat.

Obviously a young woman who liked to be taken seriously, he noted with amusement.

'Is something funny?' the woman prompted sharply.

'Not at all,' Jonas drawled dismissively, swinging long legs from over the arm of his chair to the floor before straightening in his seat.

'Then I take it you are Mr Noble?' the woman repeated abruptly.

He looked around the luxurious but otherwise deserted private lounge before glancing back up at the young

5

woman with mocking brown eyes. 'I would think that's a pretty sure bet,' he finally drawled caustically; he didn't suffer fools any more gladly than this young woman appeared to!

Anger flared briefly in those dark green eyes, but was quickly brought back under control. 'If you've finished your coffee—' she looked down pointedly at the empty cup on the table in front of him '—your flight is ready to leave any time.'

He wasn't sure he was going to be ready, in the full sense of the word, any time today. Despite the pint of strong coffee he had consumed since his arrival fifteen minutes ago! It had been a long night, involving no sleep, and flying off to God-knew-where, to meet a man he didn't even know, was not high on his list of priorities at this particular moment.

But he had agreed—under pressure!—to today's meeting yesterday when he'd received the telephone call from Jerome Summer, and he was a man of his word. So, despite the change of circumstances which meant he hadn't actually been to bed yet, he had duly presented himself at this private lounge situated within the much larger complex of the airport. But that didn't mean he had to like it!

He stood up, flexing tired muscles. 'That's some uniform you have there,' he murmured derisively. If he had expected to be pampered by a sexy flight attendant on this short, but, his host considered, necessary flight, then he was obviously in for a disappointment!

'Uniform?' the woman repeated abruptly, looking down frowningly at her dark clothing. 'These are my own clothes, Mr Noble,' she told him coldly.

Obviously Jerome Summer ran a relaxed ship, Jonas acknowledged. It was none of his business how the other man dealt with his staff, but Jonas's own experience had taught him that familiarity bred contempt; become too re-laxed with someone who worked for you, and you were heading for disaster. His own secretary, Dorothy, was prime proof of that!

At almost fifty, over ten years his senior, Dorothy had taken on a motherly role in his life. And like most mothers with a grown-up son, she treated him with bullying affection.

However, this young woman didn't quite fit into that category! Jerome Summer was in his early fifties, and the young lady was probably only in her late twenties. Which begged the question, what role did she have in Jerome Summer's life that led to such familiarity...?

'I'll have to mention to Jerome that a flight attendant in a short skirt and silky blouse is much more conducive to comfortable travel,' Jonas said silkily.

Dark brows rose over icy green eyes as his meaning obviously became clear. 'For whom, Mr Noble?'

'Why, me, of course.' He grinned, some of the strong coffee at last seeming to kick into gear as he felt a rush of adrenaline. It would only be a temporary thing, of course, he acknowledged ruefully, but hopefully it would be long enough to get him through his meeting. 'And if, as you say, the flight is ready, where is Mr Summer?' he added frowningly. 'Or is he already on the plane?'

'Rome is at the estate, of course,' the young woman replied caustically. 'What would be the point of flying you there if Rome were already in town?' she scorned.

'Rome', was it? Jonas acknowledged sceptically. Obviously very familiar! 'I meant Danny Summer, of course,' he corrected briskly. 'I was told he would be meeting me here. He's some sort of relative, I gather?' he added hardly as the annoyance seemed to be increasing in the young woman's expression.

The mischievously slanting mouth curved. 'You gather correctly, Mr Noble,' the woman drawled. 'Do you have any luggage?'

'Only this small case.' Jonas bent down to pick up the compact black case that stood beside the chair he had been sitting in. 'I'm not expecting to stay longer than a few hours,' he added with grim determination. 'Just until my— business with Mr Summer is completed.'

Especially if all the Summer staff turned out to be as arrogantly self-assured as this young woman! He simply wasn't in the mood to bother dealing with such aggressive attitudes with any of the usual tact and diplomacy usually necessary in his work!

The young woman shot him a sidelong glance as they walked outside and in the direction of a small private jet that stood on the tarmac a few yards away. 'Exactly what line of business is it that you're in, Mr Noble?' she voiced casually.

Too casually, Jonas decided. From the little conversation they had had so far, this woman did not strike him as the sort to indulge in politeness for its own sake—which meant there had been a reason behind her question...?

'Nothing illegal, I can assure you,' he returned noncommittally.

She looked down the length of her upturned nose at him. 'You wouldn't be on your way to see Rome if it were,' she told him with disdainful certainty.

From the little he had read and heard of Jerome Summer, she was right; the man was a business legend in his own lifetime, a doctor's son who had worked his way to the top in every business enterprise he had ever been involved in.

But even so, Jonas had no intention of discussing his

business with the other man with this less-than-polite young woman!

'I'm glad about that,' he answered dismissively, grinning as he preceded her up the steps of the jet and found himself surrounded by the type of luxury he had only ever seen on celluloid before.

His own lifestyle was far from spartan, he ruefully acknowledged, but the inside of this jet was something else. It was more like a beautifully furnished sitting-room, with a comfortable cream sofa and chairs, a tan-coloured carpet on the floor, a well-equipped bar towards the cockpit. Any woodwork visible beside the doe-skin leather looked like well-polished mahogany. The only difference that he could see was that there were seat belts tucked neatly away inside the sofa and chairs.

'The bar is well stocked with food as well as drink.' The woman stood slightly behind him now, having secured the door behind them. 'Please help yourself to whatever you would like, once we have taken off, though there's a little turbulence up there today so I would advise you to wait until we've flown above it,' she added dryly as she stepped past him.

Jonas raised enquiring brows. 'And exactly what are you going to be doing while I'm helping myself to the food and drink?' he asked.

She turned in the open doorway to the cockpit, arching mischievous brows. 'Why, flying the plane, of course, Mr Noble,' she replied innocently.

She was the pilot?

To say he was surprised was an understatement—he was stunned. It had never occurred to him that—

Careful, Jonas, he inwardly taunted himself, your male chauvinism is starting to show!

But it wasn't really a question of that, he instantly defended. A male chauvinist was the last thing he was. Hell, he knew, better than most, that women were much stronger, in some senses, than men!

But this young woman had realised exactly the assumption he had made earlier in the lounge—and she had chosen to let him go on thinking it! In fact, she was still smiling her satisfaction at his mistake...

Why...?

She hadn't even known who he was when she'd come into the lounge, it had only been the fact that he'd been the only person there that had given away his identity. What had he done in the few minutes of their acquaintance to bring about such animosity?

Nothing that he was aware of. Unless...?

'Was Danny Summer not able to make the flight this morning?' he enquired lightly, looking for some sort of answer there. If this woman had been asked to pilot this flight on short notice, that could account for some of her attitude. Some of it...

Her smile faded, her mouth tight now, green eyes sparkling challengingly. '*I'm* Danie Summer, Mr Noble,' she informed him coldly. 'Jerome Summer is my father. And, to put your mind at rest,' she continued hardly as he simply stared at her, 'I'm licensed to pilot all of his private aircraft for him.'

Not just a distant relative, but the man's daughter, Jonas realised dumbfoundedly. Although how he was supposed to have realised that Danie Summer would be a woman, or indeed this particular woman, he had no idea.

He couldn't have done, he accepted, irritable at having been disconcerted in this way. And this woman—Danie Summer—had enjoyed herself enough at his expense for one day, he decided hardly.

'Then I would advise you to start piloting this one,' he

bit out harshly. 'Because my time is short, and, I believe, as valuable as your father's!'

She looked ready to pass comment on the statement, and then thought better of it, drawing in a hissing breath before going through to the cockpit, slamming the door firmly shut behind her.

Damn! Damn, damn, damn. Jonas groaned as he dropped down into one of the armchairs. He was tired, regretted ever agreeing to this appointment, especially on a Saturday, and the last thing he felt like dealing with was a woman who enjoyed nothing more than flaunting her equality, an equality that he wasn't even aware he had questioned—apart from the assumption that she had to be the flight attendant, a nagging little voice infuriatingly reminded him!—before he had even had time to indulge in a much-needed, and so far denied, late breakfast!

'Would you fasten your seat belt, Mr Noble?' her voice came coolly over the internal intercom. 'We're about to taxi for take-off.'

Jonas did as he was asked, but it did not give him a sense of well-being to know that his life was now—literally—in the hands of Danie Summer—a woman who had shown him nothing but condescending contempt so far during their acquaintance!

CHAPTER ONE

WHO was Jonas Noble?

More to the point, *what* was he?

Until a couple of hours ago, Danie had believed she had a free Saturday, had planned on having lunch with her elder sister Harrie, and Harrie's husband, Quinn McBride, before going into town to do some leisurely shopping.

But then her father had telephoned, and, despite her half-hearted objections, had managed, with his usual charming diplomacy, to talk her into flying Jonas Noble to his country estate instead.

But Rome had been less than forthcoming about his visitor, refused—again, charmingly—to be drawn as to the reason for Jonas Noble's visit.

One thing Danie hated was a mystery. And Jonas Noble himself had been no help in explaining his reason for visiting her father's home, either. He had proved just as closed-mouthed as her father when she had questioned him a few minutes ago, and his appearance was no help whatsoever in pinning down who or what he could be.

The man didn't have the look of a businessman for one thing; his dark hair was a little too long. His casual clothing—black denims teamed with a black silk shirt and grey fitted jacket—exuded none of the formal efficiency that businessmen who dealt with her father liked to adopt. Her father excluded, of course. But then, Rome was way past the stage of caring what sort of image he presented—to anyone!

Perhaps Jonas Noble was in that kind of position, too…?

Danie shook her head even as she went through the mechanics of flying; she had never heard of Jonas Noble before, and if his photograph had ever appeared in any of the business journals her father subscribed to, then Danie knew she would have remembered him. His was not a face it would be easy to forget!

It wasn't strictly a handsome face, was too angular for that; his jaw was square and determined, with a firmly sculptured mouth, and slightly aquiline nose. It was his eyes that were so arresting, Danie realised: a deep dark brown, filled with a warmth that softened all those other hard edges.

Careful, Danie, she chided herself, or you might actually start to consider Jonas Noble as an attractive man!

Well, possibly he was, she conceded, but she wasn't fooled by a man's good looks. She knew those looks invariably hid a calculating selfishness. Her experience with Ben had more than shown her—

Damn it, where had that come from? She never thought of Ben any more, considered him a part of her life that was firmly shut away from prying eyes—and prying minds. Jonas Noble was the subject under question here, not someone from her past who had cured her of wanting any romantic involvement for the last two years!

Her passenger had one piece of luggage with him, a small case, too small for a suitcase, too large to be a briefcase. So what did it contain?

Well, she wasn't going to get any answers from the man himself, she conceded wryly, so she might as well put away her curiosity until she saw her father.

She reached up to press a button above her head. 'We're levelling out now, Mr Noble,' she told him coolly over the intercom. 'This is a non-smoking flight, but please help yourself to the refreshments,' she added mockingly, a smile curving her lips as she recalled the expression on the man's face when she'd informed him she wasn't the flight attendant but the pilot! Not exactly speechless, but close enough. Obviously women didn't step too far out of their expected roles in Jonas Noble's world, Danie thought tauntingly.

But planes, and flying, had been loves of hers since she'd been a child, having travelled all over the world with her parents by the time she was five. Instead of dolls, she had had models of planes in her bedroom as she'd been growing up, rapidly progressing to ones that had worked by remote control, taking them outside and flying them for hours. Her father's pilot at the time, an older man called Edward, had been quite happy for her to accompany him in the cockpit on flights, even found a pair of overalls for her to wear so that she'd been able to help him when he'd looked in the engines.

By the time she was eighteen she had already decided exactly what she was going to do with her life. There had been a little opposition from her father, of course. But as they had recently lost her mother to cancer, those objections had been only half-hearted. Rome was so devastated by the loss. If he had thought about it at all, he would have probably expected Danie would tire of the pursuit during the months it had taken her to get her full pilot's licence, but he would have been wrong. She loved flying, it was as simple as that.

Men like Jonas Noble were a prime example of the prejudice she had come up against during the time it had taken to attain her licence! Playing at it, seemed to be most men's opinion of her chosen career, backed up, no doubt, by what they considered to be Daddy's money.

Well, she had taken enough of that over the years, Danie reflected; if she were playing at anything, it was being polite in the face of the chauvinistic intolerance she had encountered towards her chosen career from men over the last seven or eight years!

Including Ben.

Not again, she told herself impatiently. She hadn't given the man a thought for months and now she had thought of him twice in half an hour. Unacceptable!

And it was all Jonas Noble's fault, she considered. There was something about him that brought Ben to mind. She could well do without it, thank you!

She pressed the button above her head a second time. 'We will be landing in ten minutes, Mr Noble,' she told him abruptly. 'I advise you to place any debris from your food and drink in the container provided, and to fasten your seat belt.' With any luck, his visit with her father would, as he had said, be a short one, and once she had flown him back to town she might just be able to go shopping, after all!

Her father had sent Charles out in the Rolls, and not the Range Rover, to collect his guest from the private airstrip on the estate, Danie noted with some surprise as she brought the jet in to land. Curiouser and curiouser. Rome rarely used the Rolls Royce, had bought it a couple of years ago on a whim, and now considered it a little too ostentatious for his tastes. But it had been brought out of mothballs today in Jonas Noble's honour. Which again posed the question: who was he?

'Please remain in your seat until I've completely brought the aircraft to a stop, Mr Noble,' she told him brusquely over the intercom. 'I will then come back through to the cabin and open the door for you.'

She had done this trip dozens of times before, but, she

had to admit, today was the first time she had found it slightly irritating to have a conversation—one way, at that!—with an unseen person. The only consolation was that Jonas Noble probably found it just as frustrating!

Not that any frustration on Jonas's part was apparent when, a few minutes later, the plane parked on the end of the runway, she went back into the cabin area. Jonas Noble was fast asleep! From the totally relaxed look of him, he probably had been from the moment they'd taken off, Danie realised crossly.

He was still sitting in the chair he had dropped into as she'd gone through to the cockpit, although at least his seat belt was fastened. But there was no sign of him having had any of the food or drink provided, and he seemed completely unaware that they had actually landed at their destination, his lids closed, his breathing deep and even.

He looked younger in sleep than the forty or so Danie had thought him to be earlier, long dark lashes fanning out across the hardness of his cheeks, his face appearing almost boyishly handsome now that slightly mocking expression had melted from his face.

His clothes, she could see as she took her time to look at him, were tailor-made, and the black shirt was probably Indian silk. A wealthy man then?

He was really something of an enigma, Danie realised with an emotion akin to shock. Men, she had decided after her few attempts at relationships—which, for one reason or another, had always ended disastrously!—were a complete waste of her time. And she now resented having given Jonas Noble even a little of it!

She reached down and shook his arm vigorously. 'Mr Noble, we've landed—'

'I sincerely hope so,' he murmured as he opened his

eyes and looked directly up into her face. 'Otherwise there would be no one flying the plane!'

For someone who had been fast asleep seconds ago, he was a little too much awake now for Danie's liking, and she stepped back from him as if stung, putting her hands behind her back. 'There is such a thing as autopilot, Mr Noble,' she bit out in reply.

He straightened in his chair, looking out of the window beside him. 'Not when you're on the ground,' he derided, releasing his seat belt to stretch languidly.

Danie's mouth twisted even as she registered the tightening and relaxing of muscles. 'Are we keeping you up, Mr Noble?' she scorned.

He turned to look at her with brown eyes. 'As a matter of fact—yes!' He stood up. 'That half an hour is the only sleep I've had in the last twenty-four,' he explained.

Danie's eyes widened at this disclosure, her expression disapproving. 'I hope she was worth it!' It wasn't too difficult to guess that a woman would have been the reason for his lack of sleep the previous night. Those warm brown eyes hinted at a certain sensuality about Jonas Noble!

His expression softened. 'She was.' He gave an inclination of his head by way of acknowledgement. 'Now do you intend keeping me locked in here?' he enquired. 'Or do you plan on taking me to see your father some time today?'

At the taunt angry colour heightened her cheeks, and she moved to release the door, the steps sliding automatically to the tarmacked ground. 'Can you manage your luggage, or would you like me to carry it for you?' Danie did some taunting of her own.

His mouth quirked into a half-smile as he bent to retrieve the oversized briefcase from the carpeted floor. 'I can manage, thanks. And thanks, too, for a good flight,' he added lightly.

'How would you know it was good? You slept all the way through it!' she came back tartly.

He shrugged broad shoulders. 'Not until I knew we were safely up in the air,' he rejoined. 'I heard the bit about "non-smoking flight" before I zonked out. I'm afraid my earlier years spent as a junior doctor have meant I can usually sleep anywhere, at any time,' he explained apologetically.

Danie didn't hear any more of what he said after 'junior doctor'—this man was a *doctor*? And he was here to see her father? Was Rome sick?

She found that very hard to believe, had never known her father to have a day's illness in his life. But that didn't mean he was well now...

She moistened suddenly dry lips. 'And what line of medicine did you choose to specialise in, Mr Noble?' She tried to make her tone of voice interested rather than demanding—although by the guarded look that suddenly came over Jonas Noble's face, she had a feeling she had failed. Damn!

'I believe it's called "life", Danie; it's the oath all doctors take,' he returned enigmatically. 'Is that car waiting for us?' He indicated the gold-coloured Rolls Royce that was now parked feet away from the plane steps, the attentive Charles standing waiting with the back door open.

Danie flushed her irritation. 'For you,' she corrected tautly. 'I have a few things to do here before coming over to the house,' she amended reluctantly.

She would have liked nothing better than to arrive back at the house with him, to try and find out more about exactly what he was doing here. But, unfortunately, she had the plane to check over and refuelling to see to.

He nodded dismissively. 'I'll see you later, then.' He moved lightly down the steps, grinning his thanks at Charles as he got into the back of the Rolls.

Danie stood at the top of the steps and watched the car—and Jonas Noble!—drive away, her thoughts in a turmoil.

Why did Rome need to see a doctor? Obviously because he was ill, she instantly chided herself.

But to have a doctor flown out here to see him…! Was her father's illness *that* serious?

Danie suddenly felt unwell herself at the thought of that being the case. She couldn't bear the thought of anything happening to her handsome, fun-loving father.

But Jonas Noble's visit certainly appeared ominous…

'I trust you had a comfortable flight?'

Jonas looked across at his host. The older man had greeted him at the door of the manor house a few minutes earlier, and the two of them were now seated in an elegant sitting-room. He had known what Jerome Summer looked like, of course, as he had seen the other man's picture in the newspapers several times. But those photographs had only shown Rome Summer's still boyish handsomeness, despite the fact that he was in his early fifties, and couldn't possibly hint at the sheer vitality of the man.

But what did Rome expect him to say in answer to his question? The flight had been fine—it was Rome's daughter that he hadn't found comfortable.

Danie Summer—how could he possibly have known she would be female?—was as prickly as a hedgehog, with all the charm of a herd of stampeding elephants!

But she was beautiful, another little voice inside his head reminded him.

Yes, she was—if you managed to get past those prickles

and the acidic tongue! Personally, he would as soon not bother.

'Fine, thank you,' Jonas replied brusquely, waving away the offer of a cup of coffee poured from the pot on the table that stood between the two men. 'You explained the situation to me on the telephone early yesterday evening,' he continued in businesslike tones. 'So perhaps I could carry out my examination, and then we can talk some more?'

Jerome Summer didn't move, his expression agonised now, blue eyes clouded with worry. 'Before you do that, could I just stress, once again, how delicate this situation is—?'

'I've already gathered that,' Jonas assured him dryly. 'Danie doesn't know, does she?' he prompted gently.

Rome grimaced, shaking his head ruefully. 'Has my daughter been asking you awkward questions?'

Jonas shrugged. 'One or two,' he confirmed. 'Oh, don't worry,' he assured as the other man began to frown, 'a patient's confidentiality is guaranteed as far as I'm concerned.'

Rome shook his head. 'That won't stop Danie.' His frown deepened. 'Maybe it wasn't such a good idea to have her fly you here. It just seemed the best option at the time—'

'I think it's a little late in the day to worry about that,' Jonas cut in. 'Besides, Danie is your problem, not mine,' he added firmly. 'I came here to carry out an examination…?' he prompted again pointedly.

The half an hour or so of sleep he had managed to get on the plane had temporarily refreshed him, but he was no longer a young 'junior doctor' when a couple of hours sleep grabbed here and there had been enough to keep him

going. At the moment the previous night's lack of rest
made him feel every one of his thirty-eight years!

'I don't mean to sound terse,' he excused as he realised
he had been exactly that. 'I had a difficult case to deal
with last night,' he explained. 'And lack of sleep means
I'm a little short on patience today!'

'Of course.' Rome Summer stood up quickly. 'I'll explain a little more to you as we go upstairs.'

Jonas picked up his case of instruments, listening politely to the other man as they ascended the stairs, realising
Rome needed to talk, that he found all of this extremely
difficult to deal with.

Jonas sympathised with him, could imagine how the
older man must be feeling. For a man who had controlled
his world, and that of his family, for the last thirty years,
Jonas realised this must all have come as a bit of a shock
to Rome Summer. It was something he had no control over
whatsoever. But even if the other man's suspicions proved
to be correct, it wasn't the end of the world. Other people,
other families, had gone through this sort of thing before.
And would no doubt continue to do so for a long time to
come!

But Rome Summer looked less than capable of dealing
with it, Jonas realised a short time later, Rome haggard
now as the two men returned to the sitting-room, Jonas's
diagnosis conclusive.

'I just can't believe it.' Rome groaned, his face buried
in his hands. 'I had my suspicions, of course—'

'You wouldn't have telephoned me otherwise,' Jonas
pointed out dryly, handing the other man a cup of the now
cool coffee; in the circumstances, cold or not, the caffeine
would do the other man good.

'But somehow I didn't really believe it.' Rome shook

his head dazedly, sipping the coffee without even seeming aware of what he was doing.

Jonas let the other man sit quietly for several minutes, giving him time to get over his initial shock; no doubt the coffee would help do that, too. Once the other man had accepted the diagnosis as fact, the two of them could get down to talking over the practicalities of what needed to be done over the next few months.

Rome finally raised his head, looking across at Jonas with slightly moist eyes. 'I'm sorry,' he said heavily. 'I realise I'm not taking this too well.' He gave a rueful grimace. 'I was wishing the girls' mother were here. She would have known what to do.'

'How many daughters do you have?' Jonas enquired politely, knowing the other man still needed to talk, and remembering having read somewhere that Rome Summer's wife had died several years ago.

'Just the three.' Rome sighed. 'But sometimes it seems like twenty-three!'

Jonas imagined that Danie Summer could quite easily account for twenty of those in her own right; she was certainly spirited enough to cause any man a headache, let alone her harassed father!

'Do they all live at home with you?' he asked lightly, curiosity prompting him to find out if Danie had some poor man as her husband somewhere in the background!

'None of them.' Rome shook his head. 'Harrie was married last month,' he said with obvious pleasure and pride. 'Andie is usually based in London, although she's been staying here with me the last few weeks.'

'And Danie?' Jonas persisted softly.

'I'm based, not wherever I hang my hat, but wherever I fly my aircraft!' the woman in question told him coldly as she walked unannounced into the room.

Jonas stiffened at the sound of that caustic voice, although he literally froze with shock once he had turned to look at her. The black baseball cap was gone, and he found that those dark lashes and brows had been deceptive. Hair of the most gloriously deep red now cascaded in loose waves down the length of Danie's spine.

If Jonas had thought her beautiful before, that red hair was definitely her crowning glory, giving prominence to her high cheekbones, bringing out the deep green colour of her eyes. There was no doubt about it—Danie Summer was one of the loveliest women he had ever set eyes on!

He stood up slowly. '*Your* aircraft?' he questioned silkily, feeling suddenly defensive in the face of this woman's arresting beauty.

A look of irritation darkened her features. 'Rome's aircraft,' she corrected, before turning to her father. 'Everything okay?' she prompted sharply, looking at him searchingly.

Rome seemed to have undergone a transformation in the last few seconds, Jonas noted wryly, that boyish grin back on his face, his worried expression of a few minutes ago completely dispelled. For his daughter's benefit, Jonas didn't doubt. Although there was no way Rome would be able to keep the truth from Danie indefinitely...

'Everything is fine,' Rome told Danie lightly. 'Jonas and I were just discussing having lunch before he returns to town.'

Jonas hesitated at the totally erroneous statement. Considering he hadn't even had breakfast yet...! But, he had to admit, food of any kind did sound rather tempting at the moment...

'As long as I'm not inconveniencing anyone...?' he accepted questioningly.

Glittering green eyes were turned in his direction. 'Since

when has inconveniencing someone bothered you?' Danie snapped.

Jonas's mouth firmed at the insult, Rome chuckling softly as he saw his reaction. Well, Rome might find his daughter's rudeness amusing, but Jonas found it exactly what it was—bad-mannered!

'You can have lunch with Harrie and Quinn any time, darling.' Rome put his arm lightly about his daughter's shoulders.

'But I was having lunch with them today,' Danie complained.

So she *had* had other plans for today, after all... Jonas fumed inwardly; it wasn't his fault she hadn't been able to carry them through—her father was responsible for that.

'Wouldn't you rather have lunch with two attractive men?' Rome teased his daughter.

Danie turned to give Jonas a slowly dismissive glance from head to toe. 'Not particularly,' she finally replied, before turning back to her father.

What this young lady needed was a smack on the backside, Jonas decided grimly. If her father didn't feel capable of administering it, Jonas was sure there must be plenty of other men who would!

Including him...?

Jonas frowned. He had never lifted so much as a finger against a woman in his life, and no matter how much Danie Summer might deserve a good spanking, he knew he wouldn't be the one to give it.

He had grown up in a totally female household; his mother had been widowed while still in her early thirties, and left with the sole care of Jonas and his two older sisters. Beautiful and warm-natured though she was, she had remained a widow in the succeeding years, managing, with only the help of a housekeeper, to bring the three children up alone. Meaning that Jonas, as the only male in the household, had been cosseted and spoilt by not just his mother and sisters, but the housekeeper, too.

It had been a charmed and loving childhood, instilling him with a deep respect for his mother and sisters, and a liking of women in general.

Except Danie Summer! he realised irritably.

But that, he considered, was mainly her own fault. Danie was obviously, despite her own privileged background, an accomplished and capable woman, who took her work very seriously. It was just the sharpness of her tongue that needed a little attention. A little…? Make that a lot, Jonas corrected himself firmly.

'Pity,' he drawled finally, easily able to meet the challenge in Danie's dark green eyes.

Danie's mouth twisted. 'A little sincerity wouldn't have come amiss in that statement!' she countered.

'Danie!' Rome chided. 'Must I remind you that Jonas is here as my guest?'

Jonas watched as Danie underwent a transformation, the tension leaving that beautiful face, to be replaced by a smile of gentle concern as she turned to look at her father.

Jonas felt something lurch in his chest at the difference that gentleness made to Danie; it was akin to the sun coming out in the midst of a stormy sky. And well worth waiting for, he acknowledged a little dazedly. Stripped of the cynicism that seemed to temper most of her conversation, Danie Summer was incredibly lovely.

'Perhaps lunch would be nice,' she finally conceded grudgingly. 'Would you like to freshen up before we eat, Mr Noble?' she offered with a politeness that had so far been lacking from their acquaintance.

He looked across at her with narrowed eyes, not fooled for a moment by her change in attitude, only to be met with a look of such innocence that he knew his suspicion was correct; Danie Summer had her own reason for her sudden politeness. And he had a feeling it could have something to do with the reason for his presence here today!

Well, she was wasting her time if she thought a little polite civility—something that should have been there from the beginning!—would charm out of him the reason for having come here to see her father. As he had assured Rome earlier, his relationship with his patient was always completely confidential.

As Danie Summer was going to quickly find out if she tried to pump him for information!

CHAPTER TWO

WHAT a complete waste of her time this had been, Danie muttered to herself as she pushed her food uninterestedly around her plate. She had intended originally to go upstairs and have lunch with her sister Andie. She'd only conceded to eating down here with her father and Jonas Noble in the hope of being able to find out a little more of the reason for the younger man's visit. But her father was close-mouthed on the subject, and Jonas Noble was also like a clam!

Which only succeeded in making Danie's imaginings even darker than they already were—and they were bad enough already!

Her father didn't *look* ill. A little strained perhaps, his ready smile not always reaching the warmth of his blue eyes, but other than that he seemed his normal self.

The trouble was, Danie felt so alone in her wonderings. She couldn't talk to Andie about it; her younger sister had been far from well herself since a bout of flu the previous month. Her other sister, Harrie, had only been recently married, and it would be a pity to spoil that happiness, especially if it should turn out to be unnecessary.

Audrey!

Of course, her father's assistant of the last twelve years was sure to know exactly what was going on. She might not tell Danie, perhaps, but she couldn't possibly be as clam-like as these two men had turned out to be!

'I think I'll give coffee a miss, if you don't mind.' Danie put her dessert fork neatly down on her plate before stand-

27

ing up. 'I have a few things to do before flying back this afternoon,' she told her father as he looked across at her enquiringly.

They were seated very cosily around the dining table; Danie grimaced at the scene: her father at the head, Jonas and herself sitting either side of him, facing each other across the table. Jonas's appetite, Danie had noted disgustedly, had been more than healthy in comparison with her own picking at the food. Obviously the seriousness of his work didn't affect him!

'Of course, darling,' her father accepted lightly. 'I'll give you a ring when Jonas needs to go. Oh, and I shouldn't bother to go and see Andie,' he added, looking concerned. 'She was sleeping when I called in on her room earlier.'

'Perhaps you should get Dr Noble to look at Andie before he leaves?' Danie suggested tauntingly.

'What on earth for?' her father exclaimed.

She shrugged. 'This flu seems to have been dragging on a long time. Or perhaps general medicine isn't his field?' she questioned challengingly.

Brown eyes levelly met the mockery in her gaze. 'It's been a few years,' Jonas conceded dryly. 'But I'm sure I could manage.'

'I—'

'And it's Mr Noble, Danie,' Jonas continued hardly. 'Or Jonas, if you would prefer that?'

She would prefer to know exactly what sort of doctor he was! But she knew, especially since lunch, that she would get nowhere on that subject with either of these men. A talk with Audrey definitely beckoned!

'I'll see you later—Jonas,' she dismissed him pointedly—after all, he'd called her Danie without ever having been invited to do so!

It wasn't too difficult to locate Audrey; the other woman was as much of a workaholic as Rome, busy dealing with some correspondence in his study when Danie entered there a few minutes later.

The older woman looked up with a warm smile, having become like another member of the family in the twelve years she had worked for Rome. At forty-two, she was tall, blonde, and beautiful.

'Uh-oh.' Audrey grimaced, putting aside the letter she had been working on. 'Who's been upsetting you?'

Danie scowled, sitting on the side of her father's desk. 'Is it that obvious?'

'Yes!' Audrey laughed unabashedly.

Danie chose her next words carefully. Very carefully. Because, although she knew Audrey was fond of all of them, the older woman was also completely loyal to Rome. And the last thing Audrey would ever do was break a confidence of his, business or private.

'Have you met Jonas Noble?' Danie asked lightly.

Audrey frowned. 'The man who was with Rome earlier?'

Danie looked at Audrey searchingly. Was she just delaying answering, or did she really not know anything? Danie would be surprised if it were the latter; Rome trusted his assistant implicitly. But if that should turn out to be the case... It made the whole situation seem even more ominous!

'That's the one.' She nodded casually.

'As a matter of fact, no,' Audrey replied. 'Who is he exactly?'

Danie frowned. 'I was hoping you might be able to tell me that!'

'Sorry,' Audrey said. 'But I don't have a clue.'

Damn, damn, damn! This was much worse than Danie

had thought. Never having married herself, Audrey had
become one of the family, and Danie knew that Rome had
absolutely no secrets from the other woman. But it now
appeared Rome hadn't told Audrey anything about Jonas
Noble, either…

'All I've managed to find out is that he's some sort of
doctor,' she told Audrey.

'Oh,' Audrey murmured slowly.

Was it her imagination, or did Audrey's expression suddenly look guarded? But the other woman had told her she
knew nothing about Jonas Noble, and Danie believed her.
So why did Audrey suddenly look so wary?

'Any help?' Danie went on, watching Audrey intently.

Audrey turned away from the intensity of that searching
gaze. 'Not particularly. Rome simply hasn't mentioned
him.'

Rome might not have mentioned Jonas Noble, but Danie
was sure that revealing his identity as a doctor had given
Audrey some idea of exactly what he was doing here…

And why shouldn't it have done? Audrey spent more
time with her father than anyone else, was sure to be aware
if Rome was ill. Even if she wouldn't talk to anyone else
about it…

Danie stood away from the desk, knowing she would
get nothing further out of Audrey. 'I had better go and see
if he's ready to leave yet.' She pulled a face at the prospect
of spending yet more time in the company of Jonas Noble.

'Have fun,' Audrey replied distractedly, her thoughts
obviously elsewhere.

Were they with Rome? Danie pondered as she walked
slowly back to the dining-room. Because she had no doubt
whatsoever, now that Audrey knew Jonas Noble was a
doctor, she also knew exactly what he was doing here!

Danie gave an impatient sigh. If her father *was* ill, then

she had a right to know. She wasn't a child; for goodness' sake, none of them was, and, although it would be upsetting to find out Rome had serious health problems, it couldn't be any worse than how not knowing was turning out to be!

'Why the long face, Danie?' her father asked as he met her out in the hallway.

He was alone. Which posed the question; where was Jonas Noble?

Although, for the moment, Danie put that question aside, and looked intently at her father. 'What's going on, Daddy?' she demanded.

Her father steadily held her eyes. 'I—'

'And don't try and fob me off by telling me you don't know what I'm talking about,' Danie cut in determinedly, her expression mutinous. 'Because you know exactly what I meant!'

Her father raised blond brows reprovingly. 'I wasn't about to do that, Danie,' he answered softly, that very softness telling her that he was becoming angry himself. 'But I'll talk to you—to all of you—when I'm good and ready.'

Danie drew in a sharp breath. Her father was tough when it came to his business dealings, had needed to be to become the successful man he was, but he rarely, if ever, became angry with any of his daughters. The very fact that he was angry with her now told Danie just how serious this all was...

'Where's Jonas Noble?' she asked tautly.

Her father relaxed slightly, a teasing light entering the blue of his eyes. 'Unless I'm mistaken, you didn't seem in too much of a hurry to spend time in his company earlier.'

Danie grimaced. 'You weren't mistaken. But as it appears I don't have any choice in the matter—'

'Oh, but you do.' Rome grinned. 'I've had Charles drive Jonas back to London,' he explained at her sharply questioning look.

Danie blinked her surprise. Jonas Noble had already left? He was being *driven* back to town?

'And whose idea was that?' she snapped resentfully. Damn it, she might not have wanted to spend any more time in the man's company, but it would at least have given her another chance to find out more about him!

'Mine, actually,' her father replied matter-of-factly. 'Although Jonas seemed quite happy with the arrangement too,' he added.

Danie would just bet he had! She hadn't been unaware of Jonas Noble's dislike of her, knew that he had found her brash and rude. Which she had been, she conceded ruefully. But she had also been aware, when she'd entered the sitting-room before lunch, that he had been surprised by, if not attracted to, the difference in her appearance without the baseball cap, that he had been momentarily stunned by her looks. Only momentarily, she acknowledged wryly; she was sure that not too many things wrong-footed the arrogant Mr Noble for long!

'I was only talking to Audrey,' Danie muttered resentfully. 'You said you would give me a call when Jonas was ready to leave.'

Her father's humour disappeared. 'I preferred him to be driven back with Charles,' he stated firmly.

Effectively removing any chance she might have to talk to Jonas Noble again!

She didn't like this. Not one little bit. And if her father thought he had got the better of her, then he was going to be disappointed. Jonas could only have left with Charles minutes earlier, which meant they couldn't have got very far yet.

'Where are you going?' her father called after her as she turned to run up the wide staircase.

Danie glanced back only briefly. 'I think I'll go back to town too,' she told him.

'But—'

'You'll have to excuse me, Daddy,' she interrupted his protest, turning to go up the stairs two at a time. 'I'm in rather a hurry.'

It took very little time to collect the things she needed from her bedroom, and race back down the stairs again. On her way to the front door she heard the murmur of voices coming from the sitting-room.

'—will have to be told soon, Rome,' Audrey was saying gently. 'Very soon, I would have thought. This isn't something you can keep to yourself for very much longer.'

It wasn't in Danie's forthright nature to eavesdrop, but those few words held her transfixed in the hallway, her heart beating faster, her eyes dark with apprehension as she listened to the rest of what Audrey had to say.

She'd believed Audrey when the other woman had told her earlier that she didn't know who or what Jonas Noble was, or what he was doing here, but obviously the little Danie had told the other woman about him had given Audrey the answer to the latter at least…!

'I realise that,' Rome groaned in a pained voice. 'It's just that— This isn't the sort of thing you can just blurt out over breakfast one morning!' he rasped impatiently.

Audrey sighed. 'I know, but if I've been able to guess…'

'Yes, yes,' Rome muttered heavily. 'I will tell them. But in my own time,' he said grimly. 'I have to get used to the idea myself first!'

'I know, Rome,' Audrey returned huskily. 'I do know.

I just— Oh, Rome!' she choked emotionally. 'It will only be a matter of weeks before they all realise—'

'It's all right, Audrey,' Rome soothed, appearing to be the comforter now. 'It will be all right, you'll see.'

Danie couldn't stand and listen to any more, hurrying from the house, closing the door softly behind her, loath to let her father or Audrey know she had heard any of their conversation.

Weeks...! My God, did that mean—? Was her father—?

She didn't care whether Jonas Noble wanted to see her again or not—he was damn well going to. Because she was determined to get some answers from somewhere— and at the moment Jonas Noble seemed to be the man who had them all!

It was warm and comfortable in the back of the Rolls Royce, and Jonas could feel the effect of that warm comfort as his eyes once again began to close sleepily. Thank goodness it was the weekend and he could sleep in late tomorrow.

You're getting too old for this, Noble, he told himself. One sleepless night had reduced him to being almost a walking zombie. *Almost*, he smiled to himself sleepily. He had been awake enough to visit his patient today.

And he had certainly been awake enough to appreciate the beautiful, if caustic, Danie Summer!

He shook his head as it rested back against the leather seat, smiling slightly, his eyes closed. Not a woman to be trifled with, he decided, knowing that she believed he had done exactly that. And had resented him intensely for it. He—

'I'm going to pull over, Mr Noble,' Charles announced from the front of the car, glancing in his driving mirror as

Jonas opened his eyes to look across at him. 'Miss Danie seems to want a word,' Charles added helpfully.

Miss Danie—!

Jonas sat up straighter in his seat, turning to look out the back window of the car. But as far as he could see, 'Miss Danie' was nowhere to be seen. There was only a motorbike behind them, a huge monster of a black machine, with its rider bent low over the handlebars—

Jonas narrowed his eyes to look more intently at the driver of the powerful black bike, instantly recognising the deep green eyes that could be seen clearly beneath the black crash-helmet.

When she wasn't flying planes, it seemed Danie Summer rode a motorbike that looked powerful enough to crush her if it fell on her! Not that it ever would, Jonas decided; it wouldn't dare!

A woman who liked to live life dangerously, he decided.

He turned to sit patiently in the back of the car while Charles got out to talk to Danie. The back passenger door opened seconds later and Danie Summer herself climbed into the back of the vehicle to sit beside him.

Jonas raised dark brows as he looked at her. She had taken off the black helmet, releasing that cascade of flame-red hair. The black leathers she wore seemed moulded to the curves of her body—and very sexy it looked too, Jonas realised as he felt a faint stirring of his own body in response to such feminine perfection.

'To what do I owe the honour?' he prompted sarcastically, annoyed with himself for his own reaction to this woman. Beauty, he knew, was only skin deep; Danie Summer was the most outspokenly rude woman he had ever had the misfortune to meet.

Her mouth twisted derisively. 'You forgot to say goodbye,' she murmured huskily.

Jonas looked at her through narrowed lids. He didn't believe for one moment that was the reason she had followed him. Although it was becoming patently obvious that was exactly what she had done...

'Goodbye, Danie,' he said.

She smiled. 'Very politely delivered, Jonas.'

He gave an acknowledging inclination of his head. 'My mother made a point of instilling good manners into all of her children,' he returned.

Danie nodded. 'But does it have to be goodbye?' She quirked dark brows, eyes gleaming brightly.

With what, Jonas wasn't sure. A cross between challenge and flirtation, he thought; although the latter seemed unlikely in the circumstances!

He eyed her warily now. 'What did you have in mind?' he asked slowly.

Danie shrugged, colour heightening her cheekbones even as she spoke. 'I was wondering if you would have dinner with me this evening?'

Jonas drew in his breath quickly. He wasn't fooled for a moment into believing this young woman really wanted to have dinner with him—her motives for the invitation, in view of her earlier curiosity concerning the reason for his visit to her family home today, were all too obvious!— but at the same time, he was intrigued in spite of himself...

'In a word—no,' he told her bluntly, his gaze becoming amused as he saw the way angry colour suffused her cheeks now; obviously not a young lady who was used to hearing that particular word!

She swallowed hard—doing her best to swallow down a blistering response at the same time!—eyes flashing with resentment. 'Why not?' she demanded.

Jonas smiled at the return to her previous bluntness. She certainly hadn't been able to maintain that air of flirtatious-ness for long! But, he realised, he thought he preferred her rudeness; it was certainly more honest, and at least he knew where he stood!

And there was no denying that Danie was amazingly beautiful...

'I wasn't saying no to dinner, Danie, just not tonight,' he heard himself say. 'It probably hasn't escaped your notice, but I'm having trouble keeping my eyes open!'

Her anger at his refusal rapidly faded, to be quickly replaced by scorn. 'Of course.' She nodded. 'You mentioned earlier that you had very little sleep last night.'

And, of course, she had already drawn her own conclusions concerning that sleeplessness.

Jonas gave an inward smile at the knowledge. Not that he hadn't had relationships in the past, and they had certainly quite often involved getting a minimum of sleep, but this particular period of time there wasn't a woman in his life. Nor had there been for some while. Mainly because he had found he was tired of relationships that seemed, ultimately, to be leading nowhere.

In fact, he had found himself doing quite a lot of soul-searching in recent months. He enjoyed his work, and good relations with his mother, and his sisters and their respective families, but just lately he had wondered if there wasn't something missing from his own life, had found himself possessed of a restlessness that neither his work nor his family could assuage.

But maybe it was the fact that there wasn't a woman in his life at the moment that had caused that restlessness in the first place!

While he didn't think having dinner with Danie Summer would help that situation, he had no doubts it would prove entertaining.

'Tomorrow evening, however, would be no problem—if that would suit you?' he suggested.

And then wondered if he weren't making a big mistake. While she might be breathtakingly beautiful, he hadn't particularly liked Danie Summer so far in their acquaintance, and he was halfway sure she shared the feeling. Halfway? Damn it, she had given every indication she heartily disliked him!

Tomorrow evening should be fun, Jonas thought. If Danie accepted... Which, right now, she seemed to be having difficulty doing, Jonas noted shrewdly. From what Rome had told him about his daughters, Danie wasn't married, but that didn't mean she didn't have someone in her life. Which might make seeing him tomorrow evening something of a problem...

Well, that was *her* problem, Jonas dismissed. If she could offer to see him this evening, then she could make it tomorrow evening instead.

Unless she just didn't like the delay of twenty-four hours...?

Which was probably more than likely the case, Jonas decided. Danie Summer had come over to him as an 'instant' person. If something needed doing, then deal with it now, not later. Which probably accounted for the way she had followed him on her motorbike!

'Well?' he prompted impatiently; his own time, as he had told her earlier, was no less valuable than was her own, or her father's, and quite frankly he had used up enough of it on this family for one day. Besides, falling into bed—alone—beckoned.

Those green eyes flashed her anger once more before it was quickly brought under control. Danie even went so far as to force a smile to those poutingly inviting lips. 'Tomorrow evening will be fine,' she answered in measured tones. 'In fact, it will probably be better,' she continued as she warmed to this change of plan—her plan! 'I'm sure I'll have no problem booking us a table at my favourite Italian restaurant on a Sunday evening.'

And Jonas was sure, if Danie decided to eat at her favourite Italian restaurant on New Year's Eve without a booking—one of the busiest evenings of the year—that a table would be found for her somehow! There was about her an assured arrogance that would ensure not too many people said that word no to her...

So it came as no surprise to him either that Danie would be the one to book the restaurant. 'What time do you intend picking me up?' he enquired tauntingly, laughing softly as she looked momentarily nonplussed at the suggestion. 'I usually call and collect the people *I've* invited out to dinner,' he informed her.

Danie looked irritated at the reminder that she had been the one to do the inviting. 'Would seven-thirty suit you?' she said tautly.

'That depends on what time you book the table for.'

Her mouth tightened at his deliberate awkwardness. 'How about eight o'clock?'

'Then seven-thirty will be fine,' Jonas returned, enjoying her momentary discomfort. Momentary—because he was sure she wouldn't remain disconcerted for long! 'In fact,' he went on softly, 'I'll look forward to it!'

It was obvious from her expression that Danie didn't share the sentiment.

Jonas laughed to himself. He did not think Danie was the answer to the restlessness that had been plaguing him recently, but she had certainly brightened up what might otherwise have been a very arduous day. In fact, he was even starting to look forward to continuing another verbal fencing-match tomorrow evening!

He glanced down at the plain gold watch on his wrist. 'If you'll excuse me, Danie,' he told her briskly. 'I have another patient to see before I call it a day.'

Impatience once again flared in those revealing green eyes at his obvious dismissal, only to be dampened down again as she made an effort not to lose the fiery temper he had already glimpsed more than once today.

'You're certainly kept busy,' she finally replied.

'Unfortunately, I don't very often get flown around in luxurious planes!'

'Where exactly do you work?' Danie asked casually.

She would never make it in the diplomatic corps, Jonas concluded; she was as transparent as glass. 'Here and there,' he answered enigmatically, having to stop himself from laughing out loud this time at the angry frustration she wasn't quick enough to hide.

'Then I had better not keep you any longer,' she said, bending to pick up her helmet and leather gloves from the carpeted floor where she had placed them earlier.

'Haven't you forgotten something?' Jonas reminded her as she threw the car door open with her usual impatience.

She turned back to him, looking puzzled. 'I don't think so…?' She shook her head, red hair framing the loveliness of her face.

So much perfect beauty, Jonas mused. What a pity her only reason for wanting to see him again was the hope of trying to get him to be less than discreet about his visit to the Summer estate today…! A wasted hope, he was afraid, but it would be interesting to see how she went about it…

'You have no idea where I live,' he told her, taking a pen and small notebook from the breast pocket of his jacket, quickly writing down his address before ripping the sheet from the pad and handing it to her. 'I'll be ready and waiting at seven-thirty tomorrow evening.'

Danie shoved the piece of paper in the pocket of her leather jacket, obviously annoyed with herself at the oversight. 'I'll try to be on time,' she snapped before getting out of the car and slamming the door shut behind her.

Charles had barely had time to get back in behind the wheel of the Rolls Royce before the black motorbike, Danie bent grimly down over the engine, shot past them with a roar, then rapidly disappeared into the distance.

Jonas relaxed back onto his seat, a smile playing about his lips. Danie Summer's tongue was as sharp as a knife, and she had an arrogance that bordered on contempt. But she was also incredibly beautiful, and the most intriguing woman Jonas had met for a very long time. If ever!

What a pity her only reason for wanting to see him again was the selfish one of wanting to know why he had been to see her father today.

And what a pity—for Danie!—that she was going to be unsuccessful!

CHAPTER THREE

'DRESSED to kill', she believed it was called. Danie studied her reflection in the mirror. The short green sequinned dress clung so lovingly to her body that she could wear only the minimum of clothing beneath it; she had dispensed with a bra altogether, and her panties were of the sheerest silk. Her hair was loose about her shoulders, like a rippling flame—red, with the merest hint of gold as it shimmered down her spine.

She had applied a little more make-up than usual, too—in fact, she didn't usually bother with it at all!—her lashes long and silky, her eyes outlined with black kohl, giving them a look of wide innocence, her cheekbones aglow with blusher, the deep red gloss on her lips a match for the colour of her hair.

If Jonas Noble didn't find her appearance attractive, then he simply wasn't a normal flesh-and-blood man!

She had been so irritated when he'd refused her invitation to dinner yesterday, even more so when he'd then suggested they meet over twenty-four hours later. She had wanted to know what was going on then, not the next day!

But, in retrospect, the delay had been fortuitous. She'd had time to calm down, to collect her thoughts, to think rationally about how she was going to go about finding out the reason for Jonas's visit to her father yesterday. And the only problem with the plan she had come up with, that she could see, was if she would be able to hold on to her temper long enough to try and seduce the information out of him!

She knew Jonas found her attractive, had seen his admiration for her looks in his face. There was no doubting the fact that he was handsome enough himself for her not to find flirting with him too arduous a task. It was the fact that he also annoyed her intensely that could pose a problem!

Besides, finding her physically attractive and actually being attracted to her as a person were two entirely different things—and Jonas had given every indication that he found her as irritating as she found him!

Not exactly a recipe for success, she acknowledged ruefully. Oh, well, she would just have to set about changing his opinion of her...

If she could have done this any other way, then she would have. She had gone back to the estate earlier today intending to talk with her father, only to find that he and Audrey had driven up to Scotland in preparation for a deal he was to complete there early tomorrow. Andie had also gone—back to her apartment in town, Danie assumed. Which was no help at all; Danie still had no intention of worrying either of her sisters with this until she was more sure of her facts.

Jonas Noble alone, it seemed, was the only person available to give her them...

Time to go, she decided firmly, picking up her small evening bag before throwing a light black cashmere wrap about her shoulders; she didn't want to add tardiness to the list of faults Jonas had no doubt already found in her!

The address he had given her was in Mayfair. But she had expected to find Jonas owned an apartment, and the tall imposing three-storey house came as something of a surprise to Danie. Obviously, whichever field of medicine Jonas Noble had chosen to go into, it was very lucrative!

Jonas looked absolutely stunning in a black dinner suit

and snowy white shirt, Danie discovered a few minutes later, when he opened the door to her ring on the doorbell!

The suit was obviously tailored to his broad shoulders, narrow waist, and long legs, the white of the shirt showing that he had a healthy tan. But it was his face, no longer looking fatigued, that took Danie's breath away, the hard planes once again softened by the warmth of his deep brown eyes.

Perhaps seducing this man wasn't going to be so easy after all—for her own peace of mind; she might actually find herself genuinely attracted to him!

'Danie Summer, I presume?' he drawled, obviously mocking the change in her appearance from her workman-like garb of yesterday.

Steady, Danie, she warned herself as she instantly felt a flash of anger at his derision. 'Jonas Noble, I presume?' she returned with dry sarcasm at the change in his own appearance.

He smiled, eyes crinkling at the corners with genuine amusement. 'You're exactly as I remembered you, Danie!'

She wished she could say the same! But now that he was no longer exhausted by lack of sleep, showered and decked out in his own finery, relaxed with the prospect of the evening ahead of them, Jonas Noble was dangerously attractive!

She gave a nod of her head. 'I'll take that as a compliment,' she returned—knowing it had been no such thing; Jonas's remark was obviously referring to the sharpness of her tongue. Then she had better not disappoint him! 'Are we going to stand here on the doorstep all evening, or are you ready to leave?'

His grin deepened. 'I wonder if you would like to come inside for a drink before going to the restaurant?'

She was disconcerted enough by the change in his appearance and demeanour without finding herself alone in this beautiful house with him. She definitely would feel more comfortable going straight to the restaurant. Although she couldn't help feeling an inner curiosity about his bachelor home...

'Perhaps we could come back for coffee after our meal?' she suggested as a compromise—if she hadn't managed to wheedle the information she wanted from him during the meal, perhaps she would stand more chance in the intimacy of his home...

'Perhaps we could,' Jonas agreed, those brown eyes seeming full of laughter now.

At her expense, Danie guessed. Could she help it if this particular man brought out every defence she possessed? Besides, he was intelligent enough to realise that her about-face yesterday had to have a motive of its own!

Which didn't bother her in the least, Danie mused on the drive to the restaurant. She would think him conceited in the extreme if he hadn't put two and two together and come up with the right answer. But he was still here, accompanying her to dinner, and that was all that mattered.

'Danie!' Marco, the Italian-born, but brought-up-in-England, owner of the restaurant greeted warmly as she entered at Jonas's side. 'It's so good to see you again. And you too, Mr Noble.' He turned to Jonas. 'I didn't realise the two of you knew each other,' he added speculatively.

'We don't,' Jonas said, shaking the other man's hand. 'Yet,' he amended with an enigmatic glance at Danie.

Danie forced the smile to remain on her lips, determined Jonas shouldn't see that his remark had caused her any alarm. Even if it had!

She had no intention of getting to know Jonas Noble, tonight or any other night, and his own professionalism should have told him that to do so would be very indiscreet. She totally dismissed the idea that she was behaving less than fairly herself. She wasn't the doctor in attendance to a member of her family, Jonas was, and if he didn't feel it was unprofessional to become intimately involved with her, then perhaps he damn well ought to!

'You are looking as beautiful as ever, Danie—'

'Cut the flattery, Marco,' she told the restaurateur shortly. 'I've had very little to eat today, and I'm starving!' she continued indelicately.

'You heard the lady, Marco,' Jonas drawled, taking a light hold of her elbow. 'I have a feeling Danie is a woman who may turn violent if she isn't fed! What do you think?' he bent to murmur softly in Danie's ear, as they followed a smiling Marco through the noisily crowded restaurant to their table.

She arched dark brows as she turned to look at him from beneath her lashes. 'I've been wondering for years why I seem to have this impatience with the rest of humanity—and you've solved the riddle for me only a short time into our acquaintance!' she said with a sweetly insincere smile.

Jonas laughed huskily. 'You only "seem" to have impatience, Danie...?' he returned pointedly.

She shrugged, moving to sit down as he held back her chair for her. 'Sometimes I'm merely baffled by their lack of imagination,' she dismissed airily.

Jonas looked admiringly at her across the width of their window table once Marco had left them to peruse the menu. 'And have you always had an answer for everything?' he finally said.

'According to my mother my first word wasn't "Daddy", it was "no"!' she told him.

A smile played about his lips now as he looked at her. 'I can believe that.' He nodded slowly. 'What was she like?'

Danie blinked her bafflement at this sudden change of subject. 'Who?'

'Your mother.' Jonas sobered. 'She must have been a pretty incredible woman to have entranced a man like Rome. And she produced some incredibly beautiful daughters, too,' he opined admiringly.

'Flattery, Jonas?' Danie taunted softly.

'Not at all,' he returned. 'Physical beauty is all too easy to see.'

'As opposed to inner beauty...?' Danie challenged.

'That's sometimes a little more difficult to find,' he acknowledged hardly.

This was all becoming a little too serious for what Danie had in mind for the evening. 'My mother was one of the lucky ones; she had inner as well as outer beauty,' she explained at Jonas's questioning look. 'She was tiny, with deep auburn hair that could look almost black in some lights, and then the fiery red of my own in sunlight. She had beautifully tiny features, almost like a doll,' Danie remembered gruffly. 'But it wasn't her looks that drew people to her.' She shook her head. 'She was one of those people who was possessed of the ability to make others happy, to only see the positive rather than the negative in people. In fact,' she added briskly, 'my mother was the complete opposite of me!'

Instead of coming back with an affirmative comment, Jonas continued to look at her for several long, timeless seconds. 'You still miss her,' he finally murmured gently.

Danie flinched, a shutter coming down over her emotions. She had been seventeen when her mother had died, had spent all of those years secure in her mother's love, within the warm glow of her mother's world of sunshine and laughter; of course she still missed her! But it wasn't something she intended discussing with Jonas!

'I would be singularly lacking in emotion if I didn't,' she answered scathingly.

Jonas nodded. 'My own mother brought my two sisters and myself up virtually alone after my father died when I was very young.'

Danie didn't want to know that, either, didn't want to know anything about his private life—it only succeeded in making Jonas seem more and more like a person in his own right. And that would never do!

'Life can be a bitch, can't it?' She was deliberately flippant. 'What do you feel like eating?' She changed the subject, lifting her own menu up in front of her face.

She was more shaken than she cared to admit by the talk of their respective mothers. She had loved her mother with an innocent completeness, and she had heard Jonas's admiration for his own mother in his one brief comment before Danie had turned to the menu so rudely.

But her own feelings about the cruel loss of her mother were other things that were locked away, only to be looked at when she was alone; she simply couldn't share them with a man she barely knew...

'Pasta, and then garlic prawns, I think,' Jonas decided before placing the menu to one side. 'If that's okay with you?' He quirked dark brows. 'There's nothing worse than having someone breathing garlic all over you when you haven't eaten the stuff yourself,' he explained at her questioning look.

Danie frowned. She had intended being friendly towards him—even if she hadn't quite managed it so far!—in order to ask him the questions she wanted answers to, but she certainly hadn't intended getting close enough for him to breathe all over her!

'Go ahead,' she answered casually. 'I was going to have the garlic mushrooms, anyway.' She made it obvious she certainly hadn't intended asking *his* permission before eating garlic!

His brown eyes gleamed with laughter as Jonas easily read her mutinous thoughts. 'And a red wine to go with it—if that's okay with you?' he enquired.

'Fine.' She put aside her own menu. 'As I'm driving I'll only be having one glass, anyway.'

'We can always get a taxi back to my house,' Jonas pointed out.

Which then posed the question; how would she get home from there…?

'I rarely drink, anyway,' she told him tautly, wondering if this man wasn't perhaps taking too much for granted by her invitation, after all…! 'And I prefer it when other people don't, either,' she added before he could comment. 'I find it tends to make people rather silly, most unlike their normal selves.'

Jonas leant towards her a little. 'Then I'm glad I don't drink alcohol in great quantities, either!'

Danie didn't see why he should be glad; so far he hadn't given any indication he cared one way or the other whether she approved of him or not.

'Please don't deny yourself the pleasure on my account,' she told him frostily.

'I wasn't about to,' he assured her before turning to order a bottle of the red wine from the waiter who had been hovering beside their table for some minutes.

Luckily the ordering of their food took some time too—time enough for the subject of Jonas's pleasure to be forgotten! She could have phrased that a little better, Danie berated herself. Although the subject of alcohol did give her another opening…

'I don't suppose it's very sensible, in your profession, to ever have too much to drink,' she voiced casually, although her gaze was narrowed sharply as she watched Jonas across the table. 'You must be constantly on call to your patients?'

Jonas appeared unfazed. 'Even doctors have some time off,' he replied.

Deliberately so, Danie was sure. 'And is tonight one of those occasions?' She made her tone deliberately light; they were at least heading in the right direction in their conversation now!

His mouth twisted ruefully. 'Unfortunately, I'm not just a doctor, Danie, I'm a consultant. I deal mainly with private patients, with fees to match. Those patients expect a personal service for those fees.'

'That sounds fair enough,' Danie agreed, anticipation beginning to well up inside her. 'Are you—?'

'Jonas!' a pleased female voice cried out in recognition.

The woman appeared to have been on her way past their table when she spotted Jonas. She was a tall, willowy blonde, her beautiful face alight with pleasure, blue eyes glowing warmly.

Jonas stood up as he recognised the other woman, the smile on his own face as warm. 'Grace!' He bent and kissed her. 'You're looking extremely well,' he told her approvingly.

The woman, Grace, looked better than 'extremely well', Danie thought irritably; she was absolutely stunningly beautiful, and her long straight hair shone like spun gold. From the familiar way Jonas had just greeted her, the two of them had—or still did—know *each other* 'extremely well'!

Wonderful. Danie had come out this evening with the purpose of wheedling information out of Jonas Noble concerning her father, and almost within minutes of their arrival it appeared they had been interrupted by a woman who obviously knew Jonas on more than a friendly basis!

It was bad enough that it was proving difficult to pin Jonas down to the conversation she really wanted to have with him, without having the woman—or one of them!—in his life interrupting them too!

Jonas's comment concerning the way Grace looked had been completely genuine, but as he turned and saw the disgusted expression on Danie Summer's face he knew that she had completely misconstrued the situation.

He gave a slight shake of his head, his mouth thinning at the accusation he could read in Danie's eyes. His annoyance at that accusing look wasn't helped by the fact that ordinarily he would have felt no compunction about explaining his acquaintance with Grace. But, in the present circumstances, he simply couldn't do that...

'Danie Summer, this is Grace Cowley,' he introduced stiffly. 'Danie is a friend of mine, Grace,' he explained, knowing Danie—sharply astute Danie!—wouldn't fail to pick up the fact that he hadn't said what part Grace played in his life.

Because he had no intention of explaining that to Danie. She was bright and intelligent, and, once an explanation was given as to how he had first become acquainted professionally with Grace, Danie would put two and two together and come up with the correct answer of four! He had to remember that a patient's privacy, albeit that of a member of Danie's family, was at stake here...

'How lovely,' Grace greeted Danie with warm sincerity. 'It's way past time some lucky woman snapped this gorgeous man up and made a family man out of him!' The last was accompanied with a merry look in Jonas's direction.

He smiled in appreciation of the suggestion, knowing his bachelorhood was considered a challenge by the majority of women in his acquaintance; the married ones tried to set him up with single female friends of theirs, and the single ones thought he was fair game.

'I'll marry when I'm good and ready,' he said firmly. 'How are Gerald and the family?' he went on, knowing by her tense expression that Danie was listening avidly to every word of this conversation. Probably hoping to pick up some snippet of information on him that she could use once they were alone together again!

'Gerald is sitting over there.' Grace turned and waved across the restaurant at her husband. 'And the twins are doing marvellously. Growing fast, of course,' she added wistfully. 'You must come and see us all some time,' Grace encouraged determinedly.

'I'll do that,' he returned noncommittally. 'Now, we really mustn't keep you from Gerald any longer...'

Grace gave a throatily appreciative laugh. 'I can take the hint that the two of you want to be alone!' She reached up and kissed Jonas on the cheek. 'Nice to have met you, Danie.' She smiled. 'And remember, Jonas, I love weddings.' At that, Grace wended her way back to the table where her husband waited.

Jonas sat down, deliberately avoiding looking at Danie, although he could feel her scathing glance on him. She had obviously drawn her own conclusions about his relationship with Grace, regardless of her husband and children.

Damn it, he wasn't going to disabuse Danie of those assumptions! Why should he? Besides, he simply couldn't, not without breaching a professional confidence...

Danie's mouth pursed at his continued silence. 'What an absolutely beautiful woman,' she commented.

'Absolutely,' he answered tersely.

'I—'

'Our first course appears to be arriving,' Jonas interrupted thankfully, sitting back to let the waiter put their respective plates in front of them.

Danie looked irritated by the interruption, and picked listlessly at her food, clearly having little interest in what she ate.

In contrast Jonas enjoyed every mouthful of his own starter with apparent relish. He hadn't been needed at the clinic today, giving him a chance to catch up on chores that had necessarily to be put off until the weekend, and as a consequence he had eaten very little all day.

'Obviously being in the company of a beautiful woman gives you an appetite,' Danie suddenly bit out tartly. 'I wasn't referring to me!' she exclaimed as he raised his eyebrows.

He glanced across the restaurant. 'Grace is beautiful, isn't she?' he acknowledged clinically. 'She's also very happily married.'

Danie looked sceptical. 'But obviously that wasn't always the case.'

Jonas sighed. 'It has been during our acquaintance. Look, Danie—'

'Hey, it's none of my business.' She made an obvious effort to dismiss it lightly. 'What happens in your private life is your own affair—'

'This dinner is taking place in my private life,' he interrupted.

'Not exactly.' Danie gave a laugh. 'We met in your professional life.'

'The two are completely separate as far as I'm concerned,' Jonas told her.

'Are you telling me the two never overlap?' Danie looked at him with assessing eyes.

'Never,' Jonas answered firmly.

She was far from happy at his reply, he could see. But he couldn't help that. It was the truth; he never mixed his professional life with his private one. He had agreed to have dinner this evening with Danie Summer, not with the relation of his patient, and the sooner Danie accepted that the better!

He sat forward in his seat, reaching across the table to touch her hand where she distractedly crumbled her bread roll on the plate at her side, his clasp tightening on hers as she tried to remove her hand from his. 'I'm having dinner with *you*, Danie, not your family,' he murmured huskily. 'Can we just leave it at that?'

'But—'

'Who knows?' he said teasingly. 'If we forget all about how we met yesterday, you may just find you start to enjoy yourself!'

From the look on her face—frustration mingled with anger—there didn't look as if there was too much chance of that!

Which was a pity. Because he was actually starting to enjoy this verbal fencing-match with Danie Summer. Not only was she an amazingly beautiful woman herself, but, once you got past that brittle shell, she was also bright and intelligent.

A highly lethal combination as far as he was concerned, Jonas was quickly discovering!

CHAPTER FOUR

DANIE studied Jonas disgruntledly beneath lowered dark lashes as she ate her main course. It hadn't changed: clams *couldn't* be any more close-mouthed than he was turning out to be. Whatever direction she approached the subject of his work from, somehow he seemed to avoid giving her an answer. Which, from her point of view, made this dinner a complete waste of time!

Except…

She didn't know what she had expected of this evening, but actually finding herself attracted to Jonas Noble certainly hadn't been part of the plan!

His physical good looks weren't in doubt, those warm brown eyes like hot molasses. But she was quickly discovering that he was also wittily charming, and that he had an integrity where his work was concerned which, while being irritating in her case, was nevertheless admirable in this day and age.

The truth of the matter was, Jonas Noble was the most attractive and interesting man she had met in a very long time—if ever!

'Care to share the reason for the smile?'

She gave Jonas a startled look—she hadn't realised she had been smiling. What was there to smile about in finding this man attractive? Her experience of men so far had taught her that first impressions were usually the wrong ones!

Except… This was her second opinion where Jonas was

concerned, a little voice mocked inside her head; her first had been much less flattering!

But after Ben she no longer trusted her own opinions where men were concerned—second, third, or fourth! Jonas appeared to be a highly eligible bachelor, charming, successful, rich, but that didn't mean that was what he actually was.

Coward, that voice mocked again.

Well, she couldn't help it; experience had taught her never to take anything or anyone at face value. Besides, Jonas was far from forthcoming in one particular area of his life!

'Not really,' she snipped. 'How's your food?'

'Excellent. As usual,' Jonas answered smoothly.

Danie nodded. 'Marco obviously knows you quite well.'

'Quite well, yes,' Jonas confirmed enigmatically.

And as it wasn't the sort of restaurant where one ate alone, that posed the question: who did Jonas usually come here with? It would be a woman, of course. Maybe even the beautiful Grace—before her marriage, of course, Danie allowed. He—

'My youngest sister,' Jonas said softly.

Once again Danie gave him a startled look, this time mixed with irritation. 'What about her?'

'You were wondering who I've been here with in the past; the answer is, my youngest sister,' he repeated.

Danie felt the warmth that coloured her cheeks. Was she that transparent? If she was, she was losing it; most people claimed she was extremely difficult to know. Maybe they had just meant that literally, she wondered self-derisively; she knew her brittle sense of humour certainly wasn't everybody's cup of tea!

'We came here together a lot after her separation and subsequent divorce,' Jonas explained.

'I'm sorry,' Danie murmured politely. Divorce was so common nowadays, it was coming to be a pleasant surprise to see a marriage that was surviving!

Her feelings were jaundiced, she knew that, but nevertheless she had decided long ago that if she couldn't have the sort of marriage her parents had had together, then she didn't want to bother. And so far none of the men she had met had even remotely changed that opinion.

Except Ben... But, in retrospect, he had turned out to be even more dishonest than most.

Were there no men left in the world who wanted a one-to-one relationship, who would return the kind of love Danie knew she was capable of giving herself? Again, her experience had told her no.

'I'm not,' Jonas answered her. 'Her husband was a first-class bastard; she's well rid of him.' The warmth had gone from those brown eyes now, to be replaced with a cold implacability.

This was a side of Jonas that Danie hadn't seen before, giving his character a new dimension. But it wasn't one she disliked. His obvious anger towards his ex-brother-in-law spoke of strong family ties—something else most men seemed to be lacking in nowadays. It seemed to be an utterly 'me' culture at the moment, and it wasn't one that Danie particularly admired.

She gave Jonas a warm smile. 'I'm sure your sister was glad of your love and support during such a difficult time.'

Jonas gave her a sharply searching glance, as if he suspected her of mockery.

Danie met that gaze for long, timeless seconds. 'I come from a close family myself, remember, Jonas?' she finally said.

He relaxed slightly. 'So you do,' he drawled. 'We've

come back full circle to the reason you invited me out to dinner, haven't we?' he mocked lightly.

Her smile became guilty now. 'Was I that obvious?'

Jonas chuckled, relaxing back in his seat. 'You were,' he confirmed without rancour. 'How do you think you're doing so far?'

'Lousy!' she acknowledged with a self-deriding grimace. 'You're better at this than I am.'

Once again he reached out and touched her hand. 'I don't mean to be obstructive, Danie,' he apologised. 'It's fine for us to have dinner together, but you have to understand—I have no choice but to respect my patient's privacy.'

'Even with the relatives of that patient?' she persisted intensely, making no move to take her hand from beneath his.

'Especially then,' Jonas replied quietly. 'On the basis that if my patient wanted you to know then they would tell you.'

Danie felt a flash of anger at this logic, but it was quickly followed by a grudging return of respect for this man seated opposite her. He was telling her as gently as he could that he wasn't going to reveal anything, no matter what methods of persuasion she might try to bring into play! And she could hardly criticise him for one of the qualities she was learning to admire in him.

Although she wasn't sure admiring Jonas Noble was a good idea. Because with a man who looked like this, was as charming as this, it wouldn't stop there. A relationship between the two of them, in the circumstances, was surely going nowhere. She—

'Don't analyse things so much, Danie,' Jonas cut in huskily on her thoughts, his thumb moving caressingly across the back of her hand. 'Have you never thought of just letting life run its course?'

'Several times.' Now she did remove her hand from under his, although the tingling sensation his touch had aroused continued long after she had thrust it beneath the table. 'It was always disastrous!'

Jonas sat back with a laugh. 'Maybe your judgement has just been at fault.'

'Maybe it still is,' Danie rejoined.

'I can't argue with the logic of that,' Jonas mused.

She looked across at him keenly. 'Have you ever been married?'

'Have you?' he came back smoothly.

'Certainly not!' she snapped.

'Why not?'

Danie frowned at his persistence. 'Why haven't you?' She wasn't even sure he hadn't been, but she felt slightly under attack by this line of questioning.

He shrugged his broad shoulders. 'Simple enough. I haven't found the right woman yet.'

'The right woman?' she repeated dazedly.

'Of course,' Jonas replied.

Danie stared at him. The right woman! Was he serious?

Jonas chuckled once again. 'Don't look so horrified, Danie.' He grinned. 'I'm one of the old-fashioned breed, I'm afraid. One man, one woman. As long as—'

'She's the right one,' Danie finished for him huskily, unable to tear her gaze away from him now.

And she wasn't horrified. Far from it. His words had just echoed her own thoughts...

This man couldn't be for real—could he?

'And until I find her,' Jonas continued lightly, 'I'm quite happy in my bachelor state.'

No doubt he was, with beautiful women like Grace in his life!

She was being unfair now, Danie castigated herself. The man had just echoed her own feelings, and all she could do was question his statement. Had her cynicism really become that entrenched?

'You haven't told me yet why *you've* never married,' Jonas said.

There was no way she was going to admit that it was for the very same reason *he* hadn't! 'Haven't you noticed, Jonas? I'm a pilot,' she returned. 'And in my job I fly whenever and wherever my father wants to go; there can't be too many men that would have patience with that!'

'Why not? You would have been a pilot when they met you, a relationship shouldn't make you less than you are.'

Again Danie wondered, was this man for real? Besides, it was easy to theorise about such a situation, but the reality of it was much different.

'Would you be tolerant of a woman's career?' she asked disbelievingly.

'I'm not *that* old-fashioned, Danie!' he rebuked her. 'And I'm not saying it would be easy,' he answered seriously. 'But if you love someone—'

'You can work these things out,' Danie finished scathingly. 'The words are easy to say, Jonas, actually doing it is something else entirely.'

He remained relaxed. 'As I said, it wouldn't be easy. But I wouldn't expect to give up being a—my career,' he corrected. 'So why should I expect my wife to do so?'

Danie shook her head. 'As I said, Jonas, words. It's all just words.'

'At the moment, yes, but I hope I'm big enough to put it into practice one day. I— Would you like dessert, Danie?' Jonas offered as the waiter returned to their table.

'I'm not really a dessert person,' she refused reluctantly. Because she wasn't at all anxious for this evening to end just yet, not when the conversation had just become so interesting!

'Me neither.' Jonas smiled up at the waiter. 'Just the bill, thanks.'

'No coffee?' Danie prompted once the waiter had departed.

'My place, remember?'

Vaguely, she did. But while it had seemed a good idea earlier as a last-ditch attempt to prise some information out of him, she was no longer sure it was a good idea for her to go back to this man's home with him. No longer sure at all...

'Thank you.' Danie waylaid the waiter as he returned and would have handed Jonas the bill.

'Danie—'

'*I* invited *you* out to dinner, Jonas—remember?' she deliberately used the same word he had a moment ago.

Those brown eyes glowed warmly. 'I remember, Danie. How could I forget? It's the first time a woman has ever invited me out rather than the other way round!'

'Really?' Danie smiled as she took her credit card from her small bag and handed it to the waiter; she was glad she was a first at something for Jonas.

'Really.' Jonas returned her smile.

They were becoming altogether too friendly, Danie realised with a start. Actually coming to really like each other hadn't been something she had envisaged when she had made that invitation.

Or maybe it was the effect of the red wine? No... She had kept to the one glass, as she had said she would, and Jonas hadn't drunk much more than that himself.

Damn—they really did like each other!

'Would you return the compliment and come out to dinner with me one evening this week?' Jonas cut in softly on her chaotic thoughts.

She swallowed hard. A second dinner together? They hadn't got through the first one yet!

'Aren't you being a little optimistic, Jonas?' she parried. 'We still have a way to go on this one yet!'

'So we do,' he laughed. 'But I have to tell you, I've enjoyed it this far!'

So had she. In fact, for the most part she had forgotten the purpose of the evening altogether. Which was a terrible admission, she thought self-disgustedly.

She wanted to know what was wrong with her father, not—not—not to stand on the brink of an affair with Jonas Noble!

Because that was what was happening here. She knew it as surely as if they had spoken the words out loud. Jonas was as aware of her as she was of him. And that could lead to only one conclusion.

Help!

Once that defensive wall was allowed to slip, she *was* transparent as glass, Jonas realised tenderly. And maybe that was the reason she had built that wall in the first place? It couldn't have been all that easy being one of Rome Summer's daughters, with all the wealth it involved, both now and in the future, when your emotions were there for everyone to see!

Whatever the reason for that wall, Jonas appreciated the fact that for some reason he was being allowed to see behind it. And to realise that Danie's sharp wit and sarcastic manner were part of the shield she used to hide her much softer nature.

And—

'I'm ready to leave whenever you are,' Danie told him tersely once the waiter had returned her card to her.

He had no doubt the wall wouldn't remain down for very much longer, Jonas inwardly finished.

Danie was a very private person, and no doubt she felt she had already shared enough of that softer side of herself for one evening. Besides, she was obviously also wary of the physical awareness that seemed to have sprung up between them during the evening.

Well, he couldn't exactly say he was overjoyed by it himself!

He had always preferred tiny, kittenish women, like his mother and sisters, women he could relax with—and instead he found himself attracted to an almost-six-foot-tall red-haired Amazon, with all the relaxing qualities of a charging tiger!

He shook his head ruefully as the two of them walked across the restaurant side by side, shocked for a brief moment when he caught sight of their reflection in one of the long mirrors that adorned the walls: they made a stunning couple.

'Don't analyse things so much, Jonas,' Danie tauntingly returned his earlier advice to her as she moved assuredly across the car park to unlock her car. 'Just let things run their course,' she added as she held the passenger door open for him with a flourish.

That was the basic trouble—in the circumstances, what possible course could there be for the two of them?

He paused by the open car door. 'Thanks for the advice, Danie.' He bent to briefly brush his lips across hers, raising his head to look down in the semi-darkness at her suddenly flushed face. 'Let's hope it doesn't lead us *both* into disaster!' he murmured before sliding into the low passenger seat of her sports car.

This woman seemed to like speed: planes, motorbikes, sports cars. Maybe she hoped that if she just kept running fast enough no one—no *man*, Jonas corrected himself—would ever catch up with her.

He sighed heavily as her anger at his audacity in kissing her manifested itself in the slamming of the car door behind him before she marched round to her own side of the car and got in behind the wheel.

Well, he had been curious to see what her reaction would be to his kissing her—and as she accelerated the car with a roar out onto the road, pressing him sharply back against the leather seat, he knew that she was absolutely furious at the liberty.

'Never offer others advice you can't follow yourself,' he pronounced as the car raced assuredly through the evening traffic. 'And this is a thirty-mile-an-hour zone, Danie,' he added, the speedometer showing she was doing fifty.

To her credit she did slow the car down to the appropriate speed, but the mutinously angry expression remained on her face, those cat-like eyes seeming to shoot green sparks.

Jonas continued to watch her in the semi-darkness of the lit streets that led to his house. The phrase 'you look beautiful when you're angry' sprang to mind—but, as he wanted to retain his own teeth, he wisely kept quiet. Even if it were the truth!

'Coming in for that coffee?' he asked once Danie had brought the car to a screeching halt only feet away from his front door.

At least she had stopped the car—he had been beginning to wonder!

Plainly, she also fought an inner battle with herself before answering him. He could sense her dogged curiosity was at war with those alarm bells ringing in her brain that told her to get as far away from him as possible!

Jonas held his breath as he waited for her answer, knowing that if she decided to accept his invitation it could change things between them, irrevocably.

'Coffee sounds—good,' she finally answered stiltedly.

Don't expect anything else, her tone was telling him, Jonas realised with amusement. Although why he should be amused, he had no idea; he didn't particularly like the idea that she believed he would take the invitation a step further and try to seduce her into bed.

There was no doubting Danie's beauty, or that he was very attracted to her; he just felt he should have more than a few hours' acquaintance with a woman before attempting to make love to her. Why, he hoped that, even in his student days, he had had a little more finesse than that!

'I've had no complaints so far,' he said curtly, ignoring the sharp look she gave him as he stepped out of the car.

He unlocked the front door, switching on the lights as he made his way assuredly to the kitchen through the silence of the house, Danie trailing behind him.

He had had a cook-cum-housekeeper for a short time several years ago, but his work was such that he was never sure when or if he would be home for meals, and after several weeks of ruined or uneaten food the housekeeper had predictably handed in her notice. Never to be replaced. He liked his privacy, he had decided, was quite capable of cooking his own meals if necessary, and a daily cleaner took care of that side of things.

'Have a seat while I make the coffee,' he advised Danie, moving capably about the kitchen as he prepared the coffee-machine.

'You've done this before,' Danie observed dryly, watching him as she sat at the pine kitchen table.

Jonas turned to her with raised brows. 'Done what before?' he said innocently.

Colour darkened her cheeks, and she sat up straighter in her chair. 'Made coffee, of course,' she returned shortly.

Jonas smiled before turning back to the coffee preparation. He couldn't help it. Danie, whether caustic or sweetness itself—and the latter didn't happen too often, he had to admit!—had the ability to make him smile.

'Do you live here alone?'

Her tone, Jonas surmised, was deliberately light, which probably meant it had never occurred to her that he wouldn't have at least a housekeeper to take care of his needs. In other words, she hadn't expected to be completely alone here with him!

'Completely,' he drawled unconcernedly, turning to look at her with laughing brown eyes, the coffee-machine now bubbling away nicely behind him.

She moistened red-painted lips. 'How on earth do you manage?'

'A man alone, and all that?' Jonas queried amiably. 'As it happens, I'm pretty self-sufficient, quite capable of washing and cooking for myself.'

'I find that surprising. Having been brought up by your mother and two older sisters,' Danie explained at his questioning look.

Jonas grinned. 'My mother made it plain to me, as soon as I was old enough to understand, that women were not put on this earth solely to cater to a man's needs!' He laughed at Danie's wide-eyed expression. 'She was right, of course.'

'She sounds—'

'Very forward-thinking,' Jonas finished affectionately. 'She still is.'

'I was going to say she sounds wonderful,' Danie corrected.

'She's that too,' Jonas agreed warmly. 'Once my sisters and myself were old enough to be left she took herself off to university, got a degree in history, before going on to teach. She only retired last year,' he added proudly.

Because he *was* immensely proud of his mother. A lot of women in her position, widowed with three children, would have chosen a much less productive avenue. But Jeanette Noble was made of much sterner stuff. Hopefully, her children had inherited that steely backbone.

'She's the reason you have such a tolerant attitude towards women having careers of their own,' Danie realised knowingly.

'Partly,' he acknowledged, pouring their coffee. 'Shall we go through to the sitting-room with this?' He held up the tray of coffee things.

Danie looked disappointed. 'It's quite cosy in here.'

Too cosy, Jonas was quickly discovering. The kitchen, as the heart of his home, was encircling them in an intimacy he wasn't sure Danie was ready for—and he knew he wasn't! Damn it, the woman had only invited him out in the first place because she wanted to know the reason for his being at her family home yesterday.

'If you're cold I'll put the fire on for you in the sitting-room,' he told her, not waiting for her to answer before leading the way through to the sitting-room and, as good as his word once he had put down the tray, flicking the switch on the gas fire.

Danie was staring curiously around the room when he straightened to look at her, taking in the relaxing cream and gold decor, the mahogany furniture, her gaze coming to rest on the piano that stood near the French doors that led out into the garden.

'Do you play—or is it just somewhere for you to put your photographs?' She dryly referred to the dozens of framed photographs that stood on the piano's top.

'I play,' Jonas ventured. 'But very seldom, so it's also somewhere for me to put photographs!'

Danie strolled over to the piano, tall and graceful in her clinging green gown, having left her wrap in the car. 'You must have dozens of relatives,' she said admiringly.

'Actually, no.' Jonas walked over to join her beside the piano. 'My sisters are extremely doting mothers, and, as I'm godfather to all their children, I receive a deluge of photographs of the little darlings every Christmas and birthday—mine as well as theirs! They would notice if even one of those photographs were missing.'

Danie turned to smile up at him. 'You know you love it,' she teased laughingly.

Jonas smiled back at her. 'I cannot tell a lie...' he murmured huskily, knowing a sudden awareness of Danie as she stood only inches away from him. He had only to reach out and—

Danie's eyes widened in alarm before she quickly turned back to the photographs, obviously as aware of Jonas in that moment as he was of her. And she was not at all happy about it!

Her hair smelt of lemons, Jonas discovered as he moved slightly closer, admiring its silkiness, aching to run his fingers through that molten flame. As she gave a nervous glance back at him he knew he wanted to taste her lips too, to drink in that pouting loveliness, to—

'Don't, Jonas,' she groaned throatily.

He hadn't been aware of it, but his actions had followed his thoughts, and he found himself coming to a halt with his lips only centimetres away from Danie's. 'Why not?'

he asked gruffly, their breaths mingling warmly as he looked straight into those alarmed green eyes.

She swallowed hard. 'Because—because— What about that patient confidentiality you talked about?'

'Not good enough, Danie. You're not my patient. And it was far, far too slow in coming,' he murmured softly before his lips gently claimed hers.

She tasted of fruit and honey, and as his arms moved about the slenderness of her body, moulding those soft curves to his much harder ones, it was as if the other half of himself had finally been put in place.

Jonas wrenched his mouth from Danie's, looking down at her disbelievingly. He didn't really know this woman—

So what? a little voice mocked inside his head; he might not know her, but his body certainly did!

Physical attraction, that was all it was, he told himself firmly. And he was past the age of wanting a relationship based only on that.

Only...?

Yes, only!

He turned away abruptly to move over to the low table to pour their coffee into the waiting cups. The sooner this was drunk, then the sooner Danie Summer would leave. And that was something he knew she had to do. Very soon!

He glanced across at her. Her face was turned away from him as she once again looked down at the photographs on the piano top. But even so he could see how pale her cheeks now were, green eyes huge against her pallor.

Jonas straightened slowly, frowning across at her. 'Danie—'

'I have to go!' she told him sharply, avoiding his gaze as she quickly crossed the room.

'Danie…?' He reached out and grasped her arm as she would have walked straight past him to the door.

She tossed back flaming red hair as she looked up at him challengingly, green eyes flashing her anger. 'I said I have to go, Jonas,' she bit out tautly, looking down pointedly at his firm grasp on her upper arm.

Jonas's frown deepened. 'It was a kiss, Danie. The customary thank-you at the end of a pleasant evening. Nothing more. Nothing less,' he added, not sure himself if that was strictly accurate.

It might have started out that way, but he had quickly discovered there had been a lot more to that kiss than a thank-you. Which was the reason it had come to such an abrupt end!

Danie's mouth tightened. 'The words would have been sufficient!'

Maybe so—they would certainly have been less disturbing! But now that it had come time for Danie to leave, Jonas found that he couldn't let her do so without knowing he was going to see her again. And he didn't mean at her father's home when he revisited his patient!

Jonas retained his hold on Danie's arm. 'You haven't given me an answer concerning our having dinner together again some time this week,' he reminded huskily.

Her throat moved convulsively. 'I don't think that would be a good idea, do you?' she finally returned gruffly.

'Caution seems to be something that disappeared from my thought processes the moment I met you!'

Danie again swallowed hard, wrenching her arm free in such a way Jonas was sure it must have hurt her. Although she gave no sign of that as she gave him a hard look. 'Then it's as well I've maintained mine,' she bit out. 'To me you're only my father's doctor, Jonas, with information that I want, but that you refuse to give me. As far as I'm concerned this is the end of our acquaintance,' she told him coldly.

Jonas knew she was being deliberately rude, and he could take an educated guess that it was the kiss they had just shared that had caused this knee-jerk reaction. Rationally he could reason all that out—but that still didn't mean he was unaffected by her deliberate nastiness!

'Do I take it that's a no to dinner?' he rasped with obvious sarcasm.

She had the grace to blush in the face of what they both knew to be her ill-mannered behaviour, sighing heavily. 'I just don't think it would be a good idea, Jonas, for us to—'

'Confirmation of your refusal will suffice, Danie,' he cut in.

Her gaze dropped from his. 'My answer is no, Jonas,' she said a little shakily. 'I—I have to go. I— My wrap…?' She looked about her agitatedly.

'You left it in the car,' Jonas told her flatly.

'Fine. Then—goodbye, Jonas,' she told him before hurrying from the room, the front door to the house closing behind her seconds later, to be quickly followed by the roar of the car engine as she drove away.

Jonas dropped down into one of the armchairs, brooding darkly. Not the most successful evening he had ever had, he acknowledged.

But he would see Danie again. And very shortly, if he weren't mistaken.

Because there had been something completely unbelievable about her earlier statement concerning his visit to her father yesterday. Once she discovered the truth of that, Jonas had a feeling he would see Danie again. Probably with all guns blazing!

CHAPTER FIVE

'BETTER late than never, I suppose,' Harrie said merrily as she sat down opposite Danie at the restaurant table. 'And so much nicer to eat out.' Danie's older sister looked about them appreciatively. 'I feel quite sorry for Quinn, having to miss out on this treat,' she chattered on, seeming to have no idea of Danie's misery as she sat listening to her. 'Although not too much, of course,' Harrie laughed. 'It will be nice to have a girlie chat before Quinn and I go away tomorrow for a few days— Good grief, Danie; what on earth is the matter?' Harrie exclaimed as she finally became aware of Danie's lack of input into the conversation. 'You look as if you've found a pound but actually lost five!'

Probably because that was exactly how she felt, Danie acknowledged to herself heavily. She had finally met a man she admired as well as felt half in love with already— and after Sunday evening she knew he was as far removed from her as the stars in the sky.

She had felt totally miserable about the whole affair the last day or so, finally knowing she had to talk to someone about it. She had always been close to Harrie...

'Harrie, I think I'm in love.' She attempted to add a smile to the starkness of that statement, but knew she had failed in that attempt as it came out as more of a grimace than anything else.

'But that's wonderful— No, it isn't, is it?' Harrie said slowly, looking concerned once more at Danie's misery.

'If it were, you would look a damn sight more cheerful than you do! It isn't another Ben, is it, Dan—?'

'Certainly not!' she cut in sharply. 'Although it might just as well be,' she added emotionally. 'I—' She broke off as the waiter hovered near their table waiting to take their order. 'Shall we have a bottle of wine?' she suggested agitatedly, the mere mention of Ben throwing her into renewed misery.

'A bottle of Chablis, please,' Harrie told the waiter lightly before turning back to Danie. 'This one hasn't driven you to drink, has he?'

Danie gave a humourless smile. 'He hasn't driven me to anything.' Literally. Because so far in their acquaintance she had flown and driven Jonas wherever they had gone together!

'Then what—?' Harrie broke off the conversation again as the waiter reappeared efficiently with the requested bottle of wine, pouring some out into a glass for each of them before disappearing again. 'Sometimes they can be a little too attentive,' Harrie observed.

Danie took a sip of her wine. The last day or so had been awful, as far as she was concerned, but now that it actually came to it she wasn't sure what to say to Harrie. Not without bringing their father into the conversation, and she had no intention of doing that...

'So who is he?' her older sister probed. 'And why do you look so unhappy?'

Instead of ecstatic, as a woman in love should be, Danie accepted. It wasn't as if Jonas didn't find her attractive, or want to see her again, because she was sure that he did, on both counts. There were just reasons why that could never be. After Jonas's reassurances on Sunday evening they had nothing whatsoever to do with his professional relationship with her father.

She drew in a ragged breath. 'You know the reason I broke up with Ben—'

'But you just said this situation wasn't—like that,' Harrie reminded her.

'Jonas isn't married, that's true.' Danie sighed, knowing her sister still hesitated to mention that was the reason Danie had stopped seeing Ben Trainer.

Not that she had known he was married when she'd gone out with him; that knowledge had come much later in their relationship.

It had all seemed so idyllic at first; Ben was a television interviewer who had come to talk to her father concerning appearing on his current affairs programme. Ben was tall, and dark, with wickedly teasing blue eyes; Danie had been attracted to him from the first, more than happy to accept when he'd invited her out to dinner.

The weeks that had followed had been some of the happiest she had ever known, Ben being an amusing as well as attentive companion. The end had come the day she'd walked into a restaurant and seen him seated at a table with a pretty blonde woman, the two of them obviously well acquainted and in deep conversation.

Nevertheless, Danie, in her innocence, had made her excuses to her sister Andie and crossed the restaurant to say hello to Ben. Only to find herself being introduced to his wife, Nikki!

Danie had looked at Ben in stunned disbelief before beating a hasty retreat, grasping Andie's arm as she'd told her sister they were going to eat somewhere else.

Of course, Ben had called round to her apartment that evening, full of excuses and apologies, insisting that Nikki was his wife, but that the two of them had been parted for months, that they had actually been discussing their divorce and the arrangements for the children when Danie had seen them together.

Danie hadn't believed him; she hadn't believed him for a very good reason. She had seen the look of pain and disillusionment on Nikki Trainer's face as Danie had greeted Ben with intimate warmth, knew that the other woman had guessed at the relationship between the two of them. And been totally devastated at the realisation!

Danie had also seen Nikki Trainer's face on Sunday evening, in several of the family photographs that stood on top of Jonas's piano! She didn't need to be told that Nikki Trainer was the youngest sister he had talked about. The one that had divorced her husband...!

Danie cringed as she recalled her shock on seeing those photographs at Jonas's on Sunday evening. For the second time in her life she hadn't been able to get out of a place fast enough—and Ben Trainer was responsible for both of those times.

Jonas had described his ex-brother-in-law as a 'bastard'—but somehow Danie had the feeling that he didn't yet know about her own unfortunate relationship with Ben. Nikki Trainer obviously hadn't regaled her big brother with all the messy details!

How would Jonas react to being told she had been involved with the 'first-class bastard'?

Danie didn't even want to think about it!

Just as she dared not go out with Jonas again. Because she had no doubts she was falling in love with him. And if, by some miracle, he should ever learn to return those feelings, he would want to introduce her to his family, to his sister, Nikki...!

Danie knew she was thinking way ahead of where she was now with Jonas, but even the possibility of it was horrendous to contemplate! Which was the reason she had turned down his invitation to see her again, and also the reason why she had left so abruptly on Sunday evening.

But the knowledge that she dared not go out with Jonas again, because of her past involvement with Ben, was hurting her so deeply she didn't know what to do about it. Or if she could do anything...!

'Jonas...' Harrie repeated appreciatively. 'That's a strong-sounding name.'

Jonas was strong. He was a dedicated and responsible doctor, too. Unfortunately, one of the other qualities Danie had admired in him, that of being a caring son and brother, precluded any further relationship between the two of them!

'So who is he?' Harried probed interestedly. 'And where did you meet him?'

Both questions Danie couldn't answer. Not without bringing Jonas's visit to their father on Saturday into the conversation, and she really didn't want to do that. Harrie had only been married a few weeks, she and Quinn obviously ecstatically happy together, and Danie did not want to be the one to burst that bubble of happiness by encouraging her older sister into helping her second-guess the reason why Jonas had attended their father. No doubt they would all be told in time.

But, in the meantime, Danie was stuck in a dilemma about Jonas. She longed to see him again, ached for him, but the part of her that had been so badly hurt by Ben in the past told her she would only be leaving herself open to further pain.

But she still *wanted* to see Jonas again!

'Where I met him isn't important.' She pretended disinterest. 'Neither is who he is,' she added firmly.

Harrie shook her head. 'Then what's the problem? Is it a one-sided attraction—is that it?' Although her tone of voice seemed to imply that was something she just didn't believe.

Danie felt grateful for her sister's confidence in her ability to be attractive to men, but at the same time she knew that wasn't the issue. 'Not exactly,' she hedged.

'But there is a problem?' Harrie pressed.

Danie wished she had never started this! But she also knew it was too late to stop now. Her sister could be tenacious when she chose, and she was obviously intrigued by this situation.

Danie drew in a deep breath. 'Harrie, he's Ben's ex-brother-in-law!' she burst out. And then stared wide-eyed at her sister as she waited for her reaction.

Harrie opened her mouth to speak. And then closed it again. Opened her mouth. And then closed it again.

Danie couldn't help it—she laughed. 'This has to be a first. I've certainly never seen a speechless Harrie before!'

'I—I just—' Harrie shook her head dazedly. 'How do you do it, Danie?' She pulled a face. 'Of all the men—'

'In all the world, he had to walk into my life,' Danie finished in a not-bad imitation of Humphrey Bogart, even if the quote was completely incorrect. 'And to answer your question, Harrie; I have no idea.' She sighed. 'He was just there. And—and he's gorgeous. And when he kissed me it was like—'

'It's gone as far as him kissing you?' Harrie squeaked. 'Just how long have you been keeping him a secret?'

It seemed as if she had always known Jonas, but she knew that in reality it was only a matter of days. Harrie simply wouldn't understand her problem if she told her that, would tell her to just cut her losses and move on. But, unlike with Ben, where Jonas was concerned that was something she didn't feel able to do.

'That isn't important,' Danie said impatiently. 'What is

important is the fact that Jonas's sister was married to Ben
when I was going out with him. I'm probably the reason
his sister divorced her husband!' she added emotionally.

'Now you don't know that—'

'Does it matter?' Danie interrupted heatedly. 'I met
Nikki. Only briefly, granted, but I could see by the look
on her face that she knew I was involved with Ben. She
isn't likely to have forgotten me, Harrie!' She winced.

And Jonas, once he knew she had been involved with a
married man—even if it were unwittingly!—with his own
brother-in-law, simply wouldn't want to know her!

There just didn't seem to be a way forward for Jonas
and her!

Harrie drew in a deep breath. 'It is a little complicated,
I grant you—'

'Thanks!' Danie returned.

Harrie mock-glared at her. 'But not unsolvable, surely?
If he doesn't already know, have you thought of simply
telling Jonas the truth?'

Danie had thought of nothing else since Sunday! But
she knew that, once she had done that, there would be no
possibility of seeing Jonas again; his loyalty to his sister
was a solid fact. As was his disgust with Ben. That disgust
was sure to include any woman who had been involved
with him…!

'He simply wouldn't understand, Harrie,' she persisted
heavily.

Harrie pursed her lips thoughtfully. 'Are you sure you
aren't underestimating him, Danie? Obviously I don't
know Jonas, but anyone with a grain of sense would know
that Ben was nothing but a charming rogue—'

'Thanks again!' Danie said. Her own common sense
seemed to be something that had been distinctly lacking
during her brief relationship with Ben.

'I didn't mean you,' her sister reproved. 'But you said there are children in the marriage—'

'Don't!' Danie cringed at the memory of discovering that not only was Ben married, but that he also had two children, innocents, who certainly didn't deserve to have the feckless Ben as their father.

'You're missing my point, Danie,' her sister continued. 'If there are children, then Ben had been married to Nikki for some years—certainly long enough, probably, for your Jonas to have realised Ben wasn't exactly faithful to his wife!'

'Maybe. But then again, maybe not...' Danie shrugged. 'And he isn't *my* Jonas,' she corrected.

'But you would like him to be,' Harrie guessed. 'Now come on, Danie; where's the determined sister I know and love? Because I can tell you now, *that* Danie wouldn't let a little thing like Ben Trainer keep her from the man she had set her heart on!'

Harrie was right, Danie knew she was. It was just that, after two years of refusing to get involved with any man, these feelings she had discovered she had for Jonas were unsettling enough, without the realisation that he was the ex-brother-in-law of the man who had caused her to be so wary of involvement in the first place!

It didn't seem to matter from which direction she approached the problem, she always came back to the fact that Nikki Trainer was Jonas's sister...!

'When are you seeing Jonas again?' Harrie asked thoughtfully.

Danie drew in a ragged breath. 'I'm not.'

'Not? But—' Harrie broke off as the waiter came to take their food order.

But it turned out that neither woman was particularly

interested in food any more, each ordering only a Caesar salad.

'Why aren't you seeing Jonas again?' Harrie demanded to know as soon as the two of them were alone again.

'I've just told you—'

'Forget about Ben for the moment—'

'I can't!' Danie groaned. 'Do you think Jonas has forgotten about him? About the way Ben betrayed his sister? With me!' she added forcefully.

'Do you want to know what I really think, Danie…?' her sister replied.

'I wouldn't have asked if I didn't!' she came back tautly.

Harrie nodded. 'Oh, I think you would. What you really want me to do, Danie, is agree with everything you've said, condone your decision not to see Jonas again. And you know something? I'm not going to do it. The last thing I've ever thought you were was a coward, Danie—'

'Because I'm not!' Danie's eyes flashed deeply green in warning.

'Then stop acting like one.' Harrie gave her hand a reassuring squeeze to take the sting out of her words. 'If you remember, things weren't exactly smooth-running for Quinn and myself at first,' she reminded her sister wryly. 'And look how marvellously that's turned out.'

'That's different—'

'No, it isn't,' Harrie told her. 'Give Jonas a call and invite him out to dinner.'

Danie hesitated. 'I did the inviting last time.'

'You—? No, don't tell me.' Harrie raised her hands in frustration. 'The only advice I can give you, Danie,' she said as the waiter approached the table with their salads, 'is not to run away from this, but face it head-on. It's the way you usually approach everything else!' she reminded her affectionately.

Harrie was right. This wasn't like her at all. She had never been one to run away from situations, good or bad. And during the last two years, since Ben's duplicity, that had been more than true of everything.

Was she behaving like a coward? Had Harrie been right when she'd guessed that Danie wanted her to tell her to cut her losses with Jonas and move on? Had she really become that frightened of emotional involvement...?

Besides, there was no guarantee that if she went out with Jonas again she wouldn't end up thinking all this soul-searching had been a complete waste of time, that she was only mildly infatuated, physically attracted rather than emotionally, after all.

Maybe she *would* give him a call...

'Danie?' Jonas didn't just sound surprised at the identity of his caller, he *was* surprised. *Very.* Danie had made it more than clear on Sunday night that she didn't intend seeing him again, cuttingly so, as he remembered.

Which was why, when Dorothy had buzzed through to him a few minutes ago to tell him there was a Miss Summer on the line for him, Danie had been the last Summer sister he had imagined to hear!

'The one and only,' her voice came back brittlely down the telephone line. 'I acquired your telephone number from my father; I hope you don't mind?'

Jonas didn't mind at all, but he couldn't help wondering what Rome Summer had made of the request! 'What can I do for you, Danie?' he said briskly.

There didn't sound as if there were any guns blazing, but with Danie, he was quickly learning, you never could tell!

'I've decided to accept your dinner invitation, after all,' she informed him lightly.

It didn't need two guesses why, Jonas realised ruefully; Danie was obviously *still* looking for information concerning his visit to her father's home last Saturday!

'If it's still open, of course,' she ventured at his prolonged silence.

Was it still open? Part of him knew that the last thing he should be doing was deepening his acquaintance with Danie Summer, but the other part of him, the part that remembered their response to each other, gave him a completely different answer...

'It's still open, Danie,' he assured her.

'Which evening would suit you?' she asked briskly.

Tonight. Tomorrow. The evening after. Any evening, he knew, would suit him for seeing Danie again.

Then common sense kicked in. Danie wasn't really interested in him, was the relative of a patient of his, and was really only after information. Whereas he...

'Are you sure, in the circumstances, that this is a good idea, Danie?' he questioned.

'Frightened, Jonas?' she came back tauntingly.

Of falling for a woman who obviously felt nothing towards him but a casual sense of amusement while she tried to prise information out of him? Of falling for Danie Summer at all?

Hell, *yes*, he was frightened!

'I'll even cook dinner for us at my apartment, Jonas,' she broke into his jumbled thoughts. 'Amongst all those flying lessons I took in my late teens, I also spent a year in France learning how to cook. My father, practical soul that he is, thought I should have more than one string to my bow,' she explained dryly. 'I think the theory was that as well as flying all over the world, I would at least be able to feed the man in my life, when I *was* at home!'

That sounded like the Rome Summer he had come to

know over the last few days, Jonas thought. But how much more dangerous would it be—for him!—to eat alone with Danie at her apartment...?

'Tomorrow evening will be fine,' he heard himself accept tersely. 'Although I believe the suggestion was that I take you out to dinner?'

'Take a rain check,' Danie dismissed easily.

Nothing threw this woman, Jonas acknowledged. She was completely in control, of herself, and every situation that was thrown at her.

Once again Jonas had the feeling of getting involved when he would be wiser not to...!

But wasn't it too late for that? Even if he turned down this idea of dinner together, the two of them would still see each other again. And the last two sleepless nights told him that he didn't need to see Danie to think about her until sleep became impossible!

'Okay, Danie, dinner at your apartment it is,' he accepted decisively. 'But I'll bring the wine.'

'You don't know what we'll be eating,' she said.

'Then I'll bring a bottle of red and white so that I cover all contingencies,' Jonas rejoined. 'Now I'm rather busy at the moment, so if you would just give me your address, we can continue this tomorrow evening.'

Not the best of ways to end the conversation, he decided a few seconds later once the call had been terminated by a seemingly cheery, undampened Danie.

Damn it, he had decided, during the last two days, that he would be a fool if he saw Danie on a social basis again. One telephone call from her and those well-intentioned decisions had flown straight out of the window!

Damn, damn, damn!

'Jonas, I wondered if you could just— What's wrong with you?' Dorothy, his middle-aged assistant and secretary of many years, had come to an abrupt halt in the doorway, looking across at him now with questioningly raised auburn brows.

Come to think of it, Dorothy was a redhead, too, Jonas realised as he looked at her properly for the first time in years. He was starting to feel that they had him surrounded!

'Nothing,' he snapped. 'What do you have there?' He indicated the papers she held in her hand.

'Just some letters for you to sign,' she replied distractedly, still studying him thoughtfully. 'Your call from Miss Summer seems to have—disturbed you?'

Jonas glared at his secretary across the width of the room. 'My mood has nothing to do with the call from Miss Summer,' he informed her.

'Oh.' Dorothy nodded slowly. 'But you accept you are in a mood? In fact,' she added before he could make a reply, 'you've been like a bear with a sore head all week.'

'It's only Tuesday!' Jonas came back tersely.

'Quite long enough to put up with your snappiness,' Dorothy informed him as she crossed the room to place the letters on the desk in front of him.

'Dorothy—'

'Yes, Jonas?' she answered innocently.

He let out a deflated sigh. What was the point? Dorothy ran his practice with the ease of an efficient sergeant major, always polite but necessarily firm with his patients, while at the same time safeguarding his privacy. He was in no position to complain if that allowed her a lot of leeway where the two of them were concerned. Besides, Dorothy knew him too well to be fobbed off by any cutting remarks on his part!

He gave a half-smile. 'I'm sorry if I've been less than—

cheerful, the last day or so,' he apologised. 'I have a lot on my mind at the moment.'

'Miss Summer, for example,' Dorothy put in knowingly.

'Her name's Danie, Dorothy,' he put in heavily, knowing Dorothy wouldn't be satisfied until she knew at least that about the other woman.

'Danie?' Dorothy frowned. 'But I thought—'

'Never mind what you thought, Dorothy.' He sighed. 'There are three Summer sisters: Harriet, Danielle, and Andrea. And not necessarily in that order.'

Dorothy gave an amused smile. 'Bit of a handful, is she?'

His mouth twisted ruefully. 'Something like that. Now could we get back to work, do you think?' he continued briskly. 'Danie Summer has taken up enough of my time for one afternoon!'

Dorothy gave him another knowing look before turning on her heel and leaving the room.

Jonas relaxed back in his high-backed leather chair for the first time since he had answered the telephone several minutes ago and had stiffened in recognition at the sound of Danie's voice.

Strangely enough, although he had no idea where this was going to take him—if he did know he would probably start running now and not stop!—he felt more relaxed than he had since Sunday.

And he knew the reason for that was that he was going to spend tomorrow evening with Danie...

Danie of the sharp tongue. Danie the derider. Danie of the flaming red hair... Danie of the beautiful green eyes... Danie of the kissable mouth...!

She was heaven and hell, Jonas decided affectionately.

But she was also the only woman he wanted to spend time with.

Well...tomorrow evening, at least!

CHAPTER SIX

PERFECT, Danie decided as she looked at the dinner table she had prepared for Jonas and herself. It was a round table, and as such the two of them should have been able to sit opposite each other. But Danie had chosen to seat them next to each other on the curve.

Much friendlier, she acknowledged with satisfaction. Friendly…? Was that what she now wanted to be with Jonas?

All her father's remarks about the contrariness of women came flooding back. But Danie didn't consider she was being contrary; she had just been kissed by the man who had seemed to be the other half of herself!

Their bodies, at least, had seemed to recognise each other on Sunday night, even if, at twenty-seven and thirty-eight respectively, their hearts were a little more jaundiced than that. And if Danie hadn't spotted that photograph of a relaxed and smiling Ben, standing beside his wife— Jonas's sister!—and two daughters, heaven knew what would have happened!

But it was what was going to happen tonight that filled her thoughts now!

She had tried to think of something about Jonas that she disliked—but the truth was, she just couldn't find a thing. He was attractive, charming, obviously successful, and he appeared to have the same family values that she did. Even that habit he had—annoying though it was!—of sidestepping her questions concerning her father's health was merely another indication of his professional integrity.

But there must be something; it simply wasn't possible to fall in love with someone on a few days' acquaintance—was it...? Tonight would give her the answer to that. It must!

The table looked great, the food was ready for cooking in the kitchen, so now she could concentrate on her own appearance. On Sunday she had deliberately dressed to attract; tonight, in her own apartment, she would wear something a little less dazzling.

The simple black knee-length dress that she finally decided upon—half a dozen other dresses lay on the bed, considered and discarded—was certainly that, but it nevertheless showed the slender perfection of her body, her hair a scarlet flame against its darkness, green eyes huge, if a little wary, in the creamy beauty of her face.

Jonas, when she opened the apartment door a few minutes later in answer to the ring of the bell, seemed to have had a similar problem as to how he should dress for the evening, although his choice of cream shirt, teamed with brown trousers and a casually fitting brown jumper, certainly took Danie's breath away. As did the bunch of yellow roses he held in his hand.

He grinned as he saw her wide-eyed gaze on the flowers. 'It was instilled in me at an early age that it's polite to arrive with a suitable gift for my hostess,' he said, holding out the roses towards Danie, maintaining his hold on the two bottles of wine he also carried, one red, and one white, as he had promised...

He couldn't have known—of course he couldn't!—but yellow roses were her favourite! Her mother had always grown roses, all the year round, in the hothouse Danie's father had built especially for her. Danie had spent hours herself in that hothouse as she'd followed her mother around. But the yellow roses, deep, almost gold, had always been Danie's favourite...

'You can take them, Danie,' Jonas teased softly as she stared at the roses. 'They aren't going to bite!'

As he'd said, they were a gesture of politeness from a guest to his hostess, nothing more. 'Thank you,' she accepted. 'Oh...!' she gasped as she took the blooms into her own arms, their heady perfume bringing into play aching nostalgia.

'What is it?' Jonas asked concernedly.

Snap out of it, Danie, she instructed herself firmly; otherwise Jonas was going to regret ever having accepted her invitation!

'Nothing.' She smiled brightly, opening the door wider for him to come in. 'Help yourself to some wine.' She indicated the tray on the side-dresser, the bottle of white wine already uncorked. 'I'll just go and do something with these.' She almost ran from the room with the roses in her arms.

She wasn't being exactly hospitable, Danie realised as she filled a vase up with water and dumped the roses unceremoniously into it. Yellow roses! Jonas couldn't have chosen to give her anything more disconcerting, her head now filled with memories of those happy hours she had spent with her mother amongst her own roses. But Jonas couldn't have known that, she chided herself, and there was no reason why he should guess now, either. As long as she pulled herself together and stopped behaving like an idiot!

'Oh, good.' She smiled brightly as she returned to the lounge and found Jonas seated in one of the armchairs, a glass of white wine dangling from his fingers.

'I poured one for you too.' Jonas nodded in the direction of the second glass as it stood on the dresser next to the two bottles of wine he had brought himself. 'Are you sure you're preparing dinner in there?' he teased, nodding in the direction of the kitchen. 'I can't smell any food cooking.'

Danie gave him a sidelong glance. 'I have the feeling, Mr Noble, that you may doubt my previous claims to culinary greatness.'

Jonas grinned. 'Well...'

'Agas don't give off cooking smells,' she assured him, picking up her own glass of wine and taking a sip.

His eyes widened. 'You really do cook!' he exclaimed appreciatively. 'My mother says only serious cooks have an Aga nowadays.'

'She's right,' Danie agreed.

'And here I've been imagining an army of caterers delivering trays of pre-prepared food, with strict instructions to be away from here before I arrived at seven-thirty!' Jonas mocked.

'Dream on,' Danie said with satisfaction, knowing that the mushroom soufflé, followed by Dover sole and summer vegetables, were going to be a success, and as for dessert—! Strawberry meringue, followed by a selection of cheeses, couldn't be faulted, either.

'I can hardly wait,' Jonas murmured, looking at her between narrowed lids.

Danie gave him an assessing look, wondering what he couldn't wait for. After all, they had been discussing dinner. At least, she thought they had...

'I'll just go and check on our first course,' she announced, before hurrying back into the kitchen, heaving a deep sigh of relief once in there.

She was, she decided breathlessly, sadly out of practice with the art of flirtation! If she had ever been in practice. Harrie was right: Danie's approach had always been forthright and to the point. But somehow, with Jonas, that didn't seem the way to go. She—

'Problems?' Jonas queried as he followed her into the kitchen, standing mere feet away from her.

Only with her equilibrium. It just wasn't decent to want to forget all about dinner, and instead rip this man's clothes off, quickly followed by her own, before the two of them became nakedly entangled in the pleasure of lovemaking!

She swallowed hard. 'On the contrary,' she assured him in a slightly higher pitched tone than was natural to her. 'I was just about to serve our starter.' She moved away from him towards the Aga, instantly feeling a lessening of that magnetism that seemed to surround her when Jonas was too close to her.

So much for the hope that she would discover, on seeing Jonas again, that she had been imagining that physical attraction between them! If anything, it was more intense tonight than it had been on Sunday. Almost as if no time had elapsed at all and they were continuing where they had left off…!

She looked up sharply as Jonas made no move to leave the kitchen but instead stood watching her as she arranged the miniature soufflés on the already prepared plates. 'I'll bring these through in a moment,' she told him as she straightened.

'I'm fine where I am, thanks.' And as if to prove the point, he leant back against one of the kitchen units, taking a leisurely sip of his wine. 'Actually, to be completely honest,' he continued, 'I'm enjoying the sight of all this domesticity on your part—I never would have believed it of the tough lady pilot in the baseball cap and combat trousers that I met on Saturday!'

Danie felt the angry flush that darkened her cheeks. 'Then let's hope you aren't disappointed,' she snapped.

'What's the saying? "The proof of the pudding is in the eating"?' She picked up the two plates and swept past him out of the kitchen and into the dining-room.

This time the reason for her racing pulse wasn't Jonas's close proximity but pure annoyance. Damn the man! Being a pilot didn't mean she was bereft of feminine traits. Besides, as he was now going to discover, she was a very good cook.

She wished now she hadn't put their place settings quite so close together at the table, but as Jonas quietly entered the room behind her she knew it was too late to do anything about it, so she indicated his seat to the left of her.

'This is a nice big apartment,' Jonas murmured as he sat down.

'I pay the rent myself,' she said heatedly as she sat next to him, that angry flush still in her cheeks.

Jonas raised dark brows. 'I was merely commenting on the size of the apartment, Danie; I wasn't suggesting anything else,' he returned levelly, picking up his fork to eat the soufflé.

Danie cooled down a little. 'Most people, given my family background, seem to think I only play at working.'

Jonas looked at her with steady brown eyes. 'I don't believe you play at anything, Danie. And I'm not "most people",' he added huskily.

She swallowed hard, completely aware of the truth of that statement! Jonas was totally unlike any other man she had ever met.

'Eat your food,' she instructed abruptly.

'Yes, ma'am,' he responded in an amused voice, suiting his actions to his words. 'My God…!' he said after his first mouthful. 'If you ever get tired of flying, Danie, I suggest you open up a restaurant!' He told her this with genuine appreciation.

She smiled her own pleasure at the compliment. 'I'll never tire of flying, Jonas.' She laughed softly as she shook her head.

He paused in his eating, his gaze intense now. 'You changed your mind about seeing me again,' he reminded gruffly.

Danie turned away from his searching gaze. 'I thought that was a woman's prerogative,' she answered—which was no answer at all! But she didn't want to get into a conversation about why she had changed her mind!

Jonas's mouth curved upwards. 'I'll grant you, you're much more unpredictable than most!'

She turned back to look at him. 'And have there been a lot of women in your life, Jonas?' She had tried to sound lightly interested—but was fully aware that she had sounded anything but.

'Some.' He shrugged. 'Nothing serious, though. And you?'

She had known almost as soon as she'd put the question to him that it wasn't a subject she wished to be pursued concerning her own life—not when her own last serious relationship had been with this man's own married brother-in-law!

She moistened dry lips. 'Nothing serious,' she echoed his words, relieved to see Jonas had almost finished his soufflé. A few minutes' respite in the kitchen wouldn't come amiss right now!

'Which just leaves unattached you and me,' he said as he looked at her thoughtfully. 'Do you think this relationship is going anywhere?'

Danie drew in a sharp breath, attempting to make a reply—and failing!—then swallowing hard before trying again. 'I thought I was supposed to be the blunt one?' she finally managed to gasp, her appetite having now disappeared completely. 'Besides, we don't have a—a "relationship"!'

'Dinner together twice in a week seems to imply something,' he corrected softly.

She pushed her chair back noisily as she stood up to remove their plates. 'It means we both have to eat!' she said restlessly.

Jonas smiled as he turned to look up at her. 'That's a good answer, Danie—if completely inadequate for the question asked.' He sobered. 'And it wasn't an idle question, Danie; I do have a good reason for asking.'

She frowned down at him. 'I can't imagine what that could be,' she said tersely. 'What happened to letting things run their course?'

Jonas shrugged broad shoulders. 'Ordinarily that would be the best thing...' he granted slowly.

'But?'

'But in our case there are—complications,' he pointed out.

Danie stiffened, eyeing him warily, her hands tightly gripping the plates she held, her cheeks pale now.

Did Jonas already know? Had he somehow found out about her brief relationship with his brother-in-law? But if—

'I was talking about my professional relationship with a member of your family,' Jonas went on slowly, watching her intently. 'Danie, what—?'

Her light, dismissive laughter cut across whatever he had been going to say next, because she had a feeling it wasn't something she wanted to hear—or answer! 'I'm sure we're both adult enough to be able to deal with that situation,' she dismissed. 'If it becomes necessary. Now, you'll have to excuse me for a few minutes, Jonas,' she said quickly, 'or our next course will spoil.'

'Heaven forbid!'

Danie was aware of his appreciative gaze on her as she left the dining-room, only breathing more easily once the door had closed behind her.

Careful, Danie, she cautioned herself. She had almost jumped to a completely erroneous conclusion just then by assuming the complication Jonas referred to involved Ben. It was a conclusion she simply wasn't ready to deal with yet.

One thing she did know—she definitely was as attracted to Jonas as she had thought she had been on Sunday night…!

Jonas tried to remember what it was he had said that had caused Danie's defensive response seconds ago, shaking his head as the answer eluded him.

Of course, he had been being a bit forward in assuming they had, or indeed would have, a relationship, and yet somehow he knew that wasn't the reason Danie had suddenly become so wary.

He gave up trying to analyse the workings of Danie's mind. She was unlike any other woman he had ever met. In fact, she was completely unique. A tough, capable pilot at their first meeting, then a beautifully, totally feminine woman on Sunday evening, and now tonight—! Not only did she look good enough to eat, but she also cooked like a dream.

Jonas couldn't help wondering what other surprises were in store for him where Danie Summer was concerned!

The perfection of the rest of the meal she served them certainly came as no surprise to him; he was quickly learning that if Danie did something then she didn't just do it well, she did it superbly.

He found himself wondering, as the two of them lingered over their coffee and brandies back in the sitting-room, his offer to help clear away after their meal firmly refused, if Danie would make love as beautifully as she did everything else...

Relaxed by the good food, complementary wine, scintillating company, he looked across to the chair where she sat opposite him, with sleepily appreciative brown eyes.

Her hair was slightly tousled from the exertions of cooking, her face slightly flushed, that pouting mouth bare of lip-gloss after their meal; Danie looked warmly desirable. Jonas was quickly approaching the time when caution concerning this attraction flew out of the window. Actually, he had probably passed that from the moment he'd accepted her invitation to dine with her at her apartment!

'Is the brandy not to your liking?' Danie seemed to pick up on his now less-than-relaxed mood.

Her choice of brandy was as excellent as her good taste in everything else. It was his own good sense that he was starting to question...

'The brandy was perfect,' he assured her, putting the empty glass down before standing up to cross the room to where she sat, his eyes intense on the beauty of her flushed face as he pulled her effortlessly to her feet in front of him. 'In fact, Danie,' he continued, 'so far, this whole evening has been perfect.'

She seemed to swallow convulsively again as she looked up at him, her eyes shining like emeralds through those dark lashes. 'So far...?'

'Danie...!' he groaned throatily even as his head lowered and his mouth claimed hers.

This was what he had wanted from the moment she had opened the door to him two hours ago. And he hadn't been mistaken on Sunday; Danie's body *did* fit against his as if it formed the other half of himself!

God, she felt so good, her soft curves moulded to his harder ones, her arms about his neck as she met the passion of his kiss.

His hands cradled each side of her face as he sipped and tasted the nectar of her lips, swollen now in her arousal, those hands then becoming entangled in the fire of her hair as he pulled her harder against him.

Jonas had never felt the rightness of this before in all of his thirty-eight years, and right now he wanted Danie too much to feel in the least wary of such all-consuming desire.

Her breast felt firm but warmly arousing as one of his hands cupped that pouting curve through the silk of her dress, knowing in that moment that she wore no bra, the material merely a whisper of fabric between his hand and her warmth. But even that whisper was too much of a barrier, and he knew a longing to have a completely naked Danie curved into his own nakedness.

The zip of the dress slid smoothly down the length of her spine. The dress, once removed from her shoulders, slipped easily to the carpeted floor at their feet.

Her nipple was already aroused against his thumb-tip, and Jonas could feel the leap of his own body as he bent and took that second aroused pink nub into the warm cavern of his mouth, his tongue lapping the creamy warmth there as Danie held him gently against her.

She wore only silky black panties, he quickly discovered as he pulled her thighs against his own pulsing ones, and her skin was as smooth as his hands moved to cup her beneath the silky material and pull her closer to his hardness.

'Jonas...!' she groaned achingly.

He raised his head to look at her, recognising the reciprocal passion in those deep green eyes, her breath coming in short gasps, her hand trembling slightly as she entwined her fingers in the thick darkness of his hair.

Jonas looked at her slender loveliness, knowing that he wanted Danie more than he had ever wanted anything, or anyone, in his life before.

'Danie, I—' He broke off abruptly as a strange ringing noise broke through that sensual aura that had enclosed them both these last few minutes. 'What the hell...?' He looked frowningly around the room for the source of that ringing.

'Leave it, Jonas. It's only the telephone—and I don't want to talk to anyone just now!' Danie told him breathlessly as she pulled his head back down to hers, their lips once again fusing in that electric desire.

But the ringing noise persisted, so much so that after a minute or so Jonas couldn't stand it any more, let alone concentrate on making love to Danie, and raised his head once more to look for the telephone. Even if he could only take the receiver off the hook so that the caller couldn't telephone back!

'Whoever it is is very persistent.' He scowled his displeasure, holding Danie at arm's length now. 'If I answer that—' he nodded darkly in the direction of the telephone on the dresser next to the drinks tray '—it isn't going to be some disgruntled boyfriend on the other end of the line, is it?' Just the thought of it made him feel like strangling someone!

It took Danie some seconds to gather her passion-scattered wits together enough to realise what he had just said, but when she finally did she didn't look at all pleased by his remark. 'It won't be a boyfriend, disgruntled or otherwise—because I don't have one!' she assured him, stepping back into her dress to zip it back into place with the minimum of movement.

As if she had done it dozens of times before, Jonas decided resentfully.

Although the fact that she was now once again fully dressed couldn't take away the fact of her passion-swollen lips, or the desire that still shone in those dark green eyes!

'Hey, let's not argue about a telephone call, Danie,' Jonas cajoled as the ringing finally stopped without either of them having answered the call. 'I apologise for the unnecessary remark I made a few minutes ago. My only excuse is that, although I've had years of being trained to answer telephone calls—for obvious reasons!—I just wasn't expecting there to be one at this particular moment.' He self-deprecatingly explained the inner disappointment he felt that the call had obviously put an end to their passionate interlude.

Danie gave a pained sigh. 'I'm no more thrilled about it than you are. I—' She broke off with an angry frown as the telephone began to ring once again. 'Persistent is about right!' she muttered as she moved to snatch up the receiver—only to find that the ringing noise continued...! She looked across at Jonas with completely puzzled eyes.

But Jonas was no longer in the least puzzled. 'It's my mobile,' he acknowledged as he moved to pick up his cellular telephone from where he had placed it on a side table when Danie had gone to the kitchen to put the roses in water; he had forgotten all about the stupid thing in his enjoyment of the evening—especially the last few minutes of it!

'The price you pay for having all those private—and rich—patients,' Danie bit out caustically before turning away.

Damn, damn, damn, Jonas muttered angrily to himself as he realised he had once again taken one step forward with Danie—only to find himself instantly taking two steps back!

'Yes?' he answered tersely into the receiver of his mobile telephone, his anger turning to concern as he instantly recognised the voice of his caller. 'Nikki...?' he cut in gently on the slightly hysterical gabble on the other end of the line.

Even as he listened attentively to the voice of his sister he glanced across at Danie apologetically for the interruption, grimacing slightly as she indicated she was going into the kitchen.

The evening, Jonas guessed, was over as far as he and Danie were concerned.

Damn, damn, *damn*!

CHAPTER SEVEN

NIKKI!

There was no surer way to put a dampener on Danie's aroused emotions than the mention of Jonas's sister's name. An actual telephone call from her had the effect, as far as Danie was concerned, of finishing their evening together completely!

After making her excuses to Jonas, Danie walked steadily towards the kitchen, knowing that he continued to watch her every move even as he carried on the conversation with his sister. It was a conversation Danie did her best not to listen to; the less she knew about Nikki Trainer, the better it would be for all of them!

She leant shakily back against one of the kitchen units once the door had closed behind her, groaning into her hands as she realised exactly what Nikki would have been interrupting if that call had come even five minutes later than it had. As it was, it was going to be difficult to face Jonas again after the intimacies they had just shared.

Seconds ago she had been almost completely naked—while Jonas had remained fully clothed!

She loved the man!

Danie knew it as certainly as she knew she would draw her next breath. But Nikki Trainer's telephone call had been a timely reminder that her love for Jonas was at best a risk, and at worst a disaster. She—

'Sorry about that,' Jonas apologised as he joined her in the kitchen, his movements tense. 'That was my sister,' he explained unnecessarily.

Danie had dropped her hands down from in front of her face as soon as he'd entered the room, straightening away from the kitchen unit now; the last thing she wanted was for him to see just how affected she had been by the passion they had just shared.

'Everything okay?' she asked, knowing by the grimness of his expression that it wasn't. Besides, it was ten-thirty at night; not too many people, even sisters, telephoned for a casual chat at that time of night!

Jonas shook his head. 'It's my niece's birthday today. She's eight. Nikki had a birthday party for her earlier. Which is the reason I'm dressed so casually, by the way. I called in to the party with Suzie's present on my way here.'

'That was nice,' Danie returned tightly—knowing he hadn't got to the problem yet...

'It was, actually,' he came back hardly. 'But apparently, shortly after I left there, Suzie's father arrived, on the same pretext.'

Ben!

Danie stiffened warily. 'I take it Nikki is the sister who's divorced?' Even as she asked the question Danie knew she was digging herself into a hole she might have trouble getting herself out of.

She *knew* Nikki was his divorced sister, knew the reason for Nikki's divorce too—she ought to!—and by pretending anything else she was putting herself into an untenable position.

'She is,' Jonas acknowledged heavily. 'And having arrived at Nikki's home with a present for Suzie, Ben is now proving very difficult to get rid of. In fact,' he bit out tersely, 'he's refusing to go at all! He was always a bit of a bully where Nik and the children were concerned, liked his own way all the time, and poor Nik was always a bit scared of his temper. She only managed to escape to telephone me now with the excuse she was going upstairs to check on the children.'

'I see,' Danie said slowly. This behaviour didn't sound like the Ben she had known at all; in retrospect, she had decided he was far too self-centred to be interested in anyone but himself! But perhaps it would be a different matter if that self-interest were challenged...?

Jonas watched her carefully. 'I hope you do—because Nikki has asked me to go over there to help get rid of him.'

Danie met his eyes. 'So what's keeping you?'

'You are,' he told her softly, reaching out to lightly grasp the tops of her arms. 'You invited me here for the evening, and it seems very rude to just eat and run.'

Danie felt the colour enter her cheeks as she easily recalled he had done far more than that, her eyes dropping away from his now. 'If it was one of my sisters who had telephoned me for help, I would be doing exactly the same as you are,' she assured him bluntly.

Jonas chuckled softly, pulling her gently into his arms, her head now resting against his shoulder. 'I was hoping you would say that!' He sighed his relief at her reaction to his predicament.

Danie raised her head to look up at him. 'Your ex-brother-in-law isn't likely to turn nasty, is he?' Ben had always struck her as being too lazy to rouse himself to physical violence, but refusing to leave his ex-wife's home seemed out of character for the man she had known too...

Jonas shrugged. 'I have no idea. But he's upsetting Nikki—and that I won't have. She's already suffered enough on his account.'

Danie extricated herself from Jonas's arms as she stepped back from him, avoiding looking at him, aware that she was one of the reasons Nikki had suffered! 'I really think you had better go,' she told him tonelessly.

Jonas looked at her with puzzlement. 'Can I call you later? Just to let you know I haven't been beaten to a pulp!'

She smiled at his attempt to joke, although she was inwardly pleased at his suggestion that he call her. This evening had come to rather an abrupt end, and her emotions were feeling a little raw. 'Please do.' She turned to find a piece of paper in one of the drawers, writing down her telephone number before handing it to him.

He slipped the paper into his shirt pocket. 'There's more than a little subterfuge to my request,' he admitted. 'This way I'll also be able to invite you out to dinner when I call!'

Danie gave a wry smile. 'That will be a novelty!' After all, so far she had done all the inviting! Well...except for that one dinner invitation Jonas had made—and which she had promptly turned down!

He laughed, before sobering at the lack of humour on her own pale face. 'Are you sure you're all right with this?' he questioned. 'Because if it bothers you—'

'It doesn't bother me. Now go!' And to suit her actions to her words she grasped him firmly by the shoulders and turned him in the direction of the door. 'Your poor sister is probably at screaming pitch by now if Ben is proving as difficult to remove as you said.'

'Hmm!' he replied. 'I don't know why the wretched man can't just leave her alone.' They walked towards the door. 'He had his chance, and he blew it, big time—'

'Maybe he's a man who just doesn't like to lose,' Danie suggested distractedly—the last thing she wanted was to hear exactly how Ben had blown his marriage to Jonas's sister!

'Maybe.' Jonas scowled. 'But Nikki has just started to

get her life back in order, has been going out with someone else for the last couple of months—'

'Well, there you have your answer as to why Ben's behaving this way,' Danie cut in knowingly, choosing her next words carefully. 'This Ben probably thought your sister would go on grieving for her lost marriage for ever,' she explained. 'Besides, it's a well-known fact that finding out an ex-partner has someone else in their life is a sure-fire reason for the ex-husband, or wife, wanting to come back.'

Jonas stared down at her as he stood beside the door. 'You seem very knowledgeable about these things...?'

'Not from personal experience, I can assure you,' she told him with a short laugh. 'Just a casual observance of human nature,' she assured him.

'Whatever,' Jonas accepted. 'Ben certainly isn't going to mess Nikki's life up a second time.'

Danie smiled at his determination, sure that Jonas was more than capable of handling his ex-brother-in-law. 'Go get him,' she encouraged—after all, she had no reason to feel in the least kindly towards Ben herself!

Jonas bent and lightly kissed her on the lips. 'I'll call you later,' he promised.

Danie's legs were shaking so badly by the time Jonas left that she had to stagger back into the sitting-room and sit down—before she fell down!

Well, she had more than answered her own questions where Jonas was concerned. She was in love with him. And the fact that Nikki Trainer was his sister was going to be as destructive to that love as Danie had feared it might be.

Jonas obviously cared very deeply for his sister, and his loyalty, if brought into question, would lie with Nikki.

Which left Danie where...?

*   *   *

Jonas's expression was grim as he faced his ex-brother-in-law across the sitting-room of his sister's home half an hour later. Ben was proving as much of an idiot as he had always been, claiming he had a right to visit his own children. The fact that those children had been in bed for the last two hours of this so-called visit seemed to have escaped him completely!

'Besides, Nikki invited me to stay for coffee,' Ben announced triumphantly.

Jonas's mouth tightened, and he didn't even glance in the direction of his pale-faced sister, his attention all focused on the petulant good looks of his dark-haired ex-brother-in-law. 'Nikki has always been polite—even to people who don't deserve such good manners!'

Ben's mouth twisted; he was confidently relaxed as he lounged back in one of the armchairs. 'I still don't understand what you're doing back here, Jonas; you've already delivered Suzie's birthday present, and Nikki and I were just sitting here talking over old times.'

Now Jonas did spare his sister a glance, knowing by the pale delicacy of her cheeks that this trip down Memory Lane had not been a pleasant experience for her. Of course it hadn't, damn it; she had once loved this man to distraction, and he had betrayed that love in the cruellest way possible.

His mouth tightened even more as he turned back to Ben. 'You've talked them over, Ben—now I suggest you leave!'

The other man raised dark brows. 'And if I choose not to do so?'

'Then I suppose I'll have to make you,' Jonas returned mildly.

Ben sat forward, his eyes narrowing angrily now. 'You always were an interfering bast—'

'And you were never good enough to even clean my sister's shoes, let alone marry her!' Jonas cut in harshly on the expletive, his hands clenched into knuckle-white fists at his sides as he scowled down at the other man.

Ben gave a humourless smile. 'You never did think I was good enough for her.'

'And I was right.' Jonas bit out disgustedly. 'Now are you going to leave peacefully—or do I have to involve the police in this?' He heard Nikki's gasp of protest at such a suggestion, but continued to meet the other man's stare challengingly. Ben might be able to bully a defenceless woman, a woman who had once loved him, but Jonas didn't have such emotions to cloud his own judgement. He was determined that Ben would leave, one way or another…!

Ben shook his head confidently. 'I very much doubt you want it to come to that any more than I do,' he drawled. 'Jonas Noble, the doctor darling of society, the—'

'That's enough, Ben.' Nikki was the one to cut in this time, her voice shaking slightly in her agitation. 'You can upset me all you like, but I won't have you being rude to my brother—'

'Of course not,' Ben acknowledged mockingly, shaking his head as he finally stood up. 'It was the biggest mistake of my life when I became involved with this family!' His eyes raked scathingly over his ex-wife. 'I can't understand what this new man in your life sees in you, Nikki; you've certainly let yourself go the last couple of years.'

Jonas felt the red tide of anger well up inside him at this deliberate hurting of a woman who had already suffered enough at this man's hands. 'Why, you—'

'Just go, Ben,' Nikki interrupted evenly, Jonas feeling proud of her as her head went back challengingly. 'And don't come back here again.'

Ben appeared unperturbed. 'The last I heard I still had reasonable access to my own two children—'

'You still do,' Nikki stated. 'But after this little fiasco I will drop the children off to you in future.' She looked at him with distaste. 'You'll just have to make sure your lady-friend has vacated your apartment before I do—otherwise the children won't be stopping!'

Ben's eyes were glacial now. 'I'll do what I please—'

'Not with my children, you won't,' Nikki told him hardly. 'I don't want any of your women near them. I don't suppose it's still the same woman?'

Ben's eyes narrowed. 'You assume correctly.'

Nikki snorted. 'She looked too good for you, Ben, very beautiful too; it's good to know she had enough sense to dump you!'

'I said *I* stopped seeing her, Nikki,' Ben retorted. 'I could have her back in my life like that—' he gave a snap of his fingers '—if I wanted to.'

'Then more fool her,' Nikki returned calmly.

For all her distaste for her ex-husband, Jonas could nonetheless see that his sister was getting close to breaking-point. Which, in the circumstances, wasn't surprising!

Ben's affairs, once realised by Nikki, had been the final ending of a marriage that had been rocky for some time. Why, Ben had even introduced his wife to one of them!

'The two of you probably deserve each other,' Jonas told the other man disgustedly. 'Now I repeat, Ben, are you going to leave, or does force have to be used?'

'Oh, don't worry, I'm going,' Ben sneered with a hard, humourless laugh. 'I find all this righteous indignation as nauseating as I did two years ago!' He strode angrily to the door. 'And maybe I should give Danie a call; at least she knows how to have a good time!' came his parting shot.

The front door of the house slammed shut behind him seconds later, but Jonas, for one, was unaware of it.

Danie!

Ben had said he would give *Danie* a call!

No, it couldn't be the same Danie. Not *his* Danie.

But she wasn't his. Admittedly, they had come pretty close to it this evening, but Nikki's telephone call had interrupted them.

Danie…?

It couldn't be the same Danie!

Could it…?

'Here.' Nikki held out a glass of brandy to him, a second one for herself in her other hand. 'After that I think we both need it!' she said with relief.

Jonas took a gulp of the fiery liquid, not even noticing as it burnt a trail down the back of his throat. It couldn't be his Danie!

Nikki sat down gratefully in one of the armchairs, sipping her own brandy. 'Every time I begin to wonder if I could have been wrong about Ben he proves to me all over again that I wasn't.' She glanced up at Jonas as she received no response. 'I'm really sorry about disturbing you this evening, Jonas,' she said. 'I just didn't want to involve Graham in this.'

Jonas could understand her not wanting to complicate matters by bringing her partner into what was already a difficult situation. 'It's okay,' he said quietly, still preoccupied with thoughts of Danie. The possibility of Danie and Ben…?

Nikki looked at him carefully. 'Did I interrupt something important when I called you earlier?'

He had thought his relationship with Danie was important. Now he wasn't so sure.

But Danie wasn't such an unusual name. It didn't have

to be the same Danie. Danie could be the diminutive of several female names, it didn't have to be the shortened version of Danielle.

All he had to do was ask Nikki for a description of this particular Danie—

No, he couldn't do that!

Because part of him didn't want to know...?

Part of him feared knowing...!

Because if Nikki's description of the other woman should confirm that it was Danie Summer they were all talking about, then Danie must have known earlier exactly who he'd been talking about, when he'd discussed Nikki and Ben!

Did he really believe that the forthright Danie he knew could be *that* underhand?

No, of course she couldn't. Danie had been blunt to the point of rudeness from the first moment he'd met her. There was no way, absolutely no way, he could ever believe she had been involved with a married man, that her relationship with him had eventually broken up the marriage.

That decided to his satisfaction, Jonas turned his attention back to Nikki. 'You did interrupt something,' he admitted with a relaxed smile. 'But luckily it was with an understanding woman.'

Nikki's eyes sparkled interestedly. 'You didn't tell me you were seeing someone, Jonas,' she reproved affectionately.

'I don't know that I am—yet,' he replied enigmatically. 'But if and when I am, you'll be the first to know,' he promised.

'Good enough,' his sister accepted, knowing better than to push the subject; she probably knew from experience that Jonas could be extremely tight-lipped when it came to his own private life. 'Goodness, I hope I never have a repeat of this evening.' She shuddered delicately. 'It seems to be my relationship with Graham that has set Ben off.'

'I've been told that often happens when an ex-partner learns you're involved with someone else.' Jonas heard himself repeating Danie's earlier words.

Nikki raised blonde brows; she was still prettily attractive at forty-one—despite what Ben had said to the contrary earlier! 'And who told you that?' she teased, obviously relieved the encounter with Ben was at an end.

Jonas grinned. 'Never mind.' He sobered. 'Now are you going to be all right, or do you want me to stay the night in case Ben decides to come back?'

His sister shook her head. 'He probably thinks that's exactly what you're going to do, so I'm sure he won't come back tonight,' Nikki said with certainty. 'Besides, he was going off to telephone this woman, Danie, remember?'

Oh, Jonas remembered all right. But it wasn't his Danie, because he was going to telephone her himself as soon as he reached home.

Danie Summer having the same first name as the woman who had wrecked his sister's marriage could prove a little complicated if his own relationship with her flourished, but that was something he would have to deal with if and when. At the moment, there were more immediate things to be done.

'You know,' his sister continued, 'if I ever see that particular young woman again, I think I may just thank her... For being instrumental in helping me make the decision to end years of hell!'

Jonas put down his own empty brandy glass. 'Don't let anything Ben said just now bother you, Nik,' he advised as he bent to kiss her on the cheek. 'It was only sour grapes on his part; anyone can see you're as lovely as ever,' he assured her. 'More so, actually,' he added as he studied her thoughtfully. 'Could it be that my little sister is in love?'

Nikki's cheeks flushed fiery-red. 'Less of the little, Buster; I'll always be three years older than you!'

'Well, that neatly avoided giving me an answer,' Jonas murmured appreciatively.

His sister's mouth quirked ruefully. 'Wait and see,' she said enigmatically. 'Dorothy approves, anyway.'

'Dorothy?' Jonas echoed, brows raised. 'My Dorothy?'

'I'm sure she would love to hear you call her that!' Nikki chuckled. 'She babysits for me sometimes so that Graham and I can go out,' she explained at his perplexed expression.

'She never mentioned it. And neither did you until just now...' Jonas felt dazed. 'You know, I think Ben may have just underestimated you, Nikki...'

His sister smiled. 'For the last time,' she said, standing up. 'I really am grateful to you for helping me tonight, Jonas—especially as I seem to have interrupted something special!' She wore a mischievous expression as she made this last remark.

Jonas smiled back at Nikki, who accompanied him to the door. 'Wait and see...' he repeated her own words concerning her own relationship.

'With bated breath,' his sister assured him. 'Mother can't wait to see her little baby married with children of his own!'

'Wait a minute!' He held up protesting hands. 'You're going way too fast for me. I've only just met—the woman,' he amended using Danie's name; it wasn't appropriate at the moment! 'Wives and babies do not figure too highly in my immediate plans!'

'Unless the first is in the singular, I wouldn't contemplate the latter at all!' Nikki pointed out. 'Bigamy is still a prosecutable offence, you know!'

'Don't get picky on me; you knew exactly what I meant!' Jonas bent and kissed his sister goodnight. 'I'll give you a call tomorrow,' he promised before strolling over to his car.

He thought briefly of lingering in the driveway to call Danie on his mobile, but, as his sister was still standing in the doorway waiting to wave goodbye, he thought better of it. Heaven knew what Nikki would make of his telephoning that certain someone as soon as he left her house!

Besides, he wasn't absolutely sure what to make of the impulse himself, he decided as he drove home. A carrying-out of his promise to Danie to call her later? Or a need to confirm, by just hearing the sound of Danie's no-nonsense voice, that she definitely wasn't the woman who had once been involved with Ben…?

Ridiculous, he told himself with a shake of his head; as if just hearing Danie speak could tell him that! He either believed it wasn't his Danie, or he didn't. It was as simple as that.

Although nothing seemed particularly simple when Jonas finally telephoned Danie's apartment fifteen minutes later—at almost midnight—to discover her line was already engaged!

Jonas's thought processes went into overdrive as he slowly replaced his own receiver. No one received casual telephone calls at this time of night. Which meant it was someone specific, someone Danie didn't mind talking to, no matter how late it was.

Ben…?

CHAPTER EIGHT

JONAS hadn't telephoned...!

That was the thought that occupied Danie's time most of the next day. Biking down to the estate. Flying her father and Audrey, recently returned from Scotland, to France. Waiting for him to conclude his business later in the day before flying them back again.

Of course, Jonas's omission could mean nothing.

Or it could mean everything...!

Damn it, why did these negative thoughts always intrude on her more positive ones?

Jonas had left last night to go and help his sister. It could have taken him a while to sort that situation out. Jonas might not have returned home until late and thought it inconsiderate to telephone her. He might have telephoned her today instead—and she had been out all day!

She had no reason—no reason at all!—to suppose she had come into the conversation last night between Jonas and his ex-brother-in-law.

Except Jonas hadn't telephoned, that taunting little voice reminded her for the hundredth time.

'Staying for dinner?' her father enquired once they had all arrived back at the house.

'Er—no,' Danie refused. 'I—er—I have to meet someone in town,' she answered evasively.

Her father raised an eyebrow. 'Anyone we know?'

Danie gave him a narrow-eyed look. 'Exactly what do you mean by that?'

'Actually...nothing,' her father returned slowly, frown-

113

ing thoughtfully as he poured a drink for Audrey and himself. 'But now that you mention it, why *did* you want Jonas's telephone—?'

'Leave the girl alone, Rome,' Audrey told him before accepting her glass of white wine. 'We're all entitled to our secrets.'

'Even you, Audrey?' Rome returned.

'Even me,' she replied enigmatically.

Rome looked less than pleased by this reply, Danie noted. As far as he was concerned, Danie knew, Audrey's job, and him, had to be her priorities in life—and not necessarily in that order!

'I have to go,' Danie told them. 'Helicopter to Yorkshire at ten o'clock tomorrow?' she confirmed.

Her father nodded distractedly, his gaze still resting thoughtfully on Audrey.

Well, at least the other woman had diverted his attention from her, Danie accepted gratefully. Although she wasn't sure Audrey had assured an easy evening for herself!

'I'll see you both in the morning, then,' Danie announced lightly, bending to kiss Audrey on the cheek before making a face at the older woman—a look that clearly said, 'Thanks. And good luck!'

Audrey gave an acknowledging smile before calmly taking a sip of her wine, her expression now as serene as always.

Danie held back a smile as she moved to kiss her father goodnight. She only hoped Audrey knew what she was doing; Rome could be relentless when he wanted to know something. And he was obviously interested in this private life Audrey had alluded to!

Danie's humour, however, evaporated as soon as she began the ride home. She hadn't been lying when she'd said she was meeting someone in town. But, unfortunately, it wasn't Jonas. And at the moment, he was the person she most wanted to see.

Maybe he would have left a message on her answer-machine? Although even if he hadn't, that didn't mean he hadn't called; some people, herself included, didn't actually like leaving messages on machines.

Stop making excuses, Danie, that little voice told her again. If Jonas wanted to telephone her, then no doubt he would do so. And she had no reason to believe, from the way they had parted last night, that he wouldn't want to.

She was absolutely shattered by the time she arrived back at her apartment, and the lack of flashes on her answer-machine told her there were no messages for her at all, adding to those feelings of exhaustion.

But she was expecting Andie here in half an hour, so she had no choice but to shower and change before her sister arrived. It would be nice to see her younger sister, although quite what the two of them were going to talk about, Danie had no idea; as far as she was aware, her younger sister still wasn't aware of their father's illness.

The best way to handle this, Danie decided as she blow-dried her hair after her shower, was to let Andie do the talking; after all, Andie was the one who had asked to come here, not the other way round.

Andie still looked far from well herself when Danie let her into her apartment twenty minutes later; her sister was still extremely pale, and she looked as if she had lost weight, too.

Although no less beautiful, Danie acknowledged affectionately. She was tall and blonde, with the same green-coloured eyes as her two older sisters, and Andie's illness and loss of weight had given her a certain air of fragility that Danie was sure a lot of men would find appealing.

'I know; I look like hell,' Andie said as she strolled into

the apartment, extremely elegant in a fitted black trouser suit and emerald-coloured silk blouse; it was a family joke that Andie had asked to wear designer-label clothes while still in her cradle!

'Actually, I was just thinking the opposite.' Danie closed the door before following her sister through to the sitting-room. 'Although maybe you really should think about seeing a doctor,' she added with concern, the brighter lighting of her sitting-room showing that Andie was bordering on gaunt rather than just delicate.

Her sister dropped down wearily into one of the armchairs. 'I've seen one,' she groaned.

'You have?' Danie didn't even attempt to hide her surprise. Andie had refused to see a doctor, unless absolutely necessary, since she'd been five years old and had had to go into hospital to have her tonsils out; she must really be feeling ill if she had actually taken herself to see one now!

'I have.' Andie nodded heavily. 'Would it be too much trouble to ask you for a cup of tea? Earl Grey, if you have it,' she asked hopefully. 'I've only just left the office, so I haven't even had time to go home yet.'

'Come through to the kitchen,' Danie gestured. 'Sit yourself down, while I make the tea,' she ordered as she heated the water on the Aga. 'Before you fall down,' she tacked on reprovingly as Andie looked even paler under the bright kitchen lights. 'You really shouldn't be working at all at the moment if you still feel this ill, Andie,' she scolded worriedly.

Her sister gave a wan smile. 'I've never understood how you got away with having that heavy thing up here.' She pointed in the direction of the Aga. 'It's amazing it hasn't gone through the floor into the flat downstairs before now!'

'Stop changing the subject, Andie.' Danie poured hot water into the warmed teapot. 'No wonder Rome is so worried about you,' she said; that worry certainly wasn't going to help his own ill health.

Andie's expression became guarded. 'What's Daddy been saying to you about me?'

'Nothing,' Danie answered truthfully, handing her sister the hot cup of tea. 'He doesn't need to say anything, I just know he's—concerned about you.'

Andie gave a sigh. 'That's one of his emotions, yes. But another one is—' She broke off as the security intercom rang from downstairs. 'Are you expecting anyone else?' Andie said with surprise.

No, she wasn't expecting anyone... But Danie couldn't deny that she was inwardly still hoping to hear from Jonas. Maybe he had decided to call round instead of telephoning?

'I'll just see who it is,' she responded, hurrying from the room before her sister could say anything further. Andie didn't look as if she were in the mood for visitors but, by the same token, Danie had no intention of sending Jonas away if her caller should turn out to be him.

If...

She pressed the button on the intercom. 'Yes?' she prompted guardedly.

'Danie, it's Jonas. Could I come—?'

'Yes!' Danie didn't wait to hear the rest of what he had to say, pressing the security button that would unlock the door downstairs, her hands shaking in her haste.

It *was* Jonas!

Her heart leapt at the thought of seeing him again. How she was going to deal with having him and Andie here at the same time, she had no idea, but no doubt she would find a way. She would have to!

She turned slowly as she heard her sister come through

from the kitchen. 'Feeling any better?' She delayed answering the question in her sister's expression.

'I don't expect to for some time,' Andie muttered, tilting her head enquiringly. 'Is that a blush I see on your cheeks, Danie?' she said slowly.

Flushed probably better described how she looked, Danie decided. At the thought of seeing Jonas again!

She moistened her lips. 'Andie, I—' The ringing of the doorbell stopped her from any further explanation. Jonas was here already! 'Just let me get that,' she told Andie breathlessly. 'And I'll explain everything later.'

Andie relented. 'Fine.'

Jonas looked wonderful to Danie as he stood on the threshold, dressed very casually in fitted denims and a dark blue cashmere sweater. Although his guarded expression didn't look too encouraging, she realised with a sinking heart.

'I hope I'm not interrupting anything,' he said politely.

Not as far as she was concerned, although she accepted Andie might not feel quite the same way!

'Of course not,' Danie assured him lightly, stepping back. 'Come in,' she invited warmly. After all, he could just look wary because he hadn't telephoned her last night and felt unsure of his welcome.

He *could* be, she told herself determinedly as doubts about that possibility instantly began to crowd into her head. Of course he could...

Although Danie certainly wasn't prepared for her sister's reaction to Jonas as he preceded Danie into the sitting-room!

'You!' Andie gasped as she stood up slowly, green eyes glaring. 'What are *you* doing here?' she demanded rudely.

Danie gaped. There was no other way to describe how

she just stood there with her mouth open at this unwarranted attack on Jonas. What on earth was her sister *doing*?

Andie turned accusingly to Danie. 'Did you invite him here?' she cried furiously, putting her cup and saucer down noisily onto the table. 'You had no right,' she continued shakily. 'Absolutely no right! Damn this family,' she muttered through gritted teeth. 'Damn you all!' Her hands were clenched tightly at her sides, her movements agitated.

Jonas drew in a controlling breath. 'Andrea—'

'Don't even try to find placating excuses for this—this intrusion!' Andie's head snapped back round to him as she butted in heatedly, the colour definitely back in her cheeks now. 'This is my problem, no one else's, and—'

'Your family is concerned for you,' Jonas soothed.

'Then they can damn well become unconcerned,' Andie snapped, bending to pick up her bag before marching towards the door. 'I never thought you would let me down in this way,' she paused to tell Danie, tears glistening in her eyes now. 'I accept Daddy has his reasons...' she continued brokenly. 'But not you, Danie.' She looked dazed. 'And as for sneaking around behind my back in this way—'

'But I—'

'Never mind,' Andie chokingly dismissed Danie's protest. 'Just another of life's little disappointments that I'll have to adjust to, I expect. I should have got used to them by now,' she added bitterly, shaking her head in disgust. 'I just never thought— Damn you, Danie,' she finished in a pained voice.

'Now just a minute.' Danie had had time to snap out of her own dumbstruck reaction to this unexpected turn of events—and now she wanted to know *what* was going on!

That Andie and Jonas already knew each other was

more than apparent, and Danie wanted to know exactly why and how that was!

'I have no idea what you're talking about, Andie,' she told her sister firmly. 'For one thing, I have no idea in what way you believe I have let you down.' It was something she would never do; the three sisters were completely loyal to each other, and their father. And as the youngest sister, Andie had always been more cosseted and protected by all of them.

Andie's mouth turned downwards. 'Maybe you don't see it as letting me down,' she replied. 'But why won't any of you understand that this has to be my decision, and my decision alone? And no amount of family pressure is going to change that! Now, if you don't mind, I think I had better leave. Before I insult—your guest, any further.' She gave a scathing glance in Jonas's direction. 'I don't believe, after tonight, that it's necessary for me to tell you I won't be attending my appointment with you tomorrow.'

Jonas looked less than pleased by this announcement, taking a step forward, his hand raised placatingly. 'Andrea—'

'I'll find myself another consultant, Mr Noble,' Andie told him with cold dismissal. 'One that I can trust,' she added bitterly.

Danie still had no real idea of what was happening here, although it had become obvious in the last few seconds that she had been completely wrong about her assumption that her father was Jonas's patient—obviously Andie was...!

She had never seen Andie like this; her younger sister had always been warmly charming, her looks impeccable. But Andie had been anything but polite to Jonas in the last few minutes, and, despite the fact that her sister was dressed as beautifully as ever, Andie did, in fact, look ex-

actly as she'd described herself on her arrival—'like hell'!
Whatever else was wrong with her, she was obviously very
ill…!

Danie turned accusing eyes on Jonas now. 'Are you just
going to let her walk out of here?' she demanded. 'Looking the way that she does?'

Jonas's hands dropped down ineffectually to his sides.
'I can only advise, Danie, I can't make Andrea do anything,' he reasoned flatly.

'Well, it's nice to know that at least one of you seems
to have realised that!' Andie broke in. 'I'll call you some
time, Danie,' she said. 'When I'm not quite so angry with
you. And I've made my mind up exactly what I want to
do.'

Danie watched as Andie let herself out of the apartment,
the door closing decisively behind her; Danie's mind was
buzzing with the things that had been said the last few
minutes.

Andie, not her father, was Jonas's patient.

But why?

What was wrong with her sister?

Oh, she knew Andie had had the flu several weeks ago,
and that her sister seemed to be having trouble bouncing
back to full health. But what, exactly, did that mean…?

Danie turned her questioning gaze on Jonas. 'Who are
you?' she breathed slowly. '*What* are you?' she added
hardly.

His cheeks were pale beneath his tan, the encounter of
the last few minutes obviously having taken its toll on him
too. But for the moment Danie was unconcerned with that.
Jonas knew the assumptions she had made concerning his
visit to the estate on Saturday—that she had believed her
father was the one who was ill—and he had let her go on
thinking that!

'Don't make me go to the trouble of finding out, Jonas,' she warned icily, starting to feel angry herself now.

Jonas had known from the beginning that she was seeing him in the hope that she could wheedle information out of him concerning what she had believed to be her father's illness. Hey, the two of them had even laughed together at her lack of success! And all the time Jonas had been laughing for an altogether different reason...

He drew in a ragged breath, his head back as he met her challenging expression. 'I don't suppose it matters now that Andrea has decided she no longer wishes to be my patient,' he said. 'I'm an obstetrician, Danie.'

An ob—

An obste—

Danie couldn't even bring herself to say the word. Because if that was what Jonas was, that meant that Andie— that Andie—

Oh, my goodness...!

Jonas watched Danie as he saw the truth finally sink into her rapidly racing brain—a truth she obviously found even more incredible than her former belief that her father was seriously ill.

He had known the assumption she had made on Saturday, of course he had. But, in the circumstances, with his professional loyalty based with his patient, what else could he have done but let her go on thinking that?

However, he could see now, as Danie's eyes began to glitter as angry a green as her younger sister's, a few minutes ago, that Danie wasn't in the least impressed by his professional etiquette!

'It wasn't my secret to tell, Danie,' he said wearily. 'It still isn't.'

'Oh, don't worry, Jonas,' Danie returned. 'You still

haven't told me anything! But I think, if you had just once mentioned your profession, I might have had an inkling my father wasn't involved in your medical examination on Saturday!' Her voice was thick with sarcasm.

This had all been rather a shock for her; Jonas realised that. But at the moment the anger Danie felt towards him was more to the forefront than the fact that her younger, unmarried sister was going to have a baby.

He couldn't exactly blame Danie for feeling that way, accepted that he had been less than helpful. At any other time he would have tried to placate her. It was just that engaged telephone line late the previous evening that held him back from attempting to get too close to her...

He hadn't slept well last night, his head full of thoughts of whom Danie could have been talking to on the telephone at that time of night. The idea that it could have been Ben, that Ben had decided to once again snap his fingers in Danie's direction, was an altogether unacceptable one to Jonas!

But the doubt that it just might have been his ex-brother-in-law had persisted, making today hell too as he'd tried to function normally and blot all thoughts of Danie from his head. Something he had only succeeded in doing for mere minutes at a time!

After picking at the dinner he had prepared for himself when he'd returned from the clinic, he had known that he had to at least see Danie. How he was going to ask her if she knew Ben, without it sounding like some sort of accusation, he had no idea, he had just known he had to speak to her face to face. As he knew only too well, Danie's emotions could be as transparent as glass on occasion.

This just wasn't going to be one of those occasions!

Oh, Danie was still transparent enough in her emotions,

and the one she was feeling most at the moment was anger—towards him! Not the ideal situation in which to ask her questions about her personal life before the two of them had met.

Jonas gave a humourless smile. 'Well, you know the truth of that visit now, so—'

'I still don't know anything that matters,' Danie cut in forcefully. 'Who? When? How?'

'I think we both know how, Danie,' Jonas gently answered her floundering questions. 'I don't know exactly when, although it's my belief the baby will be born some time around Valentine's day next year. As for the who...' he sighed '...I believe your father wants an answer to that particular question too.' He shrugged. 'But it isn't one Andrea feels like sharing with any of us.'

Danie shook her head, momentarily diverted from her anger towards him, her thoughts all inwards. 'Andie doesn't even have a regular boyfriend that I know of.' She seemed to be speaking to herself now. 'Let alone one that—' She broke off, glaring up at Jonas once again. 'Surely Andie must have told you *something*? Or would answering that come under the heading of breaching professional etiquette too?'

'It would. And it does,' Jonas replied evenly, inconsequentially noticing that the yellow roses he had brought her the evening before were arranged in a cut-glass vase on the coffee-table. After tonight the flowers would probably end up in the bin, he acknowledged ruefully. 'Danie, I think Andie is the one you should be talking to about this,' he continued. 'She—'

'She won't talk to me now,' Danie dismissed contemptuously. 'She thinks I'm in cahoots with you and my father!'

There was probably a lot of truth in that statement, but,

nevertheless, he still wasn't in a position to discuss Andrea Summer, not even with her concerned older sister.

Jonas raised his hands in defeat. 'Then I suggest you unconvince her,' he said mildly, realising as he did so that he was being less than helpful. But the truth of the matter was, he hadn't come here to talk about Andrea Summer...!

Danie continued to glare at him, tall and beautiful in a tight pale green tee shirt and bottle-green denims that moulded to her slender hips and thighs. A fact Jonas noted—and instantly berated himself for. He wasn't here to become enthralled in the way Danie looked.

Then what was he here for?

To ask a woman he had only known a matter of days, a woman he found himself very attracted to, a woman he liked—a woman he had come very close to making love to the previous evening!—if she had once had an affair with his sister's husband.

Great!

The realisation made even him wince—and he had been the one intent on asking such a question.

Well, it was a sure fact he couldn't ask it now—he would most likely end up with the vase of roses smashed over his head if he did!

'I'm sorry, Danie.' He sighed heavily. 'I know I'm not being very helpful,' he understated. 'But you obviously have a close relationship with Andrea; she wouldn't have been here otherwise—'

'No one ever calls her Andrea,' Danie told him distractedly. 'And, after tonight, I think that closeness you're talking about may be a thing of the past,' she added bitterly. 'Andie called me, asked if she could come and have a chat—a chat I now believe probably involved her—pregnancy.' She swallowed hard, obviously still having trouble coming to terms with the idea of her sister expecting a baby. 'And within minutes of her arrival here, before she even had a chance to say anything about what was bothering her—'

'I arrived and upset everything,' Jonas accepted.

Danie looked uncomfortable. 'I wasn't exactly going to say that—'

'Just think it, hmm?' he suggested.

'Maybe,' she conceded. 'Andie obviously has something on her mind.' She frowned. 'Is there a problem with the pregnancy? Is that it? Or aren't you allowed to tell me that, either?'

'If there was, I wouldn't be, no,' Jonas answered levelly. 'But as far as I can ascertain, Andr—Andie,' he amended dryly, 'is a normal, healthy, twenty-five-year-old woman—apart from a pretty ferocious bout of morning sickness, which will hopefully stop in a few weeks' time.'

'Then I don't understand,' Danie persisted. 'What—?'

Jonas carried on: 'Your sister is normal and healthy, Danie—but she is also unmarried, completely unattached, according to you; don't you think, in the circumstances, she might feel a few qualms about having this baby?' He couldn't make it any clearer than that without completely breaking a patient's, even an ex-patient's, confidence.

Danie looked at him searchingly, as the meaning of his words slowly became clear to her.

'Good Lord,' she breathed weakly, dropping down into one of the armchairs. 'Andie is thinking about not having this baby? Is that the decision she said is for her to make and her alone?'

'And wouldn't you say that it was?' Jonas said quietly, moving to pour Danie half an inch of whisky into one of the glasses that stood beside the drinks tray.

She took the glass gratefully, taking a reviving mouthful

of the fiery liquid. 'Of course it's for Andie to decide,' she finally spoke again. 'But—'

'In Andie's eyes there isn't a but, Danie,' Jonas told her kindly, coming down on his haunches beside the chair she sat in.

'Well...maybe not as far as the family is concerned,' she conceded. 'But the father—'

'Whoever he might be.'

Danie gave him a furious glare. 'I can assure you that if Andie is pregnant—'

'She most certainly is,' he confirmed, knowing this conversation had gone too far now for prevarication.

'Then Andie knows exactly who the father is,' Danie bit out.

'And she isn't telling,' Jonas pointed out, relieved to see Danie's anger had revived her.

Danie looked puzzled. 'Not even Rome?'

'Especially not Rome.'

'But why not? He'll have to know some time, we all will— If Andie decides to have the baby...' she realised faintly.

Jonas didn't know Andie very well, had met her only briefly on Saturday, when he had carried out his examination to confirm her pregnancy. But if Andie was anything like her older sister, and he had reason to believe she was, then she would make her own mind up about the future—without any interference from anyone!

'I have to go to her,' Danie decided suddenly, putting down the whisky glass before standing up. 'I'm sorry, Jonas.' She turned back in time to see him regaining his balance after almost being knocked off his feet by her sudden ascent. 'Doubly sorry,' she apologised as she realised what she had done. 'But I have to go out. I'm sure you understand?' She moved swiftly about the apartment picking up her jacket, handbag and car keys.

Oh, he understood. All too well. Danie was responding exactly as he had last night when his sister had needed him, exactly as Danie had said she would if the positions were reversed. But there was still so much unresolved between the two of them. Whether or not Danie knew Ben, for one thing... For the main thing!

Danie hesitated in the action of pulling on her jacket. 'I forgot to ask—did everything go okay with your own sister last night?' she asked guardedly—almost as if she had picked up on at least some of his thoughts.

Or was he just looking for some sort of guilty reaction in her? Quite honestly, he didn't know any more. 'Fine,' he responded, not willing to go any deeper into last night until he was more sure of Danie. 'I did call you,' he confessed, again watching her closely.

'You did?' Danie echoed. 'But I have a telephone next to my bed, and—'

'The number was engaged,' Jonas replied.

Again he watched for Danie's reaction, and for a few moments she just continued to look puzzled, and then her brow—that smooth alabaster brow—cleared. 'It was Andie,' she said heavily. 'I should have known when she telephoned me so late at night that there was something seriously wrong,' she admonished herself.

Andie...? It had been her *sister* on the telephone at almost midnight last night?

Or was she just saying that—?

God. Jonas reeled at the sickening realisation that his suspicions concerning Danie and Ben had gone so deep. Too deep to be ignored or forgotten, even though it had been her sister talking to her on the telephone last night...?

The truth of the matter was, he couldn't bear the thought

of any other man being involved with Danie, let alone a man he had nothing but contempt for!

Which meant precisely what?

'I really do have to go, Jonas,' Danie cut sharply into his muddled thoughts. 'It may take me some time to even persuade Andie into letting me into her apartment, let alone actually talking to me about any of this.'

'Yes. Fine,' he responded abruptly, pushing away those disturbing thoughts about why he felt so jealously possessive of even Danie's past. 'I— We can talk again some other time.'

'Yes.' Danie looked across at him guardedly. 'Well. We had better go, then,' she prompted awkwardly.

Part of him wanted to go. But another part of him just wanted to forget all the complications that seemed to be pushing them apart, to just sweep Danie into his arms and make love to her, forget all about—

But he couldn't forget. Even though he now knew it had been Andie on the telephone late last night, his suspicions concerning Ben and the 'Danie' he had mentioned persisted.

'Yes,' he agreed flatly.

Neither of them spoke as they travelled downstairs in the lift together, standing feet apart, a wall seeming to have dropped down between the two of them. And it was getting higher with each passing minute.

'Can I drop you anywhere?' he offered once they were outside on the pavement, his car parked across the road.

'No, thank you,' Danie refused, not quite meeting his eyes as she looked somewhere over his left shoulder. 'I may be some time,' she continued, 'and I'll need transport home.'

'Of course,' Jonas replied. 'I—I hope your meeting with Andie goes well.'

She smiled humourlessly. 'So do I.' Her tone implied she didn't hold out much hope of that, but that she had to try nonetheless.

'Goodnight, then,' he said—having the terrible feeling that it *was* actually goodbye!

Danie's eyes glistened brightly green as she looked up at him at last.

Almost as if she had tears in her eyes, Jonas realised. But that was ridiculous. Why on earth should Danie be on the verge of tears?

'Goodnight, Jonas,' she said quickly before turning on her heel and walking away, disappearing around the corner of the building seconds later on her way to the private car park at the back.

It *had* been goodbye. For both of them, Jonas thought sadly. Danie couldn't forgive him for not telling her that her father wasn't his patient. And he—he couldn't get by the fact that Danie might have had an affair with his brother-in-law!

The aching pain in his heart at that realisation told him exactly why he was so jealous of Danie's past as well as her future—he was in love with her!

CHAPTER NINE

'YOU'RE extremely quiet this morning,' Danie's father commented interestedly.

Danie didn't even turn from her attention on the controls of the helicopter as they flew above the English countryside, her father seated beside her, Audrey in the back. 'I thought you didn't like chattering women in the morning,' she replied dryly.

'A hello might have been nice,' her father said disgruntledly.

'Hello,' Danie said with dry sarcasm.

The truth of the matter was, she was not in the mood for polite pleasantries. Last night had not been very successful—on any front!—and she blamed her father for at least some of that. She was twenty-seven years old, for goodness' sake, surely old enough for him to have confided in her about Andie.

As it was, she had arrived at her sister's apartment late last night to find that Andie had already been there and gone again, leaving with a small overnight bag, according to the building's security guard.

A few telephone calls to some of Andie's friends when she'd returned to her own home had told Danie that her sister wasn't with any of them, and she couldn't be with Harrie and Quinn, either, because they were still away. So at this precise moment, she had no idea where her sister was—and so she was not in the mood to be polite to their father!

'I know about Andie, Rome,' she told him coolly.

'Oh.'

'"Oh"?' she repeated sharply. 'Is that all you can say?' She turned blazing green eyes on him. 'My little sister is in the biggest mess of her life, and all you can say is "oh"?' she accused, two bright spots of colour in her cheeks now.

'No, that isn't all I can say,' her father bit back angrily. 'But as Andie has told me all too frequently this last week, she's a big girl now, and I—'

'She's disappeared,' Danie cut in cruelly, knowing that she wasn't being completely fair. Like Jonas, her father had been entrusted with a confidence, and it wasn't for him to break it.

Jonas…!

He knew about her and Ben. Danie didn't know *how* he knew, she only knew that he did. She had seen it in his eyes last night, had felt it in the distance he kept between them. And, angry as she was with the fact that Jonas had let her carry on believing it was her father who was seriously ill, it was a distance that she didn't feel like closing at the moment, either.

After all, what did it matter? she had told herself determinedly as she had gone to bed last night. She hardly knew Jonas, their acquaintance was of only a few days' standing; she would get over the feelings she had for him. She would have to!

'What do you mean, Andie's disappeared?' her father demanded tautly. 'How—?'

'She came to my apartment last night, there was a scene, she left,' Danie told him economically.

Rome frowned. 'What sort of scene? What did you do or say to upset her—?'

'I didn't do or say anything,' Danie came back furiously. 'She—'

'Might I suggest the two of you just calm down?' Audrey spoke soothingly from behind them. 'You both love Andie; I'm sure neither of you would ever do anything to hurt her.'

'Thank you for your vote of confidence, Audrey,' Danie accepted tensely before turning back to her father. 'Andie left last night because—' she broke off momentarily '—Jonas called round, and Andie jumped to the conclusion I was in league with the both of you, and—'

'Jonas called round...?' Rome repeated. 'Just how long has Jonas Noble been in the habit of calling round to your apartment?'

'Since I invited him to do so,' she snapped. 'But that isn't important—'

'I beg to differ,' her father interrupted. 'I think it's very important.'

'Why?' she challenged, her hands tight on the controls.

'Why? I'm sure he must be breaching some sort of medical etiquette—'

'Jonas hasn't breached anything,' Danie assured him—before he dared to ask her a personal question that she certainly wasn't going to answer! 'Besides, Andie is no longer his patient,' she added reluctantly.

'You know something, Danie,' her father spoke mildly—too mildly!—resting his head back against the leather seat, although he was far from relaxed, 'I think you might have been right about my feelings concerning chattering women in the mornings! This last five minutes of conversation has given me a headache!'

She had known her father wasn't going to like Andie's decision to dismiss Jonas as her consultant. She had also known he wasn't going to like the fact that Andie had taken herself off without telling anyone.

The fact that he was also not exactly pleased that she

had been seeing Jonas was totally irrelevant; after last night, she doubted she would be seeing Jonas ever again!

And if, at the moment, that caused her some pain, it was a pain she was going to keep to herself. Jonas could have told her something, anything, damn him, to alleviate the worry he knew she had felt over her father. As far as she was concerned, he had simply chosen not to do so, and it was a choice—the past and Ben apart—that ended any sort of relationship between them.

Just another relationship that hadn't worked out, that was how she would think of it one day. One day...

'Danie, turn this helicopter around and fly us back to the estate,' her father ordered suddenly, sitting up in his seat as he once again took charge. 'Audrey, telephone and cancel our appointment for this morning. Family commitments,' he instructed. 'We have to find Andie,' he explained as Danie looked at him with a puzzled expression.

'And if she doesn't wish to be found?' Danie had already turned the helicopter around as per her father's instruction.

'I'll find her anyway,' Rome assured her determinedly. 'That's my grandchild she's carrying!'

And Danie's niece or nephew... 'Andie will make the right choice in the end, you'll see,' she said with certainty.

'Just fly, Danie,' her father ground out harshly, obviously more shaken about Andie's disappearance than he cared to admit.

She flew, and she didn't linger at the estate once they had returned, either. If her father wanted to hunt Andie down, then he was welcome to do so. Danie felt she knew Andie well enough to know that her sister wouldn't do anything stupid or impulsive; Andie just needed time and space from family pressure to get her thoughts in order. At least, Danie hoped that was all it was!

The light was flashing on her answer-machine when she got in. Two messages. Maybe one of them would be from Andie!

'Danie, it's Jonas—Jonas Noble,' the first message played. 'Could you contact me on the following number as soon as possible?' He repeated the telephone number twice after the initial message before ringing off.

The fact that he had called didn't cheer Danie at all, in fact she just felt angry all over again. There had been no reason for him to say it was Jonas Noble; just how many Jonases did he think she knew? Dozens, probably, if he believed, as she thought he did, that she had once been involved with a married man.

She played the second message. 'Miss Summer, this is Mr Noble's secretary,' the brisk female voice informed her. 'It's very important that you contact him as soon as possible.' The message ended there.

If the first message had angered her, then the second one worried her. Jonas's call couldn't have been a personal one if he had got his secretary to call again some time later. There was only one reason she could think of for Jonas telephoning her on a business level.

Andie...?

She frantically rewound the tape, playing back the initial message, noting down the telephone number this time; she hadn't bothered the first time around, because she had thought Jonas had been calling on his own behalf. At the moment, they had nothing to say to each other on a personal level!

'Dorothy Quentin, Mr Noble's secretary,' came the reply to Danie's hurriedly made call. 'How may I help you?'

Danie didn't need to be told who the other woman was, easily recognised that brisk tone. 'It's Danie Summer,' she returned politely. 'You rang me earlier.'

'Ah, yes, Miss Summer.' The woman's tone softened slightly. 'Just hold the line a moment.'

'But—' Too late, the other woman had already put her on hold.

'Danie?' The rich tones of Jonas's voice came down the line seconds later.

'Yes,' she returned tersely. She had hoped to speak to his secretary, find out what the problem was, and go on from there. Actually speaking to Jonas had not been in her immediate plans.

'I have Andie here at my clinic—'

'Is she all right?' Danie's hand tightly gripped the receiver in her panic, waves of worried sickness washing over her.

'She is now,' he came back smoothly. 'She asked me to call you. She wants to see you.'

Danie barely had time to register the fact that Jonas obviously wouldn't have called her if Andie hadn't asked him to do so... She didn't have the time to think of that now. Explanations could come later, when she had ascertained for herself that Andie really was okay.

'I'll come straight away,' she told him without hesitation. 'My father—'

'Andie doesn't want him told just yet,' Jonas put in firmly. 'And, in the circumstances, I think that might be for the best.'

What circumstances? Danie wanted to demand. But didn't. Because, she knew from experience, Jonas wouldn't tell her anything!

Her mouth tightened. 'Give me the address, and I'll be there as quickly as possible.'

Jonas gave her the address of the private clinic. 'But don't break any speed limits—or your neck!—to get here,' he cautioned dryly.

Jonas sat behind his desk, looking up from the papers he had been trying to concentrate on. Trying—because he hadn't been succeeding; Danie was still very much in his thoughts. Even more so since he had admitted her sister to the clinic.

'Who aren't?' He frowned at his secretary's enigmatic comment.

'The two Summer sisters,' Dorothy said impatiently. 'Danie just arrived,' she announced.

Jonas sat up straighter in his high-backed leather chair. 'She did?' He tried to sound only mildly interested—but he knew from the knowing glitter in Dorothy's eyes that he had failed.

Dorothy nodded. 'And very fetching she looked too. If I thought it would do the same thing for my figure I might take to wearing leather,' she added speculatively.

It took tremendous effort to keep his expression deadpan as an all-too-disturbing vision of Danie in those leathers came into his head, every shapely curve shown to perfection. 'It wouldn't,' he assured Dorothy dryly.

Dorothy appeared unperturbed by his bluntness. 'She has gorgeous hair too,' she said enviously. 'In fact, she's absolutely beautiful,' she finished approvingly.

Danie was many things, beautiful being only one of them. Until two days ago he had believed Danie to be one of those rare people, who was beautiful inside as well as out; he had thought she had the same idea of family values as he did himself. But an affair with a married man told a completely different story...!

Because he simply couldn't get away from that fact, no matter how hard he had tried to believe it couldn't have been this particular Danie. Because he had seen the apprehension in her eyes the previous evening, as if she'd been waiting for a blow. Or an accusation...! That same wariness he had seen in her face the night he'd mentioned there were complications to their having a relationship. He was very much afraid now that wariness had been because for a moment, a very brief moment, Danie had thought he'd meant Ben…!

Jonas stood up. 'Is she with her sister now?'

'She is.' Dorothy answered slowly, noting his abrupt tone. 'I had coffee sent in for both of them.'

Dorothy's expression spoke of unasked questions Jonas was not going to answer!

He nodded. 'I'll go through and see them now. You may as well go to lunch now, Dorothy,' he advised her, not wanting to give her any excuse to have to come into Andrea Summer's room while he was talking to Andie and Danie.

She regarded him speculatively. 'Will you still be here when I get back or will you be taking an early lunch yourself?'

He tensed at her attempt to find out if he intended going out to lunch with Danie once they had both visited her sister, and before his next appointment. He didn't have any intention of lunching with Danie, of course, but sometimes Dorothy kept altogether too maternal an eye on his private life.

'I have no idea whether I will still be here when you return from lunch,' he answered impatiently. 'But I'm sure you have plenty of work to keep you busy if I've already left.'

Dorothy's brows rose at his biting tone. 'Your bedside manner could use a little polishing today,' she told him waspishly.

He sighed. 'I'm not at a bedside yet.'

'Probably as well,' came his secretary's parting comment.

Jonas's second sigh was even heavier than the first. After the way the two of them had said goodbye the evening before, he hadn't expected to see Danie again quite so soon. Although he accepted it was slightly different today; this was his territory, and Danie had only been invited on to it.

Nevertheless, he wasn't looking forward to seeing her again, and took a deep breath before walking briskly into Andrea Summer's room.

The two sisters turned at his entrance. Andie was lying in bed, Danie was sitting in a chair at her side. Dorothy was right: the two sisters were unalike to look at—except for those beautiful green eyes. Right now, their expressions were totally different: Andie was warmly welcoming; Danie glared at him with hostile dislike.

'Danie.' He nodded a terse greeting before turning to smile gently at Andie. 'How are you feeling now?'

'Much better,' she answered with certainty. 'My little scare has answered a lot of questions that have been worrying me. Most of all, it's made me realise I want to have this baby very much,' she admitted emotionally.

Andie's little scare had been the commencement of pains during the night as she'd lain in bed at the hotel she had booked into so that she could avoid her family. Jonas had been the only person she'd been able to think of calling at the time to help her. Which he had been only too happy to do.

Luckily those pains hadn't been as serious as Andie had feared, although Jonas still wanted her to stay at the clinic for a few days for observation.

'That's wonderful!' Danie told her sister huskily. Squeezing Andie's hand reassuringly. 'And when you want us, the family will all be there for you.'

This woman presented a dichotomy, Jonas inwardly reflected. She was one hundred per cent loyal to her family, and yet, at the same time, she had been instrumental in breaking up another family because of her relationship with another woman's husband. No matter how he tried, Jonas couldn't get past that fact...

And he had tried; oh, how he had tried! But Nikki's months of unhappiness after she and Ben had parted were something he could never forget.

Or that look of triumphant certainty on Ben's face when he'd left Nikki's home the other evening...!

He turned back to Danie with glacial eyes. 'I'm glad you were finally able to come and be with your sister,' he bit out harshly.

Those green eyes narrowed at his barely concealed sarcasm. 'Unfortunately I was at work when you telephoned,' Danie answered just as coldly. 'I came as soon as I received your message.'

Jonas looked her up and down. 'Unconventional as ever, I see,' he referred disparagingly to the tightly fitting biking leathers she wore.

But she looked absolutely stunning with her long red hair flowing down the length of her spine, the leather suit fitting her like a glove. So much so that Jonas was sure she couldn't possibly be wearing anything underneath. Which conjured up all sorts of erotic pictures in his head. Damn it!

Danie gave an acknowledging inclination of her head, obviously holding on to her own fiery temper with effort. Jonas could easily guess the reason for that too; it had nothing to do with not insulting him in return, and everything to do with not upsetting her sister.

'Strange,' Danie said evenly, obviously unable to completely refrain from making some sort of comment, 'but I feel some of that impatience with humanity coming over me once again!' She looked across at him challengingly.

Jonas met her challenging gaze unblinkingly. 'Perhaps you need feeding once again,' he drawled unconcernedly.

Her mouth thinned scathingly. 'I can wait,' she snapped, eyes flashing brilliantly green.

'Please don't do so on my account.' Andie stretched luxuriously in the comfort of the bed. 'I think I would like to have a little sleep.' She gave a smile. 'All this excitement has made me tired. So if the two of you want to go off and have some lunch together...' she added expectantly.

The verbal fencing he and Danie had been engaged in was not conducive to them wanting to go off and have a meal together; they would both end up with indigestion!

'Unfortunately, I have to be somewhere else in just over an hour.' Jonas spoke to Andie rather than Danie.

'Don't let us keep you.' Danie was the one to answer him with hard dismissal.

His eyes narrowed at her deliberately condescending tone. 'Perhaps I could have a few words with you before I leave...?' he suggested silkily.

'Go ahead,' she invited.

'Not here, if you don't mind,' he returned smoothly, turning to open the door. 'I'm sure Andie will benefit from being left alone for a while so that she can take that nap.'

'Please go ahead,' Andie told Danie dreamily, already half-asleep.

Leaving Danie no choice but to precede Jonas out of the room! But she did it with obvious reluctance, every inch of her body tense with resentment.

She turned angrily to face him once they were outside in the carpeted corridor. 'I hope what you're going to say has something to do with Andie's condition.'

By not so much of the flicker of an eyelid did he show how affected he was by how magnificent Danie looked when she was angry. It might be a hackneyed line, but in Danie's case it was certainly true; her hair seemed to spark with flame, her eyes flashed deeply green, and as for her body—! Her breasts were pert beneath the black leather, legs long and shapely as she adopted a determined stance.

'What else could it be?' he prompted softly.

Two bright spots of colour appeared in her alabaster cheeks. 'Is Andie going to be all right now?'

'As long as she takes things easy,' he replied. 'The fact that she seems to have come to a decision about the rightness of the pregnancy will take some of the strain off her. Of course, it would probably be better for her if she had a partner to share this with, but—'

'Having a man in your life usually brings more problems, not less!' Danie pronounced scornfully.

'In your experience?' Jonas pointed out.

She drew in a sharp breath before replying. 'In my experience, yes,' she finally answered with suppressed rage. 'Why don't you just say what you want to say, Jonas, and get this over with?' She looked at him with blazing eyes, her body tense, her hands clenched about the crash-helmet she held in front of her.

Almost as if it were a protective shield...? Which was ridiculous; Danie was more than capable of taking care of herself, in any sort of confrontation.

He had stiffened at the directness of her challenge. What did he want to say? If he were to ask her if she had once been involved with Ben, and she said yes—!

He shrugged. 'I have no idea what you're talking about, Danie.' He gave a pointed glance at his wrist-watch. 'And I really do have to go now.'

She looked exasperated. 'Another wealthy patient you have to go and pander to?'

Jonas straightened at her deliberately insulting tone, wondering what Danie would have to say if she knew he was going to a rather dilapidated clinic in a run-down part of the city, that he went there two afternoons of the week, and that, far from being pandered to, his patients there were much more in need of advice on how to subsist well enough to bring a healthy child into the world than anything else. But he only wondered what she would think—because he had no intention of telling her anything about where he was going! The relationship was no longer close enough for him to want to confide anything in her.

'Something like that,' he finally replied. 'In the circumstances, your sister will be staying in for a few days' observation, so perhaps I'll see you here again,' he added politely.

'Perhaps you will,' Danie answered shortly.

Jonas hesitated, knowing that if he walked away now, left things as they were, then it was all over between Danie and himself. But, then, wasn't it all over now anyway? The two of them were more like opponents eyeing each other across the ring than the lovers they had almost become.

'Take care, then, Danie.'

'I always do,' she returned stiltedly.

But still Jonas didn't make any physical move to leave. What was wrong with him? His mind was telling him to turn and walk away, but another part of him—a part he didn't seem to have control over at the moment!—didn't want to go.

Could Danie really have been involved in an affair with Ben? What if he were wrong about that? What if—?

'Goodbye, Jonas,' Danie cut in on his thoughts, finality in her tone.

He wasn't wrong, and they both knew it...

'Goodbye, Danie,' he echoed softly, turning and walking away this time.

And he didn't look back.

Even though every part of him wanted to do just that!

CHAPTER TEN

'WE'RE all very relieved that you're going to be all right now, Andie,' Rome said warmly.

'But...?' Andie added, eyeing him ruefully from the bed where she lay resting.

Danie had caught that 'but' in their father's tone too. As she sat beside her sister's bed, she couldn't say she was any more happy about it than Andie appeared to be. The most important thing was that Andie, after a day spent resting, now looked better than she had for weeks, and the main reason for that was the realisation that she really wanted this baby. To Danie, her sister's happiness and welfare were all that mattered.

But knowing how worried Rome had been this morning, Danie realised he had to be informed of Andie's whereabouts some time, and at her sister's request she had telephoned him with the news. Only to have him arrive at the clinic within an hour of her call!

Rome stood in front of the window now, the brightness of the evening sun shining behind him making it hard to discern his expression. 'It might help if we knew who the father is,' he rasped.

'Why?' Danie was the one to defensively answer him.

'Surely it's obvious?' Rome replied.

'Not to me,' Danie told him decisively.

'Danie believes men can be an unnecessary complication,' Jonas put in from the back of the room. 'To any situation!'

She turned to give him a narrow-eyed glare. She had no

147

idea what he was doing in here in the first place. Admittedly, this was his clinic, and Andie had obviously decided he should be her consultant after all—but Danie had no idea why he should be present during this meeting between Andie and their father; she was only here herself at Andie's request.

'I'm well aware of my daughter Danie's opinion of men, thank you, Jonas,' Rome retorted. 'Although it should be an opinion she had long grown out of,' he continued, for Danie's benefit alone. 'But, in this case, I'm afraid I have to agree with that opinion; without a man being involved, there would be no—complication!'

'What a way to describe your future grandchild, Daddy,' Andie chided mockingly.

'I can see you're feeling much better!' her father commented.

'Much,' Andie agreed with a self-satisfied smile.

Danie had spent most of the day with her younger sister, and they had talked most things through—the father of the baby being the exception. But, unlike their own father, Danie wasn't particularly interested in his identity. He didn't appear to have been of any help to Andie so far, so why involve him now?

But at least Andie believed her now about not being in cahoots with their father and Jonas. Although her sister had been speculative about exactly what Jonas had been doing at Danie's apartment yesterday evening... It was speculation Danie did not intend satisfying!

Jonas had been in to check on Andie several times during the late afternoon and early evening, and for the main part Danie had ignored him. The fact that he ignored her too had rankled rather than upset her.

'I'm sure it would be beneficial to Jonas if he were to

know who the baby's father is,' Rome persisted. 'Wouldn't it?' he asked Jonas pointedly.

'It might be of some help,' Jonas replied guardedly.

'In what way?' Danie flew into the exchange.

Jonas turned his hard brown gaze on her. 'From a health point of view, of course,' he returned smoothly.

He knew of her resentment at his presence, and was responding to it. Good! Danie wanted him to know exactly how much she now resented him. He could think what he liked. After the way Jonas had let her carry on believing it was her father who was the one who was ill, she certainly wasn't in a mood to defend her actions of two years ago. She could come to regret that decision later on, but at the moment she was just too fed up to care!

'You've already told us that Andie is perfectly healthy, that the twinges she felt during the night weren't serious,' Danie persisted.

'I was referring to the baby's health, of course,' Jonas patiently responded. 'The age and health of the father can often be a good indication of other things.'

Danie gave a disbelieving snort. 'I hope you're not implying that my sister may have been involved with a sickly geriatric!' she exclaimed, with an amused look at the beautiful Andie.

Andie gave a throaty chuckle. 'Thanks for that vote of confidence, Danie!' She grinned. 'Is that what's been worrying you too, Rome? That the baby's father may be someone totally unsuitable?'

'I'm glad you now find all of this so funny!' Rome muttered impatiently.

'Not exactly, Daddy.' Andie sobered. 'It's just such a relief to know that everything is going to be okay.'

'Of course it is.' Danie gave her hand a reassuring squeeze before sparing the time to give the two men a reproachful glare. 'And I'm sure Andie would like to have another rest—now that you've satisfied yourself as to her welfare.'

Rome drew in a harsh breath, obviously having difficulty holding back his usual drive to take control of a situation. Because this was a situation of which Andie had made it more than plain she wouldn't let him be in control!

'Don't you agree, Jonas?' Danie went on. After all, he was supposed to be the specialist around here.

'I think that's up to Andie,' he replied noncommittally. 'As I've learnt only too well, the Summer women are a law unto themselves—and God help anyone who gets in their way!'

Danie gave him a sharp look, knowing that she had to be the one responsible for forming most of his opinion of the Summer women.

Was that really what he thought—or was he just referring to what he believed to be the truth of her past involvement with Ben? Did he believe that she hadn't cared that his sister was in the way of that relationship, that she had conducted an affair with Ben in spite of his wife and two young children? Jonas didn't know her very well at all if that was the conclusion he had come to...

'You're right there, Jonas,' Rome agreed with him wearily. 'I sometimes sit and wonder where I went wrong...'

'Or right,' Danie put in, standing up, no longer wearing her leathers, having returned briefly to her apartment during the afternoon to change into some lighter clothes; her red tee shirt and black denims were much more suitable for the heating necessary in the clinic. 'Time we were all going, I think,' she declared. Andie, for one, looked as if she had had enough for one evening!

Danie wasn't far behind her. It had been a long and difficult day, not helped by Jonas popping in and out when he'd come in to check on Andie, and Danie longed to get back to the peace and quiet of her apartment. To lick her own wounds in private...

She bent and kissed Andie warmly on the cheek. 'Don't worry,' she whispered for her sister's ears alone. 'I'll keep Daddy off your back,' she promised.

'And how do you intend doing that?' Andie whispered back. Both of them knew their father too well to believe he would ever stay in the background of any situation that involved his daughters.

Danie grinned. 'I'll think of something!'

'I wish you luck.' Andie squeezed her hand gratefully.

'What are you two girls whispering about together there?' their father demanded impatiently behind them. 'The three of them used to gang up on me when they were younger,' he informed Jonas wryly. 'I never stood a chance!'

'I can believe that,' Jonas acknowledged dryly.

Danie straightened, shooting him a look that said she didn't care what he believed—about anything!

'Could I have a word with you?' Jonas asked once the three of them were in the corridor outside Andie's room.

It took Danie several seconds to realise he was actually talking to her, looking up to find his steady gaze on her. She frowned resentfully. 'Which word would that be?' she challenged—sure he had a whole selection he could choose from for what he believed her to be!

'I think it's time I was on my way,' Rome announced after a glance at their two set faces. 'I'll need you at the estate at nine o'clock tomorrow morning,' he told Danie.

She didn't turn to look at her father, locked in a battle of wills with Jonas, both of them refusing to break the glance, hard brown eyes clashing with gold green. 'I'll be there,' she answered her father evenly.

'Fine. Thanks for everything, Jonas,' Rome said. 'I—
Oh, to hell with it,' he muttered as neither of the adversaries spared even so much as a glance his way, stomping
off down the corridor on his way out.

Adversaries... Was that what she and Jonas now were?
It would appear so, her own will implacable, Jonas tight-
mouthed and hard-eyed.

'I believe we may have upset your father.' Jonas finally
spoke.

Danie shrugged. 'He'll get over it,' she dismissed. 'A
word, I believe you said...?'

'In my office,' Jonas stated, looking as if he were about
to take hold of her arm, and then thought better of it, his
own hand falling ineffectually back to his side. 'If you
would like to come this way,' he told her tightly before
striding off down the corridor.

She didn't like it at all, but there was always the possibility that this word he wanted to have with her could be
about Andie. Danie doubted it, of course, but she would
listen to what he had to say anyway. And then she would
react.

There was no doubting that Jonas looked more distant
and unapproachable in the formal suit he wore today than
she had ever seen him before, the deference with which
he was treated by the staff here an indication of the respect
he commanded. But, as far as Danie was concerned, that
air of distance that surrounded Jonas could only be a bonus. She did not want to think of him as the man she had
almost made love with two nights ago!

No doubt he was excellent at his job and therefore de-
serving of the deference shown him by his staff, Danie
acknowledged; it was only as a human being that he was
found wanting!

His office, obviously also his consulting-room, was as

plush as the rest of the clinic, but Danie spared it hardly a glance as she refused the seat he offered her opposite his across the desk. She wasn't a subordinate about to be chastised by her superior!

'Could you make this quick? I have to be somewhere else.' She sarcastically repeated the excuse he had made to her this morning before leaving.

Was it her imagination, or had he stiffened at this statement?

Damn it, he had. Did he think she was still involved with Ben—was that it? Or did he think there was some other man she was meeting, despite her telling him there wasn't anyone in her life?

Damn him!

She hadn't so much as looked at a man the last two years, had been so hurt and humiliated at the discovery of Ben's deceit that she had become sceptical and wary of all men after that, never wanting to find herself in such an unacceptable—to her!—position, ever again.

She had been surprised herself, after the shaky start to their own relationship, to find herself attracted to Jonas, to such an extent that she had allowed him to slip beneath the wall of reserve she had built about her emotions. And look where it had got her!

'I won't keep you long,' Jonas grated. 'But you made a comment to me earlier today for which I would like an explanation.' He looked at her with narrowed eyes.

'Yes?' she prompted, wondering which one of her cutting comments that could have been!

'Something about not giving me the satisfaction of breaking your neck on the drive over here this morning.'

That had been during their telephone conversation this morning, for goodness' sake. And Jonas had waited all day to ask her what she meant by it...? Somehow she found that hard to believe. Which begged the question: why had he really delayed her departure a few minutes ago...?

'I was referring, of course, to the fact that you wish you had never met me—'

'I don't believe I have ever said—'

'And that equally,' she continued, 'I wish I had never met you! Oh, you didn't exactly lie to me, Jonas, except by omission, but nonetheless you did let me carry on believing something you knew to be untrue. Namely, that my father was ill.'

'You—'

'Whereas you—' again she continued as if Jonas hadn't tried to interrupt '—on even less evidence than I had, believe I've done a similar thing where you're concerned!' Her head went back challengingly, hair almost the same red as her tee shirt swinging loosely down her spine. 'The difference here appears to be that you believe you acted correctly, and so I have no justification for my anger. At the same time, you believe I have acted incorrectly, and so you do have the right to your own feelings of anger. Isn't that the way it is, Jonas?' she taunted scathingly.

Jonas drew in a sharp breath, his cheeks pale as he clenched his jaw. 'I wouldn't have put it quite like that—'

'Then how would you have put it?' Her eyes flashed deeply green. 'Please do tell me, Jonas; I'm just longing to know!'

He sighed impatiently. 'There's just no reasoning with you when you're in this mood, Danie—'

'You bet your sweet life there isn't!' she assured him furiously. 'You've set yourself up as judge and jury where I'm concerned—and I have to tell you I find your behaviour arrogant in the extreme. How dare you—?'

Her words were choked in her throat as Jonas moved forward to pull her roughly against him, his mouth coming down possessively on hers, pulling her body in close against his as he demanded a response from her cold lips.

It was a response Danie couldn't give...

She loved this man. It didn't matter that, having learnt what had happened two years ago, he believed the version he had been told without even asking her if it was the truth. She still loved him. And to have him kissing her in this savage, almost contemptuous way, not an ounce of tenderness in his kiss or touch, chilled her in a way that made her tremble.

Jonas pulled away as he felt the shaking of her body, looking down at her with darkened brown eyes. 'Danie...?' he groaned.

She looked up at him with unemotional eyes, only the bruised feeling to her lips telling her this wasn't all a nightmare—one she would wake up from in a minute! 'Let me go, Jonas,' she told him flatly, standing cold and inert within the steel band of his arms.

His arms dropped away from her as if he had been stung; he stepped back, his throat moving convulsively as he swallowed. 'Danie, I—' He broke off as the door suddenly opened behind them, looking sharply over Danie's shoulder at the intruder. 'I thought you had already gone for the day, Dorothy,' he rasped in measured tones.

'I—I had some correspondence to finish,' his assistant muttered awkwardly. 'And as I'm not going straight home this evening—I'll bring these letters back later and put them on your desk—'

'Please don't bother on my account,' Danie told the older woman lightly as she turned to face her, knowing that she had to maintain her dignity until she had at least managed to walk out of here—then she could collapse into the emotional heap of despondency that she really felt she was! 'I was just leaving, anyway.' She smiled brightly at the other woman as she walked to the doorway. 'Thank you once again for everything you're doing for my sister, Jonas.' She made the polite statement without even turning to look at him. 'Goodbye,' she added with a finality that was unmistakable.

Because it was goodbye, if not from Jonas completely, because he was obviously going to continue attending Andie, then certainly from the man she had briefly become emotionally involved with. There could be no future for them now.

If there ever had been.

'I'm terribly sorry, Jonas,' Dorothy told him agitatedly, her expression stricken. 'I had no idea you were in here, let alone that you had company. And I obviously interrupted at completely the wrong time—'

'Stop babbling, Dorothy,' Jonas said wearily as he moved to sit down behind his desk, elbows on its top as he dropped his head into his hands. 'I have a headache.'

'Shall I get you something for it—?'

'It isn't that sort of headache,' Jonas replied heavily, dropping his hands from his face to give her a humourless smile. 'Its name is Danie Summer—and I don't think any sort of pill you might choose to get for me is going to rid me of *her*!'

'I thought she just left,' Dorothy glanced at the open doorway.

'Physically, maybe,' Jonas conceded. He should have just let her leave earlier with her father, not delayed her with that lame excuse of needing to talk to her. Because he hadn't really needed to talk to her at all; he just hadn't been able to bear the thought of her leaving.

'Ah,' Dorothy said knowingly.

Jonas's eyes narrowed. 'Exactly what does that mean?' he grated irritatedly.

'I don't see what your problem is, Jonas.' Dorothy strolled confidently across the width of the office, placing the unsigned letters on his desk for his signature in the morning. 'The two of you were obviously friendly enough a couple of days ago—'

'What makes you think that?' he demanded sharply.

Dorothy shrugged. 'She felt confident enough of your reaction then to telephone you.' She reminded him of the call from Danie she had answered three days ago. 'And you certainly seemed pleased enough to receive the call,' she recalled.

'That wasn't pleasure, Dorothy; I was in a daze. I seem to have been in that state, in one form or another, since the moment I first met Danie Summer!'

Dorothy arched auburn brows. 'And just how long have you known her?'

He thought for a moment. 'Seven days—but it seems much longer!' he admitted, hardly able to believe himself that his acquaintance with Danie had only existed that long.

It seemed as if he had always known her. As if she had always been a part of his life, at first aggravatingly so, and then humorously, followed by a passion that had seemed to consume them both.

And now she had gone. If her final word meant what he thought it did, she had gone for ever.

That ache was back in his chest.

Oh, he knew—being a doctor, he should!—that the emotions didn't actually come from the heart, that it was just another organ of the body—but at this moment he definitely had an ache where he knew his heart to be!

Or, at least, where it should be.

Because he felt as if that particular part of his body had walked out of the room when Danie had…!

'Look, if you've done something stupid, Jonas—and, being a man, you probably have,' Dorothy began, 'then—'

'Not another one.' Jonas sighed his impatience. 'A man hater,' he explained at Dorothy's questioning look.

'Don't be ridiculous, Jonas; I don't hate men,' she chided lightly. 'I just happen to believe women are a little more in touch with their feelings than men, but that doesn't mean I hate men. I doubt your Danie Summer hates men, either. Although, being so beautiful, she's probably had more than her fair share of idiotic men trying to prove how wonderful they are,' she said knowingly. 'Now don't look like that.' Dorothy chuckled at his scowling expression. 'I wasn't referring to you!'

'I should damn well hope not,' he retorted.

'No… Well, to get back to what I was saying,' she continued, a smile playing about her lips at his ongoing bad humour, 'if you've done something to upset Danie then all you have to do is apologise—'

'It isn't as simple as that.' Nothing was ever that simple where Danie was concerned!

No, he was being unfair now. Danie wasn't the one who had complicated things; it was the past that had done that.

Her judge and jury, Danie had accused him of being. Was that what he had been? Had he found her guilty without hearing anything she had to say on the matter?

Possibly, he conceded grimly. But surely those words themselves had confirmed that she was the Danie from Ben's past.

'No one said that life wasn't complicated, Jonas,' Dorothy told him affectionately. 'Maybe it hasn't been for you. You had a happy and carefree childhood—your mother made sure of that. You have a close and caring family. Your career is everything that you could want it to be. You've never really had to fight for anything you wanted. In fact, Jonas—'

'I've had life easy so far,' he finished.

'I wasn't going to put it quite like that,' Dorothy said, 'but in a word—yes!'

'I hope you aren't going to put this little chat down as overtime, Dorothy.' Jonas sat back in his chair, some of the tension Danie's departure had caused starting to leave his body now. 'I'm not going to pay you for insulting me!'

'That's better.' Dorothy looked approvingly at his almost smiling expression. 'And I'm not insulting you, Jonas,' she told him softly. 'I'm trying to help you. Has no one ever told you that the best things in life very often have to be fought for?'

'My mother probably mentioned it when I was younger,' he drawled.

'But so far you've never had to put it into action,' Dorothy guessed. 'Is Danie Summer worth fighting for?'

'Oh, yes!' he answered unhesitantly, knowing he would never meet another woman like Danie, that there *was* no other woman like Danie. Not for him, anyway. One woman, one man, and he had no doubts that Danie was that woman for him.

But there wasn't only himself and Danie to consider, there was Nikki too. Nikki had just started to find some happiness in her own life. Maybe later on—

Don't be a fool, man, he instantly chastised himself; women like Danie didn't hang around waiting for someone they weren't even sure was theirs.

Because he was Danie's. Heart, body, and soul.

What a mess!

'I really don't understand your problem, Jonas—and I don't want to know,' Dorothy instantly assured him as he raised dark brows. 'But the young lady that just walked out of here looked as if her heart were breaking with each step that she took. It makes no sense if the two of you feel that way about each other.'

'No mountain is too high to climb in the quest for love, is that it?' Jonas derided. He wasn't at all sure if Dorothy had been reading Danie's emotions correctly; if they hadn't been interrupted when they had, angry as Danie had been, she would probably have ended up slapping his face before leaving! 'This particular mountain is just too damned high, Dorothy. And I was never too fond of heights!'

'You don't think an apology would do the trick?' Dorothy ventured.

'What makes you think I'm the one in the wrong?' he demanded.

'I didn't say I did think that—'

'Then why should I be the one to apologise?' Jonas persisted unmercifully.

'It doesn't matter who's to blame for the rift.' His assistant sighed her impatience with his levity. 'Someone has to make the first move, that's all.'

Jonas shook his head, remembering Danie's anger of a few minutes ago, her implacability. 'I'm afraid it won't be me, Dorothy,' he told her quietly.

'Oh, well, I tried,' Dorothy said, glancing at her wristwatch. 'I'm afraid I have to go now, or I'm going to be late; I'm babysitting for Nikki this evening,' she said fondly, having come to know all of Jonas's family during the years she had worked as his assistant.

'She mentioned that,' Jonas replied, feeling a jolt at the mention of his sister so soon after his disastrous confrontation with Danie.

Dorothy nodded happily. 'I'm all for helping the path

of true love run smoothly—and Nikki deserves to be happy after being married to that other swine for so long.'

Without even being aware of it, Dorothy had just answered her own questions concerning why he couldn't chase after Danie. Because he wanted to. He wanted to run after her, tell her that none of the past mattered, that he loved her, wanted her to be his wife. But he always came back to Nikki...

He stood up decisively, following Dorothy through to her adjoining office. 'I think I'll come with you.'

Dorothy paused in the act of pulling on her jacket. 'I don't think it needs two of us to babysit two children,' she commented.

Jonas helped her on with the jacket. 'I didn't mean babysitting,' he replied. 'I'm just ready to leave now too.'

'How cosy—you're going to walk me to my car!' Dorothy teased, moving to switch off the lights.

Jonas took a firm hold of her arm. 'Some lucky man should have snapped you up years ago—it might have helped to curb the bluntness of your tongue!'

'I wouldn't count on it,' Dorothy came back instantly.

Neither would he, Jonas agreed defeatedly.

'I don't think it will have that effect on your Danie, either,' Dorothy continued determinedly as they walked down the corridor together. 'She looks like a woman who speaks her mind, too.'

His mouth was grimly unsmiling. 'Could we just forget about Danie?' he grated.

'I will if you will,' Dorothy rejoined softly.

Meaning that Dorothy knew he wasn't going to do any such thing!

How could he forget the only woman he had ever loved? The *only* woman he would ever love...!

CHAPTER ELEVEN

'WHAT do you mean, my sister is no longer a patient at the clinic?' Danie demanded of the politely smiling receptionist. 'If she isn't here, then where is she?'

Because Andie certainly wasn't back at the estate with their father. Even though it was Saturday, Danie had just come from there after flying Rome up to, and back down again from, the north of England to carry out the business meetings he had cancelled the day before. Andie had been nowhere in sight when Danie had left.

'Miss Summer was discharged late this morning—'

'What do you mean, discharged?' Danie was aware that she sounded a little more than aggressive, but it was just such a shock to have rushed back to town, only to be told that Andie wasn't even here any more.

It had been a long and trying day, most of it spent hanging around waiting for her father to complete his business meetings. It hadn't exactly been a comfortable day either, some sort of tension seeming to have sprung up between Rome and Audrey, meaning that the flights, both ways, had been silent ones.

Danie had had no idea what their problem was, and with her own thoughts on Andie—Jonas she had put into a compartment marked 'private' for the moment; there would be plenty of time to dwell on the agony of loving him in the months ahead!—she hadn't particularly cared, either. But now it seemed that Andie, for all Danie's efforts to get back to town by late afternoon, was no longer here...

'Kay means exactly what she's saying.' Jonas spoke

smoothly as he pushed open the double swing doors to join them in the reception area, obviously having seen her arrival via the security cameras. He was once again dressed in a formal suit, a charcoal-grey one this time, with a steel-grey shirt, and conservatively patterned darker grey tie. 'Andie was discharged this morning and has since left.'

Danie gave him an impatient glance. 'I believe I understood that part,' she said with saccharine-sweetness, her tension high because of her worry about her sister. Besides, it was easier—much easier to her peace of mind—to be angry with this man…!

Jonas looked at her with steady brown eyes. 'Then which part is it you didn't understand? Never mind,' he ploughed on, as she would have snapped a reply, 'come through to my office and we can discuss this more privately.'

Danie didn't wish to discuss anything with him more privately—she just wanted to know where her sister was!

But Jonas stood beside the door he held open for her, waiting for her to precede him down the corridor. With the curious Kay watching and listening, Danie had no choice but to do exactly that, her movements swift in her irritation.

She was dressed very much as she had been the first day they'd met: a black baseball cap hiding her red hair and pulled low over her eyes, a black gilet over a black shirt, and black combat trousers completing the outfit.

If Jonas once again thought she looked distinctly unfeminine—his remarks that day about a short skirt and silky blouse had been duly noted and filed away for future use— then all well and good. She did not want him to see any remnant of the woman he had almost made love with the other evening!

Dorothy looked up to give her a smile as they passed

her office doorway, almost stopping Danie in her tracks as she also gave her a conspiratorial wink.

Now what on earth had that been about?

Obviously Dorothy had realised Danie and Jonas hadn't exactly parted as friends yesterday evening, but even so…!

Danie turned to Jonas as soon as the office door closed behind them. 'Okay, so this is more private.' She repeated his earlier words. 'Now would you mind telling me exactly where Andie is?'

Jonas looked at her impassively. 'You know, you really are one aggressive young lady,' he rasped.

She looked at him unrepentantly. 'The two of us have gone past the need to be falsely polite to each other, Jonas,' she stated. 'Way past,' she added, remembering the things that had been said and done in this office the evening before.

He gave a heavy sigh. 'It doesn't have to be like this between us, Danie. We—'

'There is no "us", Jonas,' she cut in coldly. 'Not any more. If there ever was.'

Jonas seemed to wince at her deliberate coldness. 'Won't you even try to understand—?'

'Oh, but I already do understand, Jonas,' she assured him. 'You know about my past involvement with Ben.' Again he seemed to flinch, but Danie chose to ignore that. 'And you have drawn your own conclusions from that concerning my nature! I don't think there is anything else to understand—is there?'

On closer inspection she had realised that Jonas had a strained look about his eyes and mouth, a darkness beneath his eyes hinting at a lack of sleep. But if the end of their relationship had caused these changes in him—and she wasn't completely convinced of that!—whose fault was that?

Jonas had never bothered to ask her for her version of what had happened two years ago, had simply learnt that she had once known his ex-brother-in-law, and had drawn his own conclusions. He had no idea of the heartache she had suffered once she'd learnt that Ben was a married man, of the agonies she had gone through on Nikki Trainer's behalf, easily able to empathise with the pain and disillusionment the other woman must have felt on learning that her husband had been seeing another woman. Goodness, she still shook with reaction herself whenever she thought of that!

By the same token, Jonas had never questioned the contempt she felt towards men, or the wariness she felt towards relationships. If he had, perhaps he would have realised that the mistake she had made over Ben two years ago was completely responsible for both those feelings!

'There has to be some way, Danie,' Jonas tried, his own remoteness evaporating as he looked at her with longing. 'I thought I could carry on as before, but I—I can't just let you go out of my life!' He paused. 'And you have it all wrong; it isn't your past involvement with Ben that's the problem here—it's my sister! How do you think she's going to feel about my involvement with you—?'

'We don't have an involvement, Jonas—'

'Yes, we do, damn it!' He moved forward to grasp her by her forearms. 'It's okay, I'm not going to try and force the issue in the way I did last night,' he assured her as she looked up at him, startled. 'I realise that was a mistake on my part—'

'Not the least of many!' she snapped up at him.

'Probably,' he conceded, looking at her with pleading eyes. 'Help me a little, Danie!' he groaned. 'I know I've made mistakes where you're concerned, but couldn't you cut me a little slack over that? I've never been in love before!'

Danie stared at him. She couldn't help it. Had Jonas just said he was in love with her...?

No, don't weaken, Danie, she instantly told herself. Anger. That was the emotion she had to maintain here. Because she had no intention of apologising for the rest of her life for a mistake that had come about by Ben Trainer's deceit. A mistake she had already paid for a hundred times over with her own tortured emotions...

She pulled away from him. 'If you think I'm going to just fall into your arms after that declaration, Jonas, then you're mistaken. Words, Jonas,' she derided. 'Just words. Ben used a lot of those too—and look what a liar he turned out to be.'

Jonas's face darkened with anger. 'Don't liken me to Ben Trainer!' he bit out harshly.

An angry Jonas was something to see, Danie noted abstractly, making her aware that, although she had seen him in many moods, she had only once seen him actually angry before this. Those brown eyes were hard as pebbles, his lids narrowed, his mouth drawn into a narrowly tensed line.

Danie expelled a breath. 'Then don't behave like him. He wanted to have his cake and eat it, too,' she stated.

Jonas looked at her hard. 'And in what way am I attempting to do that?' he rasped. 'I'm not a married man—'

'But if I've read you correctly you also want to keep a relationship with me a secret from your sister,' she pointed out, cutting off the description of Ben that made her cringe with embarrassment. 'I may have been naive where Ben was concerned,' she conceded, 'but I don't make the same mistake twice!'

'I'm not suggesting keeping you a secret from my sister, damn it!' Jonas replied furiously.

Danie raised dark brows. 'Then just what are you "suggesting"?' Her sarcasm was only lightly veiled.

He drew in a ragged breath. 'I think I'm asking you to help me find a way to ask you to marry me, while at the same time avoiding making any more waves in my sister's life!' Now his hands were clenched at his sides as he glared across at her.

Marry... Had Jonas really just said he wanted to *marry* her...?

'Don't tell me I've managed to render you speechless, Danie,' Jonas exclaimed. 'That must be a first!'

Danie still stared at him. To be married to Jonas... Wasn't it what she wanted more than anything? But—

There was always a but!

'Jonas,' she began slowly, 'exactly what do you believe happened between Ben and myself?' She looked at him from beneath her cap.

He withdrew slightly. 'It doesn't matter—'

'It mattered a couple of days ago—I saw the accusation in your eyes, Jonas. And no one could mistake the way you've backed off since then.'

He held up defensive hands. 'I was stunned, I admit I was. Oh, not by your relationship with Ben. I was floored by the coincidence of my having met the same Danie. What do you think the chances of that happening actually were, Danie?'

'Without Andie's pregnancy, probably no chance whatsoever,' she admitted, knowing that in normal circumstances their paths would never have crossed, that their lifestyles and circle of friends were completely different. 'Which reminds me,' she remembered. 'You still haven't told me where Andie has gone?'

'Once I had told Andie I was happy for her to go home, aware that you were away with your father all of today, she telephoned your eldest sister Harrie, who came and collected her,' Jonas explained.

So Harrie knew the truth too now, Danie realised. Well, Andie need have no worries, because as a family they would close ranks and protect their youngest member at all costs.

'Don't try and change the subject, Danie,' Jonas grated frustratedly. 'Andie is going to be fine. Your father, as far as I am aware, is in the best of health—'

'I'm aware of that too—now,' she reminded him.

Jonas looked at her searchingly, eyes narrowed. 'Is anger a good option as a defence?' he finally murmured softly.

She raised her head defiantly. 'It works for me!'

'Hmm, that's what I thought,' he said slowly, moving forward so that he stood only inches away from her now, one of his hands moving so that he gently caressed her creamy cheek, his gaze intent on her flushed face.

Danie wanted to step back, away from him, but pride made her hold her position. She wasn't frightened of anyone, let alone—

Heaven!

Jonas's mouth against hers, gently caressing, was absolute heaven...!

If he had been demanding, in the way that he had been the previous evening, then she wouldn't have found it difficult to resist responding, but that gentle sipping and tasting of his lips against hers was her undoing.

Her arms moved up about his neck as she pulled him down to her, not deepening the kiss but drinking him in in the same way he did her...

'Jonas, I— Oops!' came a female voice. 'Dorothy

wasn't in the outer office, and so—I didn't realise I would be interrupting anything.'

Danie had felt Jonas tense at the first sound of the woman's voice, his mouth instantly leaving hers. Although he made no effort to release Danie from his arms.

But even with her back towards the woman, her face slightly buried in Jonas's chest, Danie knew exactly who the other woman was. She might have only spoken to her once, and then only briefly—very briefly!—but that attractive voice wasn't one that Danie was ever likely to forget.

Nikki Trainer.

Ben's wife.

Jonas's sister…!

Somebody up there didn't like him, Jonas decided with an inward groan. A few minutes ago he had asked Danie what the chances had been of her and Nikki ever meeting, now he questioned the chances of his sister walking in on him actually kissing Danie!

Nikki rarely came to his consulting-rooms—none of his family did—and the fact that Nikki had chosen to do so, today of all days, seemed unbelievable to him.

But no, there she was, looking lovely in a peach-coloured silk suit, her face glowingly beautiful as she smiled across the room at him.

Jonas glanced down at Danie, only to find her looking up at him, green eyes dark with distress as she too recognised who his caller was. Of course—the two women had actually met each other on one occasion! Which meant that Nikki would recognise Danie as soon as she saw her face…!

He loved both these women to distraction, and, in the next few minutes, he knew he was going to hurt one of them very badly!

His arm moved possessively about Danie's shoulders as he turned her in the crook of his arm, both of them facing Nikki now as she stood near the doorway. He could feel Danie's tension at the confrontation, his arm tightening about her.

'Well, don't look so embarrassed, you two.' Nikki chuckled as she moved forward. 'Anyone would think you were a couple of naughty children who had been caught doing something you shouldn't!' She reached up to kiss Jonas in greeting before turning to include his companion in the warmth of her smile.

As Nikki came closer, Danie had moved away from Jonas, at the same time adjusting her baseball cap so that it came down low over her eyes, completely hiding her red hair, and putting her face into shadow.

She stood several feet away from them now, but nevertheless Jonas could feel the tension pulsing through her as she tensed for Nikki's recognition.

He drew in a ragged breath, turning back to his sister. 'Nikki—'

'I really should be going now, Jonas,' Danie interrupted, her voice slightly deeper than her normal tone. 'I've taken up enough of your time, and—'

'Please don't leave on my account,' Nikki said laughingly, lightly touching Danie's arm. 'I'm obviously the one who is gatecrashing here. I only called in because I wanted to share some good news with Jonas. I promise I'll be gone in a few minutes.'

Jonas had no idea whether or not Danie had noted the huge diamond solitaire ring twinkling brightly on his sister's left hand, or, even if she had, whether or not she knew of its significance. But Jonas certainly did; his sister's good news appeared to be her engagement to Graham...!

Which was certainly wonderful, and meant that his sister

was about to make a new start in her previously troubled life. But the circumstances for making such as announcement couldn't have been more unsuitable!

'I really do have to go,' Danie insisted, turning to leave. 'I— Thanks for all you did for my sister—er—Mr Noble,' she concluded awkwardly.

Mr Noble! God damn it, he was not going to start all over again where Danie was concerned. Okay, he accepted, as so obviously did Danie, that now was a little awkward, but he certainly was not going back to being called 'Mr Noble' by the woman he loved!

He caught up with her in the doorway, grasping her arm to turn her back to face him. 'I'll be at your apartment at seven o'clock this evening,' he told her.

Danie gave a brief glance in Nikki's direction. 'I don't think that's a good idea,' she muttered.

'Seven o'clock,' he repeated firmly, releasing her arm as she pulled against him; he did not want to bruise the woman he loved.

'If you think it will make any difference.' Danie sighed before striding off down the corridor towards the exit.

Jonas watched her for several seconds, loving her loose-limbed walk, the graceful sway of her hips. He loved everything about Danie—even her damned stubbornness!

'You should have introduced us, Jonas,' Nikki chided as he turned back into the room, his sister now sitting in one of the leather armchairs placed opposite his desk, slender legs crossed neatly at the knee.

He felt in need of a drink after the tension of the last few minutes, but realised that it was only four-thirty in the afternoon. 'Plenty of time for that later,' he dismissed lightly. 'So what's your good news, sis—or do I really need to ask?' He looked down at the glittering diamond ring on her wedding finger.

'Don't try that one on me, Jonas Noble,' Nikki told him reprovingly. 'I just walked into your office, your place of work, and found you kissing a very beautiful woman—and you didn't even introduce her to your baby sister!' She raised blonde brows over teasing blue eyes.

Nikki looked lovely today, glowingly beautiful, obviously extremely happy in her engagement to Graham; Jonas didn't have the right to trample on that. Not today, anyway...

'I don't recall introducing you to any woman I've kissed,' he returned dryly.

Nikki made a face. 'One or two when you were a teenager, but none since then, no,' she conceded.

'There you are, then,' he said with satisfaction, moving to sit behind his desk.

Nikki looked at him with mischievous eyes. 'Surely it's slightly different when the woman you were kissing is Danie Summer...?'

Jonas was glad that he had already sat down—otherwise he might just have fallen down, staring dazedly across the desk at his sister now. Nikki couldn't possibly have recognised Danie, not with that baseball cap hiding her face and hair. So how on earth—?

'Dorothy and I had a little chat last night, Jonas,' Nikki told him conversationally.

'You did what—?' he demanded furiously.

'Oh, do calm down, Jonas,' Nikki told him. 'Dorothy is almost like one of the family. I merely happened to mention to her that you seemed to have a new girlfriend, and—'

'My loyal and discreet personal assistant just happened to "mention" that her name is Danie Summer!' he bit out. 'Damn it, I—'

'Actually,' Nikki cut in, 'what Dorothy said was that you've been like a bear with a sore head this past week—'

'The state of my temper is no concern of either of you,' Jonas barked.

Nikki had known it was Danie beneath that baseball cap all the time! Then why hadn't she *said* something…?

'It is if the reason for that temper has anything to do with me, Jonas,' Nikki informed him softly, totally serious now, that teasing glint having left her eyes. 'Does it?'

He stood up, annoyed beyond words that Dorothy and Nikki had talked about him in this way. 'It did,' he confirmed. 'But I've decided over the last twenty-four hours that I will just have to sit you down and explain the situation to you. Because I intend making Danie my wife.'

Nikki remained calmly composed. 'I'm glad to hear it.'

'It's no good— You're *what*?' He gasped as her last comment finally penetrated his determined thoughts.

'Glad to hear it,' his sister repeated. 'Jonas, I've had months, years, to remember that last meeting I had with Danie. And the thing I remember most about her—apart from the fact that she's very beautiful,' she added, 'is the look of absolute horror on her face when Ben introduced me to her as his wife. She didn't know he was married, Jonas. And she was absolutely horrified at the realisation.' Nikki spoke with certainty. 'And she dumped Ben pretty quickly after that.'

'But the other evening you told Ben—'

'I *taunted* Ben,' his sister corrected. 'I knew damn well he hadn't been involved with Danie Summer after that day I met her at the restaurant. I'm not proud of the fact, but I had a private investigator follow Ben for several months after that day,' she admitted reluctantly. 'How do you think I came by the evidence to divorce him? Which, incidentally, had nothing to do with Danie Summer.'

Jonas had never questioned his sister's divorce, or the reasons for it, knew that the whole subject was a painful one for Nikki. But he had to admit, he was stunned by what Nikki was revealing now...

'You have to believe that I had no idea,' Nikki pleaded, 'when I made that comment to Ben the other evening, that the woman I had dragged you away from was the same Danie Summer. I would never do anything to hurt you, Jonas,' she said huskily. 'Or someone you love.'

He stayed motionless, finding this almost too incredible to take in. All this time he had been frightened of hurting Nikki with his love for Danie, only to learn that he needn't have been concerned after all.

'You do love her, don't you, Jonas?' Nikki prompted gently.

'Do I love her...!' He groaned. 'She's self-willed, out-spoken to the point of rudeness, abrasive, infuriating, ir-ritating, *kissable*—'

'You love her,' Nikki confirmed laughingly. 'And I'm here to tell you not to hold back on my account.' She sobered, looking at him intently. 'I made a mistake when I married Ben, but I have two beautiful children from that marriage, so I'm not going to complain. I certainly don't want you to compound that situation by denying yourself the woman you love out of mistaken loyalty to me!'

Jonas gave a rueful smile. 'I'm afraid that loyalty had already wavered and died. I intended asking Danie to be my wife—was actually in the middle of doing that when you arrived!—and then sorting out the problems it was going to cause within the family later,' he admitted.

Nikki grinned. 'So what's keeping you?'

'Hmm?' he murmured slightly dazedly, stunned to find that all the soul-searching he had done—and no doubt

Danie had done too, once she'd realised who his sister was!—had been completely unnecessary.

Nikki gave him a chiding look. 'You aren't really going to wait until seven o'clock to make that beautiful creature your own, are you? I was listening earlier.'

Jonas shook his head, grimacing. 'You know, I should actually be furious with you and Dorothy for having discussed my private life in this way!'

Nikki laughed. 'Show a woman a single man and she instantly starts matchmaking... We can't help it, Jonas, it's just part of our nature.'

'I'll forgive you this time,' he said. 'Just don't do it again!'

Nikki raised blonde brows. 'Once you and Danie are married there won't be a next time. Mummy is going to be absolutely thrilled,' she said happily as she stood up. 'Two weddings in the family!'

The longing he had to make Danie his wife seemed a possibility now.

If he could persuade Danie to say yes...!

CHAPTER TWELVE

'WHAT kept you?'

Danie came to an abrupt halt, staring at Jonas as he sat in the foyer of her apartment block. It was barely five-thirty, and he was the last person she'd expected to see. He had said seven o'clock, hadn't he...?

After leaving the clinic earlier she had called round to Harrie and Quinn's so that she might reassure herself of Andie's well-being. Her younger sister had been safely ensconced on the sofa in their sitting-room, the usually arrogantly self-assured Quinn fussing over her like a mother hen. A fact Harrie had found highly amusing.

In fact, Danie had still been smiling herself until she'd spotted a relaxed Jonas sitting waiting for her!

She had been stunned by things he'd said to her earlier. Had he really said he wanted to marry her? But he knew how impossible that was—the arrival of his sister Nikki only confirming how impossible!

She looked across at him warily now. 'I've been to see Andie,' she answered slowly.

Jonas stood up, grinning. 'To reassure yourself I wasn't lying concerning her whereabouts?'

Danie gave him an irritated frown as she strode purposefully towards the lift. 'I don't recall your coming into my thinking at all,' she snapped waspishly.

Jonas was laughing softly as he joined her. 'Spoken like the Danie I know—and love.'

She turned to give him one of her looks, relieved when the lift arrived at that moment. 'You said something similar to that earlier, Jonas,' she replied. 'It doesn't alter the fact that I was once involved with your brother-in-law.' She said this with deliberate hardness.

Didn't he realise that neither of them must ever lose sight of that fact? Danie felt it more than ever after meeting Nikki herself earlier. She seemed such a nice woman, obviously adored her only brother; Danie couldn't be instrumental in coming between brother and sister.

Jonas eyed her mockingly as the lift began to ascend with the two of them inside it. 'Exactly what is your definition of "involved"?' he drawled.

She gave him another glare. 'Involved is involved, Jonas,' she stated, determined to remain angry with him; it was her only defence!

'Did you love him?'

She glared darkly across at Jonas in the confines of the lift. 'That has nothing to do with—'

'I'm interested, that's all,' Jonas said.

Had she loved Ben? She had been fascinated by him at the beginning of their relationship, had found his involvement in television interesting, had been attracted to his dark good looks. But had she been in love with him, even before she'd learnt of his marriage...?

'No, I didn't love him,' she answered without hesitation, knowing that it was Jonas she loved—and that she had never felt anything like this achingly painful emotion before in her life. Certainly not for Ben. He had damaged her pride more than her heart.

'Good.' Jonas nodded his satisfaction.

Danie eyed him warily again as he added nothing to that brief statement. Didn't he realise he was just making this situation worse? There could be no future for the two of them. At least, not one that would be acceptable to Danie.

She wasn't prepared to be hidden away somewhere so that none of his family should ever know about her.

'I don't see what's good about it,' Danie said as she walked determinedly into her apartment, going straight into the kitchen to put the kettle on for a cup of tea.

'From my point of view it's very good,' Jonas responded, having followed her, sitting down at the pine table as he watched her moving about the room preparing the tea things.

'How did you explain me away to your sister?' Danie was determined he shouldn't lose sight of the obstacles that stood between the two of them ever being together!

He relaxed back in his chair. 'As it happens, I didn't have to.'

Danie's hand shook slightly as she placed the cups on their saucers. Was Nikki so accustomed to seeing unknown women in the arms of her brother that she had stopped even asking? Somehow that explanation did not go down well with Danie at all!

'I'm glad to see you didn't consign my roses to the bin.' Jonas spoke softly.

The yellow roses still stood in a vase in the sitting-room. Not because she hadn't wanted to eliminate every sign of Jonas's presence in her home, but because she simply couldn't wantonly destroy something so beautiful.

'Roses…?' She was deliberately vague. 'Oh, those.' She pretended to remember the golden blooms he had given her on Wednesday evening. 'I haven't been home much in the last couple of days,' she dismissed, placing a cup of tea in front of him, a sugar bowl at its side.

Ridiculous, she thought to herself as she picked up her own cup of tea and sat down opposite him at the table; she loved this man, and yet she didn't even know if he took sugar in his tea!

Jonas smiled across at her. 'This is better service than you gave me on the plane last Saturday!' He ignored the sugar and took a sip of the hot brew.

Well, at least she now knew he didn't take sugar in his tea. Although what good that was going to do her, she had no idea; the possibility of them taking tea together again seemed extremely remote!

'I could hardly fly the plane and serve you tea at the same time,' she observed.

Jonas eyed her, amused. 'And here was I thinking you're a woman who can do anything!'

Danie avoided meeting his mocking gaze. 'Within reason,' she muttered.

He reached out and covered one of her hands with his own. 'Danie—'

She pulled her hand away as if she had been burnt. 'Jonas, I have to tell you, having to say goodbye to you twice in one day is not something I'm particularly enjoying,' she said shakily.

'Why not?' he prompted.

She looked across at him with pained eyes. 'I'm just not!' she bit out tautly, so tense now she felt as if her spine might snap. Why did he keep prolonging this? Why didn't he just leave her alone?'

'Does it have to be goodbye?' Jonas said huskily.

Anger flared briefly in her eyes. 'I'm not the sort of woman mistresses are made of, Jonas,' she told him.

'I'm glad to hear it.' He spoke sternly. 'It's not the role in my life I had in mind for you at all—'

Her mouth twisted humourlessly. 'Just as well—*Rome* would probably beat you to a pulp when he found out!' she assured him.

Jonas sat forward, the intensity of his gaze forcing her to look at him. 'That's better,' he said as she reluctantly met his gaze. 'Danie, I love you,' he told her forcefully. 'I love everything about you. And I can't imagine my life now without you in it. Will you marry me?'

She couldn't have turned her eyes away from his now if she had tried. She loved him too. Everything about him. And imagining her own life without him in it was like looking at a barren wasteland. But—

There would always be that but between Jonas and herself…!

Had he misjudged Danie's feelings? She had never said that she loved him. He had told her earlier how he felt about her, but she hadn't reciprocated…

He watched her as she stood up abruptly to move away from the table. The baseball cap still hid the glory of her fiery hair, its peak hiding the expression in her eyes. But he could see her mouth, that delicious, kissable mouth— and he was sure he wasn't mistaken about the slight trembling of her lips before she turned away from him. Unbelievable as it seemed, Danie looked as if she was about to cry!

Jonas stood up slowly, moving to stand in front of her, his hand gentle as he reached out and removed the baseball cap before tilting her face up towards his. He hadn't been mistaken; tears were spilling over her long lashes to fall silkenly down her cheeks.

'Danie…!' he groaned, moved beyond words at this show of emotion. 'Danie, I love you,' he told her as he gathered her in his arms and held her close against him.

'Oh, God, Jonas, I love you too!' she choked, burying her face against his chest as she began to sob in earnest.

Danie loved him! Nothing else mattered. Nothing!

He pulled back to look down at her with eyes that shone brightly with his own love for her, reaching up to smooth the tears from her cheeks. 'Danie, Nikki already knew who you were when she came to my office today,' he told her as Danie's tears came to a halt, and she stared up at him apprehensively. 'Did she look like an angry or avenging woman?' he teased lightly in an effort to reassure Danie.

She swallowed hard. 'Not exactly...' she acknowledged slowly.

'Because she isn't,' Jonas told her happily. 'I have to admit, I've had more than my fair share of uncomfortable moments where you and Ben Trainer are concerned, but—'

'You see,' Danie pulled away from him. 'It doesn't matter if we love each other, Jonas. Your sister will never get over the fact that I made an idiot of myself over her husband. And you'll never be able to forget that I once inadvertently got myself involved with a married man!'

Jonas could easily imagine how angry she would have been once she'd found out Ben was married. He wouldn't like to have been in Ben's shoes during the meeting that followed Danie's discovery!

'When I said I had uncomfortable moments where you and Ben were concerned, Danie, I was referring to my own fear that you might still care for him.' Jonas considered at that moment that it would be less painful to Danie not to tell her about Ben's claim that night at Nikki's house of being able to snap his fingers and Danie would come running. She was likely to do the other man physical harm if she knew about that. Not that Ben didn't deserve it, but Jonas would prefer her to stay out of jail, if possible!

'Don't add insult to injury, Jonas,' she cried. 'I can't stand the man! And I left Ben in no doubt about how I felt about him when I saw him again that evening after I was introduced to Nikki.' She shook her head disgustedly. 'I couldn't believe how I had ever been taken in by him!'

Jonas gave a sad smile. 'I've come to realise that the last couple of days. So let's just forget about him, hmm?' he encouraged. 'Nikki has,' he added before Danie could make a reply. 'She's moved on, Danie. She's in love with someone else. The two of them intend getting married. In fact,' he continued, 'before I left her earlier I had to dissuade her from suggesting we have a double wedding with her and Graham!'

His sister had thought it a wonderful idea. But Jonas had his own ideas about the wedding he and Danie might have—and it did not involve sharing their big day with another couple.

Danie was staring up at him as if she didn't quite believe him, and he couldn't exactly blame her for feeling the way she did. He had been concerned about Nikki's reaction himself. Although it would have been a reaction, with the realisation of how much he loved Danie, he had been willing to ride out, knowing that he had to have Danie in his life.

At any price.

It was a price he had been willing to pay, although he couldn't say he wasn't relieved it was one that wouldn't be asked of him, after all. That would have been no way for the two of them to begin their life together.

'Danie.' He took a firm grasp of her arms. 'Will you marry me?'

She took a big breath. 'I have one more question to ask before I answer that,' she said. 'Why were you so tired last Saturday at the airport? And how close were you to Grace Cowley?'

Jonas gave a satisfied grin at these signs of her own jealousy where he was concerned. 'That was two questions,' he rebuked. 'But I'll answer them anyway. I had spent most of Friday night bringing a baby girl into the world. And the closest I've ever been to Grace is as doctor and patient; I'm her obstetrician, Danie. I was in attendance at the birth of her twins!'

Danie moistened her lips, the mere act making Jonas want to kiss her.

'Now answer the question, damn it, woman!' he growled frustratedly, sure that it wasn't usually this difficult to get an answer to a marriage proposal.

Danie continued to look at him searchingly for several long seconds, and then she began to smile. 'I don't think I have anything else planned for three weeks today,' she finally replied.

Now it was Jonas's turn to look perplexed. 'Three weeks today...?' he repeated.

Danie nodded, moving forward to put her arms about his waist. 'If we're going to get married, let's just get it done, hmm?' She arched one teasing brow as she looked up at him.

Danie Summer—soon to be Noble. Beautiful. Infuriating. Soon to be his.

In three weeks, in fact...

EPILOGUE

DANIE gave a happy sigh as she snuggled into Jonas's shoulder. 'I wish everyone could be as happy as we are,' she murmured contentedly.

'Impossible,' Jonas breathed lovingly into her hair.

Danie chuckled huskily, looking around the crowded table, seeing all the people she loved. Her father had insisted that she and Jonas had to celebrate their engagement a week before the wedding itself, inviting all of Jonas's family, as well as her own, to dinner at one of London's leading hotels.

This evening was the result. Danie looked at all the smiling faces: Jonas's mother, his eldest sister and her husband Jack; Nikki with her fiancé Graham; the irrepressible Dorothy; Harrie and Quinn, Andie, Audrey, and finally her father—here she came to an abrupt halt.

Because her father was far from smiling!

'I thought your father approved of our engagement,' Jonas said, obviously having been doing exactly the same as Danie.

'He does,' she confirmed.

'He doesn't look very happy.' Jonas grimaced.

'He and Audrey had some sort of disagreement a couple of weeks ago, and he's been in a foul mood ever since.' Danie shrugged.

'Audrey seems happy enough.' Jonas frowned.

Danie glanced across at her friend and her father's assistant, Audrey laughing at something Quinn had just said to her. 'Yes, she does, doesn't she?' she said. 'Then it's

184

probably nothing serious. Daddy can be a bit too fond of wanting his own way, but Audrey has learnt how to deal with it.'

'I can think of someone else that likes her own way,' Jonas teased.

Danie looked at him. 'Why, who on earth do you mean, Mr Noble?' Her lips twitched as she held back a smile.

Smiling seemed to be something she had done a lot of lately. Not least of all being after her initial meeting with Nikki after she and Jonas had decided to get married. The other woman couldn't have been warmer, or more welcoming to her family, putting Danie completely at her ease after the first few minutes. In fact, the two women had been out shopping together today in search of a wedding outfit for Nikki!

'Oh, I'm not complaining—Mrs Noble-to-be,' Jonas assured her huskily. 'In fact, I'm rather relieved you want us to be married so quickly; I don't think I could wait any longer than next weekend to make love with you!'

It had been a decision they had made together, after Danie had self-consciously admitted to Jonas that she had never had a lover. Their wedding night would be everything it was supposed to be.

Danie was as eager for that night as Jonas was, already sure that their lovemaking was going to be beautiful. After all, how could it be anything else? They were the missing part of each other...!

'I love you, Jonas,' she told him intensely. 'So very, very much.'

'And I love you too, Danie.' His arm tightened about her shoulders. 'So very, very much!'

It was enough.

And it always would be...

To Make a
Marriage

CAROLE MORTIMER

PROLOGUE

'TWICE a bridesmaid, never a bride,' he teased close to her scented earlobe.

The perfume of Andie, as he always thought of it. He had no idea what the name of the perfume was that she always wore, he just knew that whenever he smelt it, either on Andie or someone else, he was filled with warm thoughts of her...

She turned to face him now, a welcoming smile on her peach-coloured lips, green eyes glowing warmly as she reached up to kiss him in greeting.

Perfection. There was no other way to describe Andrea Summer. And today, in the frothy peach-coloured satin and lace of her bridesmaid's dress, with her long blonde hair a profusion of silky curls down the length of her spine, entwined with tiny peach-coloured tea-roses, she looked like a fairy-tale princess.

She laughed softly, a throatily husky laugh that sent shivers of pleasure down *his* spine. 'I think you'll find that it's "Three times a bridesmaid",' she corrected softly.

'It is?' he drawled with pretended ignorance. 'But you have to admit, your clock's ticking away, Andie; you're almost twenty-six now,' he continued mockingly, 'and both your older sisters have married in the last couple of months.'

She shrugged dismissively as she glanced over affectionately at those two sisters with their new husbands; the eldest, Harrie, had been married to Quinn McBride for sev-

5

eral weeks now, and this was Danie's wedding day to Jonas Noble.

'They have obviously found the right men for them,' Andie murmured fondly.

His own smile slipped for the fraction of a second, before he regained control. 'No "right man" for you yet, hmm, Andie?'

She laughed softly once again. 'I would have thought you, of all people would have known there's actually no such thing as the right person; it's all a case of taking pot luck!' she taunted contrarily.

Him, of all people...? Yes, he had always given the impression he was a confirmed bachelor; in fact, he had made a religion out of it! But this young woman—lovely to look at, always elegantly dressed, with a mischievously warm sense of humour—if she were only aware of it, could have changed all that with one crook of her little finger...!

How long had he felt that way about her? For ever, it seemed to him. Oh, there had been women in his life in the past, beautiful women, accomplished women, brunettes and redheads, as well as blondes, but none of them in any way had measured up to Andie.

'I hope you don't intend telling Harrie and Danie that!' He smiled.

Andie didn't return his smile. 'I don't happen to believe that's true for them; I'm as sure as they are that Quinn and Jonas are the right men for them.'

He was bored with the subject of Harrie and Danie; it was Andie he was interested in. It always had been. 'It's really good to see you here today,' he told her sincerely.

Andie frowned at the statement. 'I would hardly miss my own sister's wedding!'

'I can think of a couple of other family occasions you've missed this summer,' he persisted. 'The summer fête,' he added as she looked at him questioningly, referring to the fête held every June at Rome Summer's—Andie father's—estate. 'A family weekend at the estate a week later. Your father said that you had the flu.'

Andie shrugged, a smile playing about those peach-coloured lips. 'If that's what Daddy said, then that's what I had,' she dismissed. 'No mystery there.'

He took two glasses of champagne from a passing waiter; the wedding reception was being held at one of London's leading hotels. He held one of the glasses out to Andie, but was surprised when she shook her head and reached for a glass of orange juice instead. 'Don't tell me you've given up drinking champagne?' he exclaimed, knowing that in the past champagne was the only alcohol Andie had ever drunk.

'It's a new diet I'm trying out,' she dismissed, taking a sip of the juice.

'Diet?' He scowled, looking down at her already more than slender frame. 'You're far too thin as it is—'

'You're starting to sound like Rome now,' Andie taunted, blonde brows raised as she looked up at him from under thick dark lashes.

An irritated flush coloured the hardness of his cheeks. The last thing he wanted was to sound like her father, damn it! It was the very last thing he felt like whenever he was around her. Although, perhaps, to Andie, fourteen years his junior, that was exactly what he seemed...

'It's being featured in *Gloss* next month,' Andie continued lightly, referring to the monthly magazine of which she was senior editor. 'I thought I would try it and see if it really works.'

He scowled. 'You need to diet like—'

'You need to earn any more money?' she finished with

barbed sweetness. 'Have you never heard the phrase, "you can never be too rich or too thin"?'

His gaze narrowed thoughtfully at that slight edge to her tone. They had met briefly a couple of times during the last few months, never long enough to have a real conversation, as they were doing now, but he had been sure the flu excuse Rome had given him had been genuine and it hadn't been because Andie had been deliberately avoiding him. Now he wasn't so sure...

'I've heard it,' he grated. 'But I don't think you believe it any more than I do.'

'Really?' Her manner had definitely changed now, that hardness still there in her voice. 'We've known each other a long time, granted—but I don't think that gives you the right to tell me what I think!'

He reached out and grasped her arm. 'Andie—'

'I think you're going to have to excuse me,' she cut in firmly, having glanced across the room to where the bride and groom were now taking their seats at the top table in preparation for the start of the meal that was about to be served. 'It looks as if I'm needed.'

She was needed, all right. By him! He had felt this way about her since the day he'd looked at her, on her eighteenth birthday, and realised she was no longer an impish child but a beautiful, desirable woman. Almost eight years ago, he groaned inwardly.

His hold on her arm tightened. 'Andie, have dinner with me one evening next week,' he prompted forcefully.

She turned to look at him with cool green eyes. 'I don't think that's a good idea, do you?'

Good idea, be damned. This woman, it seemed, made him lose all sense of what was a good idea every time he came near her!

'I really do have to go,' she insisted, gently but firmly

removing her arm from his grasp before placing the half-drunk glass of juice in his now free hand. 'I hope you enjoy the rest of the wedding,' she added with banal politeness.

He had never enjoyed a wedding in his life, had determined long ago that he would never marry. But as he watched Andie walk gracefully across the room to take her place at the top table; he knew he would do anything to make Andie his own. Anything...

CHAPTER ONE

'I'M REALLY sorry to interrupt, Miss Summer, but there's someone outside to see you!'

Andie looked up with a frown, having been poring over a fashion layout that lay sprawled across the top of her desk. She had asked April not to disturb her for an hour, desperately trying to meet today's deadline, but as she looked at her secretary's expectantly flushed face her frown deepened.

'And who might that someone be, April?' she prompted dryly, knowing it had to be someone important—or April wouldn't have disturbed her at all.

April drew in a deep, excited breath. 'It's—'

'Adam Munroe,' the man himself announced with a smile as he strolled into the office, dressed as impeccably as usual, his charcoal-grey suit tailored across the width of his shoulders and the narrowness of his waist and thighs, his pale blue shirt made of silk, only the bright blue and yellow pattern of his tie giving any indication of the less than conservative nature that lurked beneath his outward appearance.

The arrival of Adam Munroe in the office was reason enough for April to have gone all aflutter, Andie allowed ruefully as she slowly put her marker pen down on the desk-top.

A long-time friend of her father's, Adam was a well-known film producer, but, with his tall, rugged good looks, and silver-blonde hair, he was gorgeous enough to have starred in one of the films he'd financed.

10

'Thank you, April,' Andie told her secretary dismissively, a slightly knowing smile playing about her lips as she watched April's slow retreat out of the room, the girl's avid gaze fixed on Adam the whole time.

Not that Andie could exactly blame April for that, either; Adam had been breaking female hearts with his charming elusiveness ever since she could remember. Elusive, because Adam always made it plain to the women he became involved with that the friendship would never lead to a permanent relationship. Not very romantic, but it certainly didn't seem to deter those women from becoming involved with him. In fact, the opposite!

Andie stood up slowly. 'After totally captivating my secretary so that I doubt I will get any more work out of her today—to what do I owe the honour of this visit, Adam?' she teased as she moved forward to kiss him lightly on the cheek.

He grinned, warm pale grey eyes surrounded by long dark lashes. 'I was just passing, and wondered if you would care to join me for lunch?'

She raised blonde brows. 'Isn't eleven-thirty in the morning a little early for lunch?' she queried.

He shrugged, making himself comfortable on the edge of her desk, disturbing several of the photographs that lay there in the process. 'Not when you haven't had any breakfast yet, no,' he observed pointedly.

Andie gave a wry smile, shaking her head. 'Hectic night again, hmm, Adam?' she taunted, moving back behind the desk to look up at him with mocking green eyes.

'Not particularly,' he replied dryly. 'I don't seem to be sleeping too well at the moment.'

'You—'

'Alone, that is,' he put in before she could complete her comment.

Andie chuckled. 'Maybe that's your problem; you obviously aren't used to it!'

'Very funny.' He scowled. 'The problem with you Summer sisters is that you have no respect for your elders!'

Andie held back her smile this time, although it lurked in the brightness of her eyes and the slight curve of her lips. 'Have Harrie and Danie been casting aspersions too?' She referred to her two older, now married, sisters.

Adam gave a grimace. 'When haven't the three of you teased me unmercifully?'

It was true, of course. But Andie and her sisters had known Adam, almost as an honorary uncle, for twenty years, and the fact that most women fell over themselves to meet him had been a constant source of amusement to the three of them as they'd been growing up. School friends, and then university friends, and eventually work friends, had constantly sought invitations to their father's home in the hope that Adam might be a guest at the same time.

'You know you love it, Adam,' she said.

'What I would love is some lunch.' He stood up. 'Going to keep me company?' He quirked blonde brows enquiringly.

'I'm very busy, Adam.' She gave a weary look at the layout on her desk.

'You still have to eat,' he persisted.

'Not at eleven-thirty in the morning, I don't!' she rejoined.

Adam gave an impatient sigh. 'I don't usually have this much trouble getting a woman to have lunch with me!'

Andie laughed throatily. 'A little denial is good for the soul!'

'It's *my* soul,' he returned. 'Please allow me to know what is and isn't good for it—and almost having to beg you to have lunch with me is not good for it!' he assured her scathingly.

If he weren't a mature self-assured man of almost forty, Andie would have said he had the look of a petulant little boy at that moment—one that couldn't get his own way!

She shook her head. 'You aren't begging, Adam. And I wouldn't allow you to, either,' she added seriously. 'But I'm not being deliberately difficult; I really am extremely busy.' She indicated the photographs scattered over her desk-top.

'Rome is of the opinion that you work too hard—and I have to agree with him when you can't even take the customary hour for lunch,' Adam told her, eyes narrowed on the slenderness of her frame in the silky plum-coloured trouser suit and pale cream blouse.

She had lost weight the last few months, Andie inwardly acknowledged. But she also knew it was a weight she would shortly regain. And more!

That thought sobered her somewhat, and looking up at Adam, 'Just when did you and my father have this cosy discussion concerning the amount of work I do or don't do?' she prompted.

'At Danie's wedding on Saturday,' Adam drawled challengingly. 'And there was nothing cosy—or underhand—about it; I merely remarked that you were looking at little pale, and Rome said that you're working too hard. That was the extent of our conversation concerning you,' he finished decisively.

'So you thought you would take pity on me today and invite me out to lunch.' Andie nodded, green eyes sparkling with anger now. 'It's very kind of you, Adam—'

'Don't get all polite on me, young lady,' he came back. 'For one thing—I wouldn't recognise you if you did! And for another—I'm not being in the least polite.'

'You just hate to eat alone,' she guessed.

Adam gave a reluctant smile, shaking his head as he raised his gaze exasperatedly to the ceiling. 'Either this used to be easier, or I'm just getting old!'

It wasn't either of those things, but she was busy—and, more to the point, she did not want to go out to lunch with Adam. Her life was complicated enough already at the moment, without that!

'It was a lovely wedding on Saturday, wasn't it?' She changed the subject—to one she knew he would find distasteful. Weddings and Adam Munroe just did not mix!

'Lovely,' he echoed with predictable sarcasm. 'First Harrie took the plunge, and then Danie on Saturday; I expect it will be your turn next!' he added disgustedly.

Andie looked down at her ringless left hand—knowing it would remain that way too. The man she loved, she just couldn't have...

'I doubt that very much,' she answered gruffly, blinking back sudden, unaccustomed tears. She had become so emotional lately! Definitely one of the symptoms of her condition that she wasn't too happy about. 'I'm destined to be an old maid, I'm afraid,' she explained self-derisively.

'Hey, I was only teasing.' Adam seemed to have seen that glitter of tears in her eyes, coming around the desk to put his arm about her narrow shoulders. 'There's plenty of time yet for you to fall in love and get married; you're only twenty-five, Andie—'

'Twenty-six in a couple of months' time,' she put in huskily, knowing he had completely misunderstood the reason for her emotion. It wasn't a question of falling in love and getting married; if she couldn't have the man she loved—which she most certainly couldn't!—then she wouldn't marry at all. Ever.

'That old, hmm?' Adam murmured softly, raising her chin to look into her face. 'Almost ancient, in fact.'

Andie shook her head, straightening away from him. 'You misunderstood the reason for my—emotion, I'm afraid, Adam,' she spoke firmly. 'I just find it very odd to realise that Harrie and Danie are no longer just my sisters, but are now Quinn and Jonas's wives.'

And she did find it strange. Three months ago none of the sisters had shown signs of marrying anyone, the three of them extremely close, so much so that they had never particularly needed other friends. And now to share not one of her sisters with a husband, but both of them, within the space of two months, was a little hard to take. Especially now...

Adam looked sympathetic. 'Harrie's the wife of a banker. And Danie—madcap Danie—' he shook his head a little dazedly 'is now the wife of a doctor. Amazing!'

It did take some adjusting to, Andie agreed. But there would be a lot more adjusting for Andie to do in her own life in the near future, than just to that of her sisters' marriages...

'Andie, come and have lunch with me?' Adam cajolled. 'If for no other reason than it will do wonders for my reputation to be seen with a very beautiful young woman!' he added encouragingly.

Andie looked sceptical. 'Another one?' she parried, knowing Adam had a succession of beautiful young women in his life.

He gave an irritated sigh, moving back impatiently. 'You know, I think Rome should have smacked your backside more when you were young enough to take notice!' He stood up.

'Mummy would never have let him.' Andie spoke confidently on behalf of her gentle-natured mother.

Adam sobered. 'True,' he agreed distractedly.

Andie knew the reason for that distraction. Had known it for some time. Adam had been in love with her mother…

He had been around a lot when Andie and her sisters had been children, appearing at the estate most weekends. Despite a dislike of the countryside and all things connected to it… It had only been as Andie had grown older that she'd realised the reason Adam had put aside his aversion and visited them anyway. Ten years ago her mother had died, and if the three sisters and their father had been heartbroken at the loss, then Adam had been inconsolable.

Because he had been in love with Barbara…!

Andie had been stunned by the realisation at the time, although it hadn't been a realisation she'd shared with her sisters, somehow finding the subject too difficult to discuss with her already distressed siblings. But she had wondered how her father would react, knowing Rome couldn't help but see the younger man's emotional state. Strangely enough Rome had seemed to draw comfort from the fact that Adam had loved Barbara too, an unbreakable bond developing between the two men, and now, ten years later, their friendship was stronger than ever.

Andie shot Adam a questioning look. 'Does this mean you've withdrawn your invitation to lunch?'

Adam looked crossly at her. 'No, it doesn't,' he snapped. 'And I'm no longer asking—I'm telling! Whatever that stuff is—' he waved an uninterested hand over the fashion layout she had been working on '—you'll deal with it much more efficiently once you've had something to eat.'

The fact that he was right didn't make the invitation any more palatable; she did not take kindly to being ordered about. By anyone!

She shook her head. 'The answer is still no, I'm afraid, Adam—'

'You aren't afraid at all,' he cut in harshly. 'Damn it, Andie, you and I used to be friends—'

'We still are,' she assured him coolly, completely unruffled by his loss of temper. Her father had a quiet way of doing the same thing when he couldn't get his own way, too... 'But as I've already stated—several times—I'm busy.'

'Fine,' Adam bit back, his jaw clenched. 'Perhaps I'll see if April wants to join me instead.'

Andie gave a grin. 'I have no doubt she would love to. But I'm also sure her fiancé would have a few things to say about it!'

Adam frowned darkly. 'You never used to be this difficult, Andie,' he said slowly.

She straightened in her high-backed chair, the sunshine coming in the window behind her giving her long hair the colour of ripe corn as it lay in a loose plait down her back, fine tendrils curling beside her ears and over her smooth brow.

'I never used to be a lot of things, Adam,' she told him tautly, the words tinged with an unhappiness she hoped he couldn't detect; the last thing she needed in her life at the moment was an over-curious Adam Munroe. It had been difficult enough, initially, to deal with an over-anxious Rome, without having Adam on her case now, too!

Adam looked appreciatively about the luxury of her executive office. 'You obviously enjoy being numero uno of *Gloss*,' he observed.

She gave an acknowledging inclination of her head. 'In the same way you enjoy running your own film production company,' she replied noncommittally, having the distinct feeling Adam was just making conversation now, delaying his departure for as long as he possibly could. Although why he should want to do that she couldn't imagine...

Adam gave her a considering look. 'Does that mean you've become a career woman, Andie?'

Not exactly! Especially as this was the last week she would be working on the magazine for some months to come. Which was another reason she was so determined to make sure everything was done perfectly for this, her final issue, for some time...

But despite the fact Adam was a close family friend, she had no intention of telling him any of that. Her nine months' leave of absence wasn't public knowledge, and she preferred that it remain that way!

'Not at all,' she dismissed lightly. 'Will you be coming down to the estate this weekend?' she asked, her expression still deceptively noncommittal.

Grey eyes narrowed warily. 'Why?'

'No particular reason,' Andie said casually. 'I just thought I should warn you, if you were, that Rome is not in the best of moods at the moment.'

Which was definitely an understatement! Her sister Danie had promised a few weeks ago to do everything she could to distract their father's attention from Andie and her present dilemma, but as it turned out Danie hadn't needed to do that; Audrey, their father's assistant for the last twelve years, had managed to do that quite successfully for them!

'I didn't think he looked too happy on Saturday,' Adam said. 'But I put that down to the losing-a-daughter syndrome.'

Andie chuckled softly. 'Daddy has been trying to give us away for years!'

Adam grinned. 'I wouldn't put it quite like that. He wouldn't give any of you away to just anyone.'

'That's comforting to know,' Andie replied dryly—although she knew that was actually the case. Luckily for Harrie and Danie their father approved of their choice of husband—otherwise one or both of them would have had a battle on their hands!

'Rome just wants a grandson to whom he can pass his business empire,' Adam assured her knowingly.

Andie looked down unseeingly at the photographs on her desk-top. 'And if we should all produce daughters?' she prompted gruffly.

Adam laughed, seeming unaware of her distraction. 'Then you'll all just have to keep trying until that male heir materialises!'

'I'm sure Harrie and Danie will be thrilled to know that!' Andie gave a hollow laugh.

'Look on the bright side, Andie,' Adam drawled. 'Until you find a husband it isn't a problem that need bother you!'

How little he knew…!

She didn't look well, Adam decided concernedly. Oh, there was no doubting Andie was as beautiful as ever. That would never change. Apart from her blonde hair, which she had inherited from her father, she looked exactly like her mother. And Barbara had been the most beautiful woman he had ever known…

But he knew Rome was worried about Andie, and, after seeing her at the wedding on Saturday, Adam had to admit he felt the same way. Andie still looked good enough to eat, but there was an air of fragility about her now that he had never noticed before, and a haunted look to those deep green eyes.

'So I really can't tempt you, then? To come out to lunch with me,' he pressed as she looked at him beneath mockingly raised brows.

She sighed her impatience. 'I've already explained—'

'Several times,' he agreed tersely. 'Will *you* be at the estate this weekend?'

Now her expression became guarded. 'Why?'

It never used to be like this between them! He had always had a close friendship with all of the Summer sisters, and Andie, as the youngest, had been able to twist him around her little finger. But there was a barrier between them now—and it wasn't a situation he was particularly happy with.

'No particular reason,' he replied. 'But it's a fact that I have been invited down this weekend, and, if Rome is as bad-tempered as you say he is, it might be nice to have some happier company along!'

Andie gave a loud laugh. 'Ever the bluntly honest Adam!'

He grimaced. 'You wouldn't know me if I suddenly became all charming and polite!'

'True,' she acknowledged evenly. 'It might be interesting to see, though,' she added softly.

Was it his imagination, or was there a wistful note in her voice…?

Wishful thinking, Adam, he instantly told himself.

Although there didn't seem to be anyone in her life at the moment; Andie had attended the wedding alone on Saturday. But Adam knew there had been men in her life in the past, and to even imagine that she might have been nurturing a secret passion for him all these years was the height of stupidity on his part.

'So what's wrong with Rome?' he abruptly changed the subject.

Andie frowned as she obviously readjusted her thoughts to coincide with his. 'Audrey has handed in her notice.'

'*Audrey* has?' Adam gasped disbelievingly.

Because he *didn't* believe it. Audrey Archer had been Rome's personal assistant for so long now, had become part of the Summer family life, it was almost impossible to think of any of them without including Audrey in the equation.

Andie gave an unhappy grimace. 'We're all as surprised as you obviously are, Rome most of all—'

''Surprised isn't exactly the way I would have described my own reaction,' Adam said.

'No...?' Andie looked puzzled by his words.

Were all of the Summer family blind? Adam wondered impatiently. It had been obvious to him for years that the beautiful Audrey was in love with her employer. Just as it had also been obvious that, although Rome might be unaware of it, to all intents and purposes, apart from the physical side of things—which, Adam had decided long ago, was none of his business!—Audrey had been Rome's wife in everything but name for at least the last ten years!

Audrey went everywhere with Rome, had dedicated the last twelve years of her life to all of the Summer family, becoming a surrogate mother to the three girls after their mother had died ten years ago; what on earth could have prompted her decision to leave them all now...?

With blinding clarity Adam suddenly knew the answer to that, too. Audrey had lost hope, had given up any romantic dreams she might have had of Rome one day coming to realise he loved her too.

Adam, probably more than most people, knew exactly how painful it was to love someone in that hopeless way. To have to stand in the background and watch the person one loved as they lived out their life, possibly with someone else, because that love would never, could never, be returned.

But the saddest part of this situation was that Adam was sure Rome actually did love Audrey—he just didn't know that he did! Ten years ago Rome had been devastated by Barbara's death, hadn't even seen there were other women in the world in the two years that had followed. Since that time Adam knew the other man had confined his relationships to brief, meaningless affairs, never seeing the love, or the beautiful woman who had felt that love, that was right in front of his nose!

'And what are any of you doing to try and stop her going?' he bit out tersely.

Andie looked taken aback at his accusing tone. 'What can we do?' she said. 'We're all upset, naturally—'

'Oh, naturally!' Adam came back scornfully.

Her eyes blazed deeply green as she glared at him. 'But Audrey seems to have made up her mind,' she continued determinedly, 'and so—'

'Hell!' Adam butted in furiously. 'Are all of the Summer family so wrapped up in their own lives, their own feelings, that none of you can see what this must be doing to Audrey?'

Andie's cheeks were pale now. 'Aren't you being a little unfair, Adam—?'

'No, I'm not, damn it, not even a *little* bit!' His hands were clenched at his sides. 'But I can tell you now that you've helped make my mind up about going to the estate this weekend. I shall most certainly be there—if only to lend Audrey a shoulder to cry on!' he blazed angrily.

Andie's gaze was cold now as she looked across at him unblinkingly, although a nerve pulsed in her throat. 'I'm sure she'll be very grateful—'

'You know something, Andie, I came here today full of good intentions, hoped we could share an enjoyable lunch together,' he told her harshly. 'But after listening to this I don't have any appetite for food, either. For goodness' sake, Audrey is a part of your family!' he groaned protestingly.

As I am, he could have added. But didn't. Because if

Audrey, who had been closer to Rome than anyone else these last ten years, and a second mother to Harrie, Danie, and Andie, could be allowed to just leave their lives without protest, then what chance did he have of meaning anything more to any of them?

It was certainly a leveller. One that made him feel slightly sick...

Andie gave a deep sigh. 'I'm well aware of that, Adam,' she said. 'And I have tried talking to her—'

'Obviously with little result if she still intends leaving,' he rasped.

She eyed him suspiciously. 'Maybe you will have more success this weekend,' she said softly.

Adam's mouth set angrily. It wasn't just because of Audrey, he inwardly acknowledged, shaken beyond words at the way she was being allowed to fade out of the lives of the Summer family. Could he, ultimately, expect the same fate?

He had met Rome almost twenty years ago, a young man of nearly twenty himself, with big ideas, and no money to back them up. Rome had been very much a business gambler in those days, and for several years he had become Adam's financial backer, Adam eventually in a position to pay him back, while at the same time being self-supporting. The last fifteen years had undoubtedly been highly successful ones for Adam, so much so that his film production company was worth millions.

His unhappy beginnings had been put behind him. In fact, they were something he preferred never to think about. But as a result, having no family of his own to speak of, over the years he had come to feel as much part of the Summer family as Audrey must do, had always regarded Rome as the older brother he had never been privileged to

have, and he had always looked on the three girls as indulged nieces. They were his family!

He had been a fool to think nothing would ever happen
to change that...

'Maybe I will,' he agreed grimly. 'It's a sure fact someone has to try!'

Andie looked at him wordlessly for several long, tension-
filled minutes, until finally she turned back to the work on
her desk-top. 'Perhaps I'll see you there,' she muttered,
once again picking up her marker pen.

'Perhaps you will,' he rejoined grimly, turning on his
heel and walking purposefully to the door. But he paused
before leaving and his hand on the door-handle, he inserted,
'If you can manage to drag yourself away from your own
interests long enough!'

Those green eyes were hard as emeralds as she looked
across at him. 'I'm sure that if you can I can,' she finally
answered in freezing tones.

Adam shot her a glittering glance through narrowed lids
before swinging the door open, closing it determinedly behind him as he left.

The pretty young secretary seated at the desk outside
turned to give him a shy smile, and it took tremendous
effort on Adam's part to eliminate his scowl for the few
seconds it took to give her a smile in return, before leaving.
After all, she hadn't done anything to annoy him.

Who was he really angry with? he asked himself as he
strode outside in the sunshine.

Rome, for being so blind that he couldn't see the unsel-
fish love right in front of his eyes? A love he was about to
lose...

Or Andie for seeming so indifferent about Audrey's im-
minent departure?

Or was he just angry with himself?

The latter was probably the more truthful, he accepted. He had gone along for years believing nothing would ever change, that Rome, Audrey, and the three girls would be there, as they always had been.

But nothing had stayed the same. Harrie and Danie were both married now, with homes of their own. Audrey had decided it was time for her to leave the family. And Andie—Andie had become a stranger to him.

And self-pity, he decided determinedly, was not an option!

CHAPTER TWO

AUDREY gave a wistful smile. 'It's simply time for me to move on, Andie,' she lightly answered the latter's enquiry.

Andie hadn't meant to come to the estate at all this weekend, had felt she was going to need time on her own after her enforced leave of absence from the magazine had started yesterday. But annoyed as she might have felt at Adam's remarks earlier in the week, they had struck a chord, and she had decided she had to come down after all and talk to Audrey.

She had arrived at the estate the previous evening, but this was the first opportunity she had had to talk to Audrey on her own, Rome a glowering presence at the dinner table the evening before, but luckily out on estate business this morning.

Audrey looked as beautiful and composed as she usually did, the blue of her tailored dress a match for the colour of her eyes, her blonde hair loose about her shoulders. But there was also a sadness in those blue eyes Andie had never seen there before...

'But move on where?' she questioned now as the two women enjoyed a mid-morning cup of coffee together in the sun-lounge.

Audrey gave a laugh. 'I haven't exactly thought that far ahead yet,' she admitted.

Andie's eyes widened at the admission. 'You haven't...?' she said slowly. 'But I assumed—I thought you must have found yourself a better job?' She frowned her confusion.

26

Was it her imagination, or did Audrey's gaze suddenly become slightly evasive. And if so, why had it?

Could Adam be right, after all—damn him!—and there was more to Audrey's decision to leave than was at first apparent?

Audrey shrugged. 'I'm actually thinking of not getting another job for a while. I have quite a bit of money saved—after all, what do I have to spend it on?—and so, I thought I might travel, see some of the world.'

Andie didn't feel in the least reassured by this answer. 'But you travel with Daddy all the time...'

The other woman sighed. 'Travelling with Rome is nothing more than a series of business meetings. Most of the time I have no idea which country I'm in at any particular moment; boardrooms look the same the world over!'

This explanation sounded feasible enough, Andie decided. After all, Audrey was only in her early forties, still young enough to want to do some of the things that she might have dreamed of in her youth. And yet...

Adam had put these doubts into her mind, Andie realised irritably. After all, it was Audrey's life, and she must be allowed the freedom to do with it what she wanted. The same freedom Andie had recently insisted on in her own life...

'You never know,' Audrey added with a smile, 'I might just meet someone and have children of my own. I'm not too old yet, you know.'

'You most certainly aren't,' Adam remarked firmly as he strolled unannounced into the sun-lounge. 'And whoever he is, he'll be a lucky man!' he added warmly.

Andie had known Adam would be here this weekend—he had made that more than obvious on Monday!—but, nevertheless, she was rather nonplussed at having him walk in on her conversation with Audrey in this way.

It was also a little disconcerting to hear him talking to Audrey in this slightly flirtatious way, especially as she was still processing Audrey's remark through her own thoughts!

She was ashamed to admit she had never thought of Audrey in that particular way before, had always assumed the older woman was happy with her life and career. Or maybe Adam was right, and they had all just selfishly taken Audrey's presence here for granted all these years…!

But Audrey was quite right, too; at only forty-two, there was still time for her to have a family and home of her own.

From the warmly appreciative way Adam was looking at Audrey now, he was more than aware of the other woman's attraction. And why shouldn't he be? There were only just over two years' difference in their ages…

'Thank you for that kind remark, Adam,' Audrey told him warmly as she stood up to kiss him on the cheek.

'I'm not being kind, Audrey.' He looked down at her intensely. 'I'm stating a fact.'

'I thank you, anyway.' Audrey smiled up at him as she squeezed his arm. 'I'll just go and get another cup and you can join us for a coffee,' she said before disappearing out of the room.

The silence that followed her departure was stilted to say the least, Andie decided as she glanced across at Adam beneath long lashes.

He was dressed casually today, in a black silk shirt teamed with fitted black denims, having thrown his silver-grey jacket into one of the wicker chairs as he'd entered the sun-lounge a few minutes ago. He was looking tall and lithe, his slightly overlong silver-blonde hair brushing the collar of his shirt, a slender gold watch nestling in the golden hair of his right wrist.

Adam looked exactly what he was, Andie realised: a

highly successful businessman, and a very eligible bachelor!

His expression was guarded as he looked across at her. 'You decided to come down, after all,' he murmured distantly.

He was still angry, Andie realised. But by what right? Okay, so they had all been a bit unthinking where Audrey's resignation was concerned, but Adam had no idea of the circumstances of the last few weeks—and he would remain in ignorance as far as she was concerned! He had no right to judge what he didn't understand. Besides, she still stuck by her position that it wasn't for any of them to stand in the way of what Audrey had decided she wanted to do.

'Yes, as you can see,' she replied, sitting forward in her seat as she prepared to stand up. 'You'll have to excuse me, I'm afraid; I was just about to go over to the hothouse to check on Mummy's roses.'

Adam gave her a derisive glance. 'I'm sure they can continue to grow for the next ten minutes or so without your checking on them! Long enough for you to sit with me while I drink my coffee, at least.'

She drew in a sharp breath at his undoubted mockery. She and Adam seemed to have been at odds with each other just recently—and she couldn't say it was something she was very comfortable with.

'I'm sure they can,' she acknowledged softly as she remained seated. She was feeling slightly vulnerable since her leave-taking of the magazine yesterday, and certainly didn't feel up to another confrontation with Adam. 'Did you know that it was Jonas presenting Danie with a bunch of yellow roses, just like the ones Mummy loved to grow, that confirmed for Danie that she was in love with him?' she continued conversationally.

'No.' Adam smiled as he stretched his long length in the

chair opposite hers. 'Although that sounds like the unpredictable Danie we all know and love,' he went on affectionately. 'How do you feel about having a doctor in the family?'

Her aversion to anyone in the medical profession, since going into hospital at the age of five to have her tonsils out, had become a family joke. And as Adam had been almost part of that family for the last twenty years...

She retained her casual demeanour. 'He could come in useful, I suppose,' she answered flippantly.

Adam chuckled. 'I'm sure Jonas would be pleased to hear it!'

'He's an obstetrician, did you know?' Andie said.

'I think Rome did mention it.' Adam nodded. 'I wonder how on earth Danie ever met him?' he asked thoughtfully.

Andie knew exactly how her impulsively madcap sister had met the gorgeous Jonas Noble. But that was something else that wasn't for public knowledge. And in this particular case, Adam was definitely part of the public...

'Rome is out on the estate somewhere,' she very firmly changed the subject. 'But he shouldn't be too much longer.'

'I'm not complaining,' Adam drawled, smiling warmly as Audrey returned with the promised cup and saucer. 'What man would complain about having coffee with two beautiful women?'

'One beautiful woman, I'm afraid,' Audrey announced. 'The post has just arrived, so I'll have to leave the two of you for a while,' she told them regretfully.

'Shall I pour, or would you like to be Mother?' Adam invited sardonically, once he and Andie were alone once more.

Andie gave him a sharp glance, her hands clenched tightly on the arms of her chair as she felt her cheeks lose all their colour, breathing shallowly in her shock.

Did Adam know? Had her father, despite her request for privacy, confided her condition to this man, his best friend?

Because she was going to be 'Mother'—in six months, she was going to have a baby!

The realisation of her pregnancy nine weeks ago had come as a tremendous shock to her, one that she hadn't taken to too readily initially. After all, without the baby's father in her life, it was something that she would have to go through alone.

But four weeks ago there had been the scare that she could lose the baby, and from feeling in the depths of despair, not knowing quite what to do, she had suddenly realised how much she really wanted her child. So much so that she wasn't willing to do anything that might jeopardise the pregnancy going full-term. Which was why, on Jonas's advice, she had taken a nine-month leave of absence from her high-powered, time-demanding job...

Her family knew of her pregnancy, of course, as did Audrey, but they had all been sworn to secrecy. Had her father now broken that promise and confided in Adam...?

Andie looked at him searchingly, seeing only light-hearted enquiry in his expression as he didn't wait for her answer but poured the two cups of coffee himself, and started sipping the strong, milky brew unconcernedly.

No, he didn't know, Andie realised with a thankful sigh. There would be plenty of time for that later, once her pregnancy began to show.

Strangely, she had lost weight at the beginning of her term, but Jonas had assured her that was only because of the worry and strain she had initially put herself under, because of her uncertainties, and that eventually she would start to put that weight back on. If the tightness of her clothing about her waist was anything to go by, that was starting to happen now!

But not enough, she was relieved to realise, for Adam to be in the least suspicious that his sardonic remark was actually fact! She was glad about that; Adam was the very last person she wanted to know about her pregnancy.

Because although she knew Adam had always been in love with her mother, Andie—for her sins!—had always loved Adam. Oh, she had always known it was a pointless love, that her feelings would never be returned, but she couldn't help that, she loved Adam anyway. So his pity— or even worse, his scorn!—concerning her pregnancy, were not things she felt able to cope with on top of everything else...

Adam sipped the coffee without tasting it, his thoughts broodingly introspective. He had been pleased on his arrival to see Andie had come down this weekend after all—damn it, he was more than pleased! But it had become glaringly obvious during the last few minutes that the strain which he had sensed between them on Monday was still there. In fact, it was worse!

Hell!

He drew in a ragged breath. 'How is Rome this weekend?' His coffee finished, he relaxed back in his chair.

Andie grimaced. 'About the same.'

Considering Audrey—from the little Adam had heard of the two women's conversation when he'd arrived—was still intent on leaving, he wasn't in the least surprised by Andie's reply.

He shook his head. 'I suppose I'll have to have a chat with him,' he said reluctantly; ordinarily Rome was the most genial of men, but not when it came to interference in his personal life. And whether Rome realised it or not, Audrey was very much in his personal life!

Andie gave a rueful smile. 'He's extremely volatile at

the moment, so make sure you have your body armour on first! I only asked him to pass me the pepper at dinner last night, and he almost bit my head off,' she explained with a pained grimace.

Adam groaned. 'Maybe I should come and look at the roses with you before tackling Rome.' He thought of the confrontation he would no doubt have with the older man once he had said what he felt needed to be said on the subject of Audrey's resignation. 'Isn't there some sort of saying about stopping along the way to smell the roses...?' he wondered.

Andie laughed as she stood in one fluid movement. 'I think that applies to people who need to relax more—not someone who wants to avoid someone else!'

Adam looked up at her appreciatively. Her golden-coloured hair was loose today, falling silkily down her back, framing the loveliness of her face, a face dominated by those beautiful green eyes, her skin having attained a light golden tan from the summer months.

Yet as he continued to look at her he realised there was something different about her...

But as he stood up to accompany her out to the hothouse at the back of the house, where Barbara had spent so much of her time tending her beloved roses, he couldn't quite decide what it was.

The heady perfume of the beautiful blooms assailed them as they entered the heated greenhouse, bringing back vivid memories to Adam of the woman who had first grown and tended them. Barbara had been such a lovely woman, inside as well as out, and her death ten years ago, from cancer, had been yet another blow in Adam's life. He—

Now he knew what was different about Andie! Like her mother before her, Andie always looked perfect, her make-up in place, no matter what the time of day, her clothes always beautifully tailored. Andie's make-up was still perfect, but for once she wasn't wearing any of her designer label clothes. Instead, she had on a loose green shirt over fitted denims, the former so big it looked as if it could be one of Rome's cast-offs!

Not that Andie didn't look as gorgeous as always; in fact, the casual clothing gave her a more approachable appearance, Adam decided thoughtfully. He was just surprised at the change in her, that was all…

She paused in the act of dead-heading roses, turning as she seemed to sense his gaze on her, a slight blush colouring her cheeks as she looked at him—warily, it almost seemed to him…? Had their friendship really come to that?

Probably, he acknowledged with a regretful sigh for the easy camaraderie they had once shared. But what had he expected? Nothing stayed the same. The fact that Harrie and Danie were now both married was testament to that.

'I was just thinking how much like your mother you are.' He spoke quietly, knowing, with this newfound strain between them, that Andie would not welcome any comment he might make concerning her personal appearance.

Andie's expression changed from guarded to noncommittal. 'She would have approved of Harrie and Danie's choice of husbands,' she commented huskily.

Yes, she probably would. Barbara, like Rome, had adored all of her daughters, wanted only the best for them. From the little he had seen of Quinn and Jonas, he had a feeling Barbara would not have been disappointed.

But what about Andie—would Barbara have approved of her lifestyle…? Andie was a career woman, had been the senior editor of *Gloss* for three years now, and showed no signs of wanting to change that for a husband and family of her own.

Yes, Barbara would have approved, he decided; Barbara would approve of anything that made her daughters happy.

Besides, Harrie and Danie still had their respective careers, as well as their husbands!

'I'm—'

'So here you are, Adam,' Rome's rasped comment as he entered the greenhouse interrupted what Adam had been about to say. 'Audrey said you were around somewhere.'

Adam briefly studied the older man, and he did not like what he saw. Rome's boyish good looks—blonde-haired, blue-eyed—were still the same, but there was a look of strain about those eyes and his mouth, a hardness to the latter that boded ill for anyone who got in his way.

'And, as usual, she was right,' Adam returned lightly. 'How on earth are you going to manage without her, Rome?'

Rome glared at him through narrowed lids. 'No one is indispensable, Adam,' he responded coldly.

Adam raised blond brows. 'No employee, possibly,' he returned acidly. 'But I always thought of Audrey as being more than that,' he added challengingly, aware that Andie was listening to the verbal exchange with a pained expression.

But it had taken only one look at Rome's face, at the hard implacability of his expression, to realise that the friendly chat he had intended having with his longtime friend was out of the question; Rome looked as approachable as a wounded bull-elephant!

Rome gave a dismissive shrug of broad shoulders. 'Obviously Audrey had decided differently,' he rasped harshly. 'And, as I have learnt to my cost recently, there is absolutely no point in trying to stand in the way of a woman who has made up her own mind what she intends doing with her own life!'

The remark, Adam knew, could have been directed at Harrie and Danie as much as at Audrey, and their determination to marry the men of their choice with as little delay as possible. However, Adam sensed, rather than actually saw, Andie's reaction to her father's remark, could feel the tension emanating from her as she paused in her care of the roses.

Leading Adam to wonder about the decision concerning what *she* intended doing with her own life Andie could possibly have made recently for her to assume Rome's remark was actually directed at her...?

Seeing no immediate answer to his question in either Andie or Rome's faces, he turned his attention back to Audrey; he would try and talk to Andie later on in the weekend. Try—because that hadn't been too easy to do just recently!

'And what does Audrey intend doing with her life?' he prompted the other man.

'I have no idea,' Rome answered scathingly. 'I suggest you ask her that yourself.'

'Meaning that you haven't bothered?' Adam countered, his expression deliberately innocent as the other man scowled at him.

'Meaning that Audrey has made it more than plain that it's none of my damned business!' Rome snapped.

'Hmm,' Adam murmured thoughtfully.

'What, exactly, does that mean?' Rome challenged hardly.

'"Hmm"?' Adam repeated, realising he was provoking the other man but knowing he had no choice if he was to get anywhere in this conversation at all. 'I've always thought of it as a pretty noncommittal remark, myself.'

'Then why make it?' Rome grated disgustedly. 'You—'

'Daddy,' Andie interrupted softly. 'Aren't you being just

a little—aggressive to your guest?' she said, once she had Rome's full attention.

Rome looked far from pleased at the obvious rebuke. Adam couldn't say he was exactly overjoyed by it himself; since when had he been relegated to being Rome's guest…?

But he already knew the answer to that, he acknowledged heavily. He and Andie, although still polite to each other—overly so, Adam felt!—were no longer friends, that easy camaraderie they had once shared no longer there. He knew the reason for that all too well, and regretted it more than he could say! More than he had ever regretted anything else in his life!

'I can take a little aggression,' Adam assured Andie lightly; in fact, he would relish it. His relationship with all of the Summer family had changed over recent months, necessarily so with Harrie and Danie, now that they were both married. But he had a feeling that if he were to speak as plainly to Rome as he wished to concerning Audrey, then he might jeopardise his friendship with the older man to such a degree that it would be irretrievable. Which meant his visits here would be a thing of the past…

Did he really want that?

Of course he didn't! His friendship with the Summer family had been his anchor for more years than he cared to think about!

But he couldn't just stand by and watch Rome make the biggest mistake of his life, either. He, perhaps more than most people, knew what it was like to love a woman who was completely out of your reach. As Audrey would be to Rome if he should let her leave…

'Let's walk back to the house,' he suggested to Rome as he walked over to join the other man in the doorway. 'There are a few things I need to discuss with you anyway.'

'And I thought you just came down to visit with all of us,' Andie put in with hard derision. 'How silly of me!'

Adam glanced back at her, sighing heavily at the sparks in her eyes as they easily held his.

His own friendship with Andie, it seemed, was already irretrievable…

CHAPTER THREE

SHE didn't have too much of an appetite at the moment, Andie thought—her morning sickness seemed to start in the late afternoon and continue until she went to bed! But the strained silence around this dinner table certainly wasn't helping to improve that situation!

Adam and Rome didn't appear to be talking to each other—indeed, Rome wasn't particularly talking to any of them!—and any remarks that passed between Andie and Adam were politely strained. In fact, the only person who seemed to be talking naturally and easily, to everyone, was Audrey!

The older woman looked dazzlingly beautiful this evening, her knee-length black dress shot through with silver, her smile warm and charming, her manner as friendly as usual.

But Andie wasn't fooled for a minute by the other woman's charming ease, could still see that sadness in the deep blue of her eyes...

'I thought salmon was a favourite of yours?' Adam was the one to break the awkward silence, looking at Andie as she pushed the grilled fish around on her plate.

It had been—but as with so many other foods she had once liked, now the mere smell of it only seemed to increase her nausea! The thought of actually eating any of it was complete anathema to her...

She put down her knife and fork, giving up all effort to try and hide the uneaten fish under the salad—she obviously hadn't been succeeding, anyway! 'I'm really not very

39

hungry,' she dismissed. 'In fact, if you'll all excuse me, I think I may just disappear outside for some fresh air.' She didn't wait for their response, standing up to let herself out of the French doors into the garden, breathing the air in deeply, hoping to eliminate even the smell of the salmon from her already quivering senses.

'Not exactly a lot of fun in there, is it?'

Andie turned sharply at the sound of Adam's voice; his hair looking almost silver in the half-light of this late-summer evening. She hadn't realised he had followed her—and she couldn't say she was altogether pleased at the realisation now!

She gave a rueful shrug. 'Rome has been like this for days,' she replied, wishing Adam would go back into the dining-room and leave her alone. She might have made her decision concerning having the baby, but there were still a lot of things for her to think over, and that was something she couldn't do around Adam!

Adam strolled across the patio to join her where she stood against the metal balustrade that looked out over the gardens. 'I don't think I've exactly helped,' he admitted. 'I told him earlier that he must be a fool if he's seriously going to let Audrey just walk out of his life in this way,' he explained.

Andie raised her eyebrows. 'And you're still alive to tell the tale?' she responded mockingly, well aware of how volatile her father was at the moment; she wouldn't have even dared to broach the subject with him herself! Although obviously Adam felt no such qualms...

He seemed relaxed about it. 'And to have dinner. Although from the way Rome is stabbing at his food rather than eating it, I think he wishes the salmon were me!' he joked.

Andie giggled. 'So you just left poor Audrey to face his moodiness alone!'

Adam sobered, his gaze intent on the half-shadow of her face. 'I was concerned about you.'

She stiffened. 'Me?' she echoed sharply, a pulse beating erratically in her throat. 'Why on earth should you be concerned about me?'

He gave a slight shake of his head. 'I don't know... There's something different about you.'

She turned away, swallowing hard. She was sure her pregnancy still didn't show; her black silk trouser suit, with its mid-thigh-length jacket, completely hid the thickening of her waistline and slightly larger breasts.

The latter had been quite unexpected, and were a bonus as far as Andie was concerned; she had always thought herself lacking in that particular area!

So in what way was she 'different'...?

'That bad dose of flu took a lot out of me,' she excused.

Adam disagreed. 'It isn't just that. Andie—'

'Leave it, Adam,' she cut in sharply, sure she knew what he was about to say. She didn't want to hear it!

This man had been, and probably still was, in love with her mother, and, while she might be deeply in love with Adam herself, she was not willing to be a substitute for another woman—not even her own mother!

Adam turned, reaching out to lightly grasp her shoulders as he gently turned her to face him. 'I think we need to talk—'

Her eyes flashed deeply green in the moonlight. 'Why?' she challenged, her head held back proudly.

He looked grim. 'You know why, damn it!'

'I have no idea what you're talking about,' she returned. 'Now if you don't mind, I came out here to appreciate the peace and quiet—not to engage in a verbal fencing match with you!' She glared at him. 'Besides,' she added, 'we both know how much you hate all this clean country air!'

Adam came down to the estate most weekends when he wasn't busy elsewhere, but he had never made any secret of the fact that he simply did not understand the liking Rome and his family had for country life.

'I could grow to like it, if I had to,' he said quietly.

Her mouth tightened. 'There's absolutely no reason why you should,' she responded hardly. 'I think one of us should do the decent thing—and go back inside and rescue Audrey from my father's foul temper!'

Why didn't he just let her go? She cried inwardly. His grasp wasn't tight on her arms, and yet she still tingled from his touch, warmth spreading through the whole of her body, her legs starting to feel as if they couldn't support her weight.

She still turned to liquid gold at his merest touch? After all that had happened? Despite all the complications her baby was going to cause in her life? In spite of the fact that Adam would never—could never—return her feelings!

She gave a self-disgusted shake of her head. Adam was way beyond her reach—even more so now!—and always would be...

'I—' Adam abruptly broke off any reply he might have been going to make to her suggestion as the sound of shattering glass was clearly heard from the direction of the dining-room, quickly followed by the sound of raised voices.

Andie turned back in alarm towards the house. 'You don't suppose Rome has completely lost it, do you, and actually attacked Audrey?' She gasped even as she pulled away from Adam and ran back towards the French doors that led into the dining-room.

From the scene that met her eyes as she rushed back into

the room, Andie had a feeling it was probably more a case of the other way round!

Her father was alone in the room now, standing back from the table, the front of his white shirt and the black dinner jacket looking more than a little damp, a shattered wineglass on the table-top in front of where he had previously been seated.

'What the hell have you done to Audrey?' Adam demanded, obviously having assessed the situation in a couple of seconds—and drawn his own conclusions.

Rome turned to him with blazing blue eyes, the mature handsomeness of his face contorted with anger. 'I'm sure it hasn't escaped your notice,' he replied furiously, 'but I'm the one with white wine all over me!'

The situation wasn't in the least funny, Andie inwardly thought, realising that Audrey must have been severely provoked to have thrown a glass full of wine—the glass included, by the look of it!—all over Rome. But, for some reason, she had the distinct urge to laugh!

For one thing, Rome looked ridiculous, with wine still dripping from his chin onto his already sodden shirt. And, for another—she simply admired Audrey for having the guts to act on her instincts. Andie could think of a few people she wouldn't mind throwing wine over herself!

'I noticed,' Adam drawled dryly. 'But I also know Audrey well enough to realise she must have been provoked into such an action,' he opined hardly. 'So what did you do to her?' he repeated.

'Nothing,' Rome bit out harshly, dabbing at his wet shirt-front with one of the snowy white napkins now.

'Daddy!' Andie gasped reprovingly; she also knew Audrey well enough to realise Rome must have said or done something to elicit this response.

Her father glared across at her. 'Whose side are you on?' he accused angrily. 'I—'

'I'm not taking sides,' Andie cut in. 'But I think I know the two of you well enough to be sure Audrey would not simply have thrown a glass of wine over you without good reason!' she added assuredly.

'Then you are taking sides.' Rome straightened to his full height of six feet two, throwing the damp napkin down disgustedly on the table-top. 'I never thought I would see the day when one of my own daughters—'

'If I still had the violin you forced me to learn to play when I was younger, then I would play it now!' Andie cut across this attempted emotional pressure on her father's part. 'But as I don't, and as you don't seem in any hurry to enlighten us as to the reason for Audrey's outburst, I think I'll just go upstairs and see if Audrey will be any more forthcoming!'

'She's packing,' Rome muttered as Andie turned to leave.

Andie came to an abrupt halt, turning slowly back to look at her father disbelievingly. There was certainly nothing in the least funny about this situation now!

'She isn't going to work the rest of her notice,' Rome continued. 'She intends leaving right now.'

Andie slowly shook her head as she saw the implacability of her father's expression. 'And you aren't going to do anything to stop her?'

Rome thrust his chin out arrogantly. 'There's nothing I can do.'

'Adam's right,' Andie snapped scornfully. 'You are a fool!' She turned on her heel and marched purposefully from the room, hurrying up the stairs and along the hallway that led to the bedroom Audrey had occupied for the last ten years.

But Andie hesitated outside the door, not sure how to proceed. Her father was in the wrong, she was sure of it, but that didn't mean Audrey was going to be any more pleased to see her than she would have been had it been Rome himself who came knocking on her door! But she loved Audrey, all the sisters did, and, despite what Adam might have assumed to the contrary, there was no way she was going to just let the other woman walk out of their lives in this way.

She straightened her shoulders, giving a determined knock on the door.

'Go away,' came Audrey's abrupt response.

Andie turned the handle on the door, relieved to find it wasn't locked, entering the room to find herself confronted by Audrey holding a vase of flowers aloft in her hand as she stood poised ready to throw it at whoever came through the doorway.

'I come in peace!' Andie cried even as she held her hands up defensively.

Audrey gave a shaky sigh before placing the vase of freesias back on the dressing-table. 'I thought it might have been someone else,' she admitted.

Rome... Despite Audrey's having had the vase of flowers raised as another weapon to launch at him, Andie could see that Audrey was actually disappointed it wasn't him!

Andie closed the bedroom door behind her, taking in the open suitcase on the bed, the clothes thrown haphazardly inside. Audrey really was packing to leave!

She moved to sit on the edge of the bed, realising as she looked around just how much this room had become Audrey's over the years. The décor was blue and cream, family photographs adorned the table by the window, Audrey's own as well as ones of Harrie, Danie, and Andie as they were growing up; the pastels on the walls were to

Audrey's taste too. Audrey wasn't just leaving a job; this was her home!

'Audrey.' Andie spoke firmly as the other woman continued to throw her clothes into the suitcase. 'I asked you earlier today why you were leaving, and you mumbled something about it being time to move on—'

'I believe I spoke quite clearly,' Audrey rebuked—although she didn't meet Andie's questioning gaze.

'Maybe,' Andie acknowledged. 'But now I would like you to tell me the real reason—and please, don't insult my intelligence again with that mumbo-jumbo,' she continued as Audrey would have spoken. 'I'm pregnant, Audrey, not mentally deficient!'

Audrey paused in her trips backwards and forwards between the wardrobe and the suitcase. 'I never for one moment thought that you were.'

'Well?' Andie prompted.

The other woman seemed to crumple in front of her eyes, tears filling those deep blue eyes. Audrey completely lost the tight control she had had over her emotions as she began to cry in earnest.

Andie rushed over to gather the older woman in her arms, moved beyond words at this complete breakdown of defences. She loved Audrey, they all did, and to see her hurting in this way was unacceptable.

'Audrey, you have to tell me.' Andie moved back slightly to look at her. 'I promise you I won't tell a single soul,' she promised chokingly, close to tears herself now.

Audrey gave a tearful smile. 'Surely it's obvious, Andie; I'm in love with your father! I always have been. And I always will be!'

Andie blinked. She didn't know what explanation she had been expecting; an affair with a married man possibly, perhaps even-wildly!—a past tale of manslaughter that

Audrey could no longer live with, but it certainly hadn't been this...

'Oh, Andie...!' Audrey laughed mirthlessly at Andie's stunned expression as she moved away to reach for a tissue from the dressing-table, mopping up all trace of tears from her cheeks. 'You don't see any problem with that, do you?' she asked hesitantly.

Considering Andie knew she had loved Adam as hopelessly most of her own life...no!

But, as she also knew only too well, it hurt to love someone so helplessly, to spend hours in the company of him and know that love would never be returned.

Although after the way her father had been behaving since Audrey had given him her resignation, Andie wasn't sure that was completely true in this case...

Had Adam known all the time of Audrey's love for Rome? Was that the reason he was so angry with them all?

'Doesn't this prove what I said to you earlier, Rome?' Adam demanded harshly.

'That Audrey is in love with me?' Rome repeated, moving to the side-dresser to pour himself a glass of brandy from the decanter there. 'Hardly!' He looked down pointedly at the damp stickiness of his clothing before taking a large swallow of the fiery liquid.

Adam gave the older man a pitying glance. He loved Rome like the father he had never known, or perhaps—more acceptably to Rome!—like an older brother. But, at this moment, he could cheerfully have physically shaken the other man to help try and make him see sense. In his business life Rome knew no rivals, became master of every venture he went into, and yet on a personal level he couldn't see the love right in front of his nose!

'I don't remember Barbara ever throwing wine over me

in an effort to show her love for me,' Rome commented at Adam's continued silence.

'Barbara obviously had more subtle—ways, of showing you what an idiot you can be!' Adam replied.

'Thanks for nothing!' The older man scowled.

He looked so much like a disgruntled little boy in that moment that for some reason Adam began to see the funny side of this situation, his mouth twitching as he made an effort to hold back his humour—at the other man's expense. Rome definitely looked less than his usually suave self with the sticky wine all down his shirt-front, and as for the indignant expression on his face…!

Rome's gaze sharpened suspiciously as he looked at Adam through narrowed lids. 'You wouldn't happen to be laughing at me, would you?' he accused with slow deliberation.

The grin Adam had been trying to suppress suddenly refused to be held back any longer. In fact, it came out as more of a choked chuckle!

'Damn it, you *are* laughing at me!' Rome grated indignantly, slamming down his now empty glass. 'Would it be too much to ask,' he continued between gritted teeth as Adam began to chuckle in earnest now, 'that you share the reason for this—this childish humour?'

Adam couldn't help it; Rome's angry indignation, on top of everything else, was simply too much—and he burst into a loud shout of laughter. Rome was priceless. Absolutely priceless. The man was as much in love with Audrey as she was with him—and was fighting capitulation every inch of the way!

Why else had he been in such a foul mood ever since Audrey had handed in her notice? Why else had he been so insulting to the poor woman that she had resorted to throwing wine over him? Why else had Rome brought

Barbara into their conversation just now, if not as a defence against the love he felt for Audrey...?

The man was as head over heels in love with Audrey as she was with him—he was just terrified of admitting it. To the extent he was willing to let Audrey walk out of his life?

Adam sobered slightly. 'I was just thinking it's a pity it wasn't red wine Audrey threw at you—it would have had a much more dramatic effect visually. Very much like blood, in fact,' he added with relish.

Rome didn't return the humorous smile that accompanied that last statement as he looked at Adam thoughtfully. 'You have a warped sense of humour, Mr Munroe,' he said.

'And you, Mr Summer, have no sense of humour at all at the moment,' Adam came back uncaringly.

Rome looked down at his shirt-front, pulling the damp material away from his chest. 'This shirt is silk,' he complained.

Again Adam had to hold back his humour at the other man's expense. 'Just tell the dry cleaners you had the shakes and missed your mouth!'

'Very funny,' Rome rasped—but there was at last a responding vestige of a smile on his lips. 'I've a good mind to ask Audrey to pay for it to be cleaned!'

Adam grinned. 'And risk having the bottle thrown at you next time?'

Rome looked crestfallen. 'You know, I've known Audrey for twelve years now—and I had no idea she had such a violent temper!'

Adam looked surprised. 'All that suppressed passion has to be released somehow.'

Rome was nonplussed. 'And exactly what would you know about Audrey's suppressed passion?'

Adam moved to the drinks tray to pour them both a brandy, handing one of the glasses to the other man before making his reply. 'From the mood you've been in the last few weeks—about as much as you obviously do!'

Rome gave a heavy sigh as he sat down in one of the chairs set about the dining-table—not the one he had been sitting in earlier, because that was as damp as his shirt! 'Women!' he muttered with feeling.

'Not only a different species but from another planet as well,' Adam agreed as he joined the other man and sat back down at the table.

'Obviously one of far superior intellect!' Andie snapped as she swept into the room, looking like an enraged tigress as she came to stand at the other end of the table, green eyes flashing angrily as she glared at each man in turn.

Adam gave an inward groan; his remark had been meant to mock Rome, not be taken as an insult by a member of that different species from another planet! But it didn't need anyone of superior intellect to know that Andie definitely felt insulted!

Andie continued to look at the two men with disgust. 'While the two of you have been down here discussing women like a couple of immature boys after their first date, I have been upstairs trying to persuade Audrey that whatever you said to her—' she looked straight at her father '—you didn't mean. Not only that, I assured her that you will most certainly apologise to her for making the remark.'

'You—'

'I even talked her out of smashing a vase of flowers over your head as soon as you enter the room,' Andie added scathingly as Rome would have spoken.

Rome turned to Adam. 'I think I liked the red wine idea better,' he said consideringly. 'As you said, much more dramatic!'

Adam could see by the fury of Andie's expression that this was not the time for levity, and yet he couldn't help but smile at the other man's remark. At least Rome had got his sense of humour back!

Although the look on Andie's face as she saw his smile didn't augur well for her own humour!

'When the two of you have quite finished behaving like a couple of juvenile delinquents, I—'

'Immature *and* juvenile,' Rome amended with a considering tilt of his head. 'Not bad going for men of fifty-four and nearly forty!'

'At this moment three and four is probably nearer the mark!' Andie bit back before turning to her father with glittering green eyes. 'Rome, if you don't go upstairs and apologise to Audrey right now—'

'Yes?' Rome prompted softly at the threat in her tone, his own gaze narrowed warningly now.

Adam could see by the sudden flush to Andie's cheeks that she had heard that warning—but he also knew by the following stubborn set of her mouth that it was going to be a warning she ignored. He gave a pained wince as he waited for her response.

'You're going to lose her for good,' Andie stated baldly. 'And that's something you're going to regret for the rest of your life,' she declared with certainty.

Her words were nothing like Adam had thought they would be. Or Rome either, if the stunned look on his face was anything to go by!

'What is it with everyone this evening?' Rome implored as he stood up noisily. 'Suddenly you all know what's better for me than I do myself!' He began to pace the room, stopping every now and then to glare impatiently at either Andie or Adam, finally coming to a halt near the doorway. 'Well, I've listened to what the two of you have had to say this evening—maybe not patiently, but I've certainly listened. And do you want to know the biggest conclusion I've come to…?'

Adam had the distinct impression that he, for one, didn't want to know. But quickly following on the heels of that realisation was the fact that he wasn't going to have any choice in the matter!

'The conclusion I've come to is that the two of *you* should sort out your own lives before you start telling me what I should or shouldn't do with mine!' Rome told them bluntly.

Adam looked warily across at the other man, and, without so much as glancing at Andie, he could feel her sudden tension. What exactly, he wondered, did Rome mean by that remark…? More to the point, what was he going to say next?

Rome gave a humourless smile as he took in their stunned expressions. 'Not so pleasant when it's directed at you, is it?' he derided. 'For instance, Adam—' Rome turned to him '—it's way past time you stopped this carefree bachelor life, settled down with one of those beautiful women you're always seen parading around with, and raised your own family instead of sharing mine. And, as for you, Andie—'

'That's enough, Daddy,' she told him through stiff lips, her face very pale now, her hands clenched at her sides.

'But—'

'I said that was enough!' she burst out.

Rome gave another heavy sigh. 'Maybe it is,' he conceded evenly. 'Now if you'll both excuse me,' he said as the sound of the front door opening could be clearly heard, 'I have to go out there and persuade Audrey out of doing something I'm going to regret for the rest of my life!' The door closed decisively behind him as he left the room.

The silence he left behind him was so filled with tension Adam felt as if he might reach out and touch it.

But he certainly dared not reach out and touch Andie, he realised as he looked across at her. That barrier seemed to have fallen between them again; her expression was remote, her gaze, when it met his, cold...

'Well, I must say, I'm really impressed that the two of you found Audrey's behaviour so damned funny!' she finally burst out, eyes flashing deeply green.

The adage 'attack is the best form of defence' came unbidden to Adam's mind...

He had no idea why; after all, Andie's outburst was probably merited. Except... 'I didn't find it in the least funny,' Adam told her sharply. 'If you must know, I was trying to calm Rome down by making him see the funny side of it!'

Andie gave him a scornful look as the sound of raised voices could clearly be heard outside in the hallway. 'I don't think Audrey appreciates your efforts any more than I did! Sitting down here laughing about the situation like a couple of—'

'Schoolboys,' Adam finished for her, starting to feel angry himself now. Why did this woman always misinterpret what he was trying to say or do?

'Exactly.' She gave him another scathing glance. 'A "different species from another planet!"' she repeated.

'But with superior intellect,' he repeated dryly, striding forcefully across the room to lightly grasp the tops of her arms when he received no answering smile from Andie. 'You know, Andie, you've certainly lost *your* sense of humour the last few weeks,' he told her.

Andie looked up at him unsmilingly. 'Probably because I see very little to smile about the last few weeks,' she responded. 'Now, if you wouldn't mind releasing me...? I'm tired and would like to go to bed.'

Adam looked at her searchingly. She did look tired. But it wasn't just that. There was also that hardness about her eyes and mouth. And he could tell by the way she strained against his hold on her arms that she did not like him touching her... Had it really come to that, to a point where she couldn't even bear him to touch her?

'Don't you think we should let the lovebirds have a little more time to settle their differences?' he cajoled huskily, the sound of voices outside still audible in the dining-room.

'Would you please let me go?' Andie said through gritted teeth.

She really didn't like him touching her, Adam accepted heavily. Whereas he—he wanted to touch her, damn it. In fact, he wanted to do a lot more than just touch her!

Andie's gaze narrowed glitteringly as she seemed to read at least some of his thoughts from his expression. 'Don't even think about it, Adam,' she warned softly.

Perhaps it was that warning tone. Or perhaps his patience had been tried too far. Whatever the reason, he did a sight more than just think about it!

She felt curvaceously desirable, Adam briefly had time to register as he pulled her to him. But only briefly—because as his lips fused with hers he could think of nothing but that. Actually, he couldn't think at all, could only feel! Andie felt so good to him, her body curved into the hard contours of his, her hands tightly gripping his shoulders.

Now he knew how a thirsty man in a desert had to feel when offered water. He wanted to drink, and drink, and drink, never wanted this to stop!

But even as he recognised that, that was exactly what it did, Andie wrenching her mouth away from his, pushing at his chest until he had no choice but to release her.

She stood removed from him now, her head held back defiantly, her nostrils flaring angrily as she breathed deeply.

'That was a mistake on your part, Adam,' she said grat-ingly. 'And one definitely not to be repeated.' She pushed the blonde tumble of her hair back from her angrily flushed face.

Adam would have liked to throw her words back in her face, wished for nothing more than to be able to claim that she had responded. But the truth of the matter was, she hadn't. For several long—glorious!—seconds she had re-mained impassive in his arms—rather like a wooden doll?—and then she had begun to fight him.

He drew in a ragged breath, putting a hand up to a temple that suddenly ached with tension. 'Are we never going to be friends again, Andie?' he said dully.

'Friends!' she repeated harshly. 'I've always tried to be your friend, Adam, but it obviously isn't a friend that you want—'

'Tried?' he echoed incredulously feeling as if she had just punched him in the solar plexus.

'Tried,' she repeated firmly, the coldness of her gaze easily holding his. 'But I can't even do that any more, Adam,' she told him flatly. 'I suggest that in future we just try to stay out of each other's way.'

He swallowed hard, knowing by her implacable expres-sion that she meant exactly what she had just said. But how could he stay away from her—when what he most wanted to do was the exact opposite to that?

No!

Much as he might want Andie, he certainly wasn't what Andie needed in her life.

'I think you're right, Andie,' he said shortly. 'You are tired and need to go to bed. We can talk about this again tomorrow.' When he had recovered sufficiently from this talk to be able to deal with the situation logically.

'My conclusion will be exactly the same, tomorrow or

any other day!' Andie snapped before sweeping from the room, leaving a trail of her heady perfume in her wake.

Adam almost fell into the chair, putting his hands up to cover his face as he gave a pained groan.

Andie had always tried to be his friend!

Until he had ruined even that...?

CHAPTER FOUR

'JUST how long did you think you could keep the existence of my child from me?'

Andie flinched at the sound of that angrily accusing voice, but she didn't open her eyes, or move from her prone position on the sun-lounger on the terrace of her father's Majorcan villa.

His child, he had said...

Yes, she was carrying his child. The baby was hers too, of course, but she knew him well enough to realise he wouldn't just stand by and ignore his own child.

Although, as he seemed to have guessed, that hadn't prevented Andie wanting to stop him from having that knowledge for as long as possible. Which was what she was doing in Majorca in the first place.

It had started out as a germ of an idea, a need for a complete—if temporary!—break, away from the emotional pressures being brought to bear concerning her pregnancy. With no magazine to go to each weekday, and her father's attention thankfully occupied elsewhere, it hadn't been too difficult to make the move to the Majorcan sunshine for a few weeks. To put off, for a short time longer, the confrontation that now seemed to have come to her...

How had she ever got herself into this mess?

Ah, yes...she remembered now. It had begun, quite innocently, with an invitation to attend a party as Adam Munroe's partner. She gave a rueful smile as she remembered teasing him about the unexpected invitation...

'Don't tell me the eligible Adam Munroe has been stood

57

up?' she taunted at the twenty-four hours' notice he had given her.

He shook his head unconcernedly. 'I was actually going to attend alone,' he drawled. 'But then I thought you might find it rather fun.'

'Run out of ambitious young actresses just longing to be seen on the arm of the influential film producer Adam Munroe?' Andie looked up from her desk to venture.

Adam grinned unabashedly, perched on the side of her desk. 'Tired of their unsubtle machinations,' he revealed. 'At least I know you don't have any ambitions to become an actress!'

Andie had to smile. 'Not the most charming invitation I've ever received!'

'But you'll come anyway?'

Why not? Her social calendar wasn't exactly overflowing with invitations. From choice, she acknowledged. No man, she had learnt through dating over the years, could in any way measure up to the man she was already in love with. The man who, for reasons of his own, was inviting her to spend tomorrow evening with him...

She looked up at Adam with searching eyes. What was it about this man that held her so enthralled? Oh, he was handsome enough, but then so were a lot of other men she had met. Adam could be incredibly charming too—but that wasn't unique, either. No, she had no idea why it should be this man she loved; she only knew that she did. That she always had.

And the temptation to spend an evening in his company was just too great to refuse...

'Okay, Adam,' she decided firmly—before she could have second thoughts about the prudence of going out with him at all. 'What time shall I be ready? And what do you want me to wear?'

'Eight o'clock.' He smiled his pleasure in her acquiescence. 'And I wouldn't presume to tell you what you should wear.'

Andie gave a wry smile. 'It's never stopped you before!' she clearly remembered one occasion, that of her eighteenth birthday, when Adam had been less than polite concerning the figure-hugging red dress she had been wearing!

He continued to grin. 'Maybe I'm getting more circumspect in my old age,' he drawled.

Andie quirked one mocking brow. 'I doubt that very much. Okay, Adam, I'll use my own judgement,' she assured him.

And she did, the knee-length shimmering silver dress clinging lovingly to every curve of her body, the low neckline revealing a tempting expanse of creamy breasts. Her blonde hair she left loose down the length of her spine, silver lights reflecting from the dress, her jewellery of chunky gold earrings and bracelet, giving her a delicacy that was refuted by the teasing mischief lurking in her deep green gaze.

Adam, she was pleased to note, was completely bowled over by her appearance when she opened her apartment door to him the following evening.

'May I say, Miss Summer, that you dress up quite spectacularly?' he told her.

'And may I say, Mr Munroe, that so do you?' she returned flirtatiously in an effort to hide her own reaction to his lethal handsomeness in the black dinner suit and snowy white shirt. Not that she could hide her reaction completely, conscious of a pulse beating erratically at the base of her creamy throat.

'Your carriage awaits, my lady.' He gave a theatrical sweep of his arm.

Her 'carriage' consisted of Adam's sleek green Jaguar

sports car. She showed a long expanse of slenderly silky leg as Adam held the door open for her to slip into the passenger seat.

She gave him a reproving look as he got into the car beside her, still trying to pull her dress down to a respectable level. 'I can't help thinking, Adam, that you chose such a low car deliberately!'

He quirked blond brows at her before turning the key in the ignition. 'Actually, Andie—I can't help thinking the same thing!' he returned unrepentantly.

Adam drove out of London towards Berkshire, their hosts for the evening turning out to be the Grants, the film director Daniel, and his beautiful actress wife Carla Burton, the latter heavily pregnant with their second child.

There wasn't a single guest at the party that Andie didn't recognise from either film or television, and, while her own highly indulged upbringing meant she wasn't in the least overwhelmed by so many celebrities, she couldn't say she was exactly overjoyed when, shortly after their arrival, Adam, having provided her with a glass of champagne, excused himself to go and talk to the latest darling of the film world, Elizabeth King.

In fact, Adam's attention on the beautiful redhead was so intense over the next ten minutes that Andie couldn't help wondering why on earth he had needed to bring her here with him at all!

'Actress or television presenter?' The teasing male voice at her side drew her attention away from Adam and the beautiful actress.

She turned to find herself looking at the boyishly attractive comedian Gordon Andrews. 'Actually, I work on a women's magazine,' she revealed.

His eyes widened humorously. 'How on earth did a member of the press manage to get an invitation here?' He looked around them pointedly at the less-than-well-behaved guests, the champagne flowing liberally, along with the guests' inhibitions.

Andie laughed at his comical expression. 'I'm the senior editor, not a reporter.'

Gordon waggled his dark eyebrows expressively. 'I'd love to see the junior one—she must still be in nappies!'

She liked him, Andie decided, as Gordon seemed to have decided to stay at her side, his wicked brand of humour having her laughing out loud several times through the evening, thankfully diverting her attention away from Adam. Although she was still aware that Adam didn't leave Elizabeth King's side for a single minute, attentively supplying her with champagne and food if she looked like running out of either.

Damn him, Andie decided stubbornly. Stupidly, she had looked forward to this evening out with Adam—and as far as he was concerned she might just as well not exist!

In fact, she was surprised when, the party obviously drawing to a close at about three o'clock in the morning, Adam remembered to come and get her so that the two of them could leave together, she had half expected him to leave with Elizabeth King, too!

'Good party?' Adam finally asked rigidly in the darkness of the car as they drove through the quiet London streets, the rest of the journey having taken place in tension-filled silence.

'Excellent,' Andie came back tautly. 'Gordon Andrews is as funny off stage as he is on it.'

'I noticed you were enjoying yourself,' Adam observed sarcastically.

'Really?' Andie returned just as sarcastically.

Adam turned to her sharply in the confines of the car. 'And exactly what does that mean?' he snapped.

She gave a dismissive shrug of her shoulders. 'Elizabeth King is very beautiful.'

'I—'

'You just missed the turn to my apartment,' she interrupted.

His response was to immediately do an illegal U-turn in the middle of the road—something he wouldn't have stood a chance of doing if it weren't almost four o'clock on a Sunday morning!—bringing the Jaguar to a screeching halt outside the apartment building where she lived, before turning in his seat to look at her with steely grey eyes.

'I would rather have spent the evening with you,' he ground out between clenched jaws.

'Really?' Andie's eyes flashed deeply green in the half-light. 'Then you must have hidden acting ability!' She glared at him, remembering all too clearly that if it hadn't been for Gordon Andrews she would have spent the entire evening mingling with people she didn't know—and who, on this evening's behaviour, she wasn't sure she wanted to know, either!

Adam reached out to grasp her shoulders. 'Are you seeing Andrews again?' he demanded to know—almost as if she had spoken her thoughts out loud!

Andie wrenched out of his grasp, reaching to open her car door—obviously Adam wasn't about to get out and do it for her! 'I don't think that's any of your business!' she scorned as she stepped out onto the pavement.

For such a large man, Adam moved with surprising speed, at her side as she used her key to open the security door at the entrance to the building, following her inside.

He swung her round to face him. 'I'm making it my business, Andie,' he insisted. 'Do you intend seeing Andrews again?' he repeated, his voice steely now.

She looked up at him defiantly. 'I think that's for me to

decide—don't you?' Knowing she actually had no intention of seeing the other man again.

Gordon had asked her if she would like to have dinner with him next week, but, despite having enjoyed his company this evening, Andie knew she wasn't in the least attracted to him. Much better to leave their evening together as a pleasant memory. At least, that part of it!

'Excuse me, Adam,' she dismissed as the lift arrived at the ground floor, stepping inside.

'No,' Adam returned shortly, stepping into the lift beside her. Andie looked at him frowning as the lift ascended to her floor, before stepping out into the carpeted entrance to her apartment, throwing her bag and keys down onto the table and striding through to the calm elegance of her sitting-room.

Adam swung her roughly round to face him, his expression furious in the glow of the side-light she had left on in the room in anticipation of her return.

She gave a heavy sigh, knowing that they were both too angry to continue this conversation. 'It's very late, Adam—'

'That didn't seem to bother you a short time ago when you were all over Gordon Andrews!' he shot back at her, grey eyes glacial.

Her own eyes widened indignantly at his unwarranted accusation. 'The man kept me company for the evening—which is more than can be said of you!' she returned angrily.

'Don't try and turn this round on me,' Adam rasped coldly, his hand tightening on her arm. 'By the time I had concluded my business with Elizabeth you were secluded in a dark corner with that damned clown!'

'I—!' Andie gasped her outrage, trying to pull out of his grasp—and only succeeding in bruising herself instead.

'Elizabeth King is even younger than I am!' she exclaimed. 'Which makes you nothing but a—'

'Yes?' Adam challenged hardly, his face only inches away from her own.

There was a warning in his eyes, but Andie was past caring about his anger, was only concerned with her own humiliation—and hurt, that he should have chosen to spend her coveted evening with him in the company of another woman, a beautifully luring one at that.

She had so looked forward to being with him this evening, had dressed with him in mind—and, as far as she was concerned, he had merely been using her in an effort not to arrive at the party alone, after all!

'An aging Romeo!' Andie concluded stubbornly, anger winning out over prudence.

'An aging—!' Adam's eyes darkened for a moment before they became silvery cold. 'If I'm an aging Romeo,' he bit out tautly, 'then you're nothing but a teasing flirt!'

The two of them glared at each other, nose to nose, green eyes clashing with silver, chins jutting out, neither of them willing to give an inch.

How long they would have gone on staring at each other in that way Andie couldn't have said, but suddenly Adam gave a groan, all of the anger draining out of his body, his hands no longer tight on her arms, the thumbs lightly caressing against the creaminess of her skin.

'Damn you, Andie…!' he breathed raggedly, his forehead damp against hers now.

She felt the change in him, holding her breath in an effort not to break the physical awareness that suddenly seemed to have sprung up between them, her gaze steadily meeting his as she dared him to take this one step further.

'Damn you…!' he groaned again before he moved slightly, his mouth claiming hers.

There was no gentle exploration, no slow rising of passion; as their lips met it was as if a sensual explosion had been set off between them, all thought, all caution, forgotten in the wave of feeling that engulfed them both.

With their mouths still fused in exploration, their clothes fell quickly to the floor, Andie not absolutely sure who took off what, only aware of searing emotion as she felt the naked warmth of Adam's body as it fitted perfectly against her own nakedness, Adam's hands seeking, and finding, each sensitive spot on her body, his lips heatedly following that same trail until Andie felt like liquid fire in his arms.

The carpet felt warm against her back, Adam like fire above her, his lips and hands touching the pouting yearning of her breasts, Andie groaning low in her throat as she felt a nipple drawn completely into the moist heat of Adam's mouth, the gentle touch of his tongue, the pleasure-pain of nibbling teeth, bringing a moist warmth between her thighs.

She arched against him as his hand explored her there, feeling as if she would burst with the heated sensations. And then she did burst, but it was like nothing she had ever known before, every part of her feeling suddenly hypersensitive as the pleasure coursed through her, welcoming Adam into her as his body finally joined with hers.

The pleasure that followed was even more intense than that first time, and as the heated quivering of her body brought Adam to his own peak the two of them reached that unknown plateau together in a sensation that seemed to go on and on into eternity...

His child, he had just said.

Yes, it was Adam's child she carried.

But it was a child that had been conceived in anger rather than love, a fact that had been more than borne out by Adam's dazed expression when he'd raised his head from the dampness of her breasts to look at her with unfocusing, unrecognising grey eyes.

A shiver of shocked reaction quivered through her. Because if Adam hadn't known he was making love with her, then it had to be—Oh, God!

Andie pushed frantically at his chest, feeling a momentary loss as her body ceased to be joined with his, rolling away from him to gather up her shimmering silver gown and hold it protectively in front of her nakedness. 'Go, Adam,' she told him woodenly.

He drew in a short breath, still not quite looking at her. 'I—'

'Just go, Adam,' she bit out, turning away from him so that he shouldn't see the sudden tears that welled up in her pained green eyes. 'Please!'

He swallowed hard, gathering up his own scattered clothes, not speaking again until he was once again fully dressed—and looking remotely unapproachable. 'Andie, I—I don't know what to say,' he began shakily.

Her mouth twisted into the bitter semblance of a smile. 'Then it's probably best that you say nothing,' she told him tersely. Anything he said now could only make the situation worse. If that were possible!

Adam shook his head. 'I don't know what happened,' he said. 'One minute we were furious with each other, the next—!' He gave another shake of his head. 'I'm sorry, Andie,' he added wretchedly.

Not as sorry as she was. Because, in the absence of the woman he really wanted, she had only been a substitute enough like her in looks to allow Adam the fantasy. As Andie knew only too well, that woman was her own, dead, mother!

She knew it as surely as if Adam had spoken the words

out loud—and she knew she would never forgive him for using her in that way.

She stirred herself now, finally opening her eyes to look across the terrace of the villa to where Adam stood grimly in the shadow of the purple bougainvillaea that ran along one side of the mellow stone building.

She knew as she looked at him that, despite everything, she still loved him...!

She hated him.

Adam could see it in the dark green of her eyes as she looked over at him with such cold contempt.

She had never looked lovelier to him, the week she had spent in the warm Majorcan sunshine having given a healthy tan to the silky skin visible above the green bikini, the gentle glow of early pregnancy having given a warm allure to the curves of her body.

That was his child that lay nestled inside that curvaceous body, he acknowledged possessively. His child! And Andie's...

He watched warily as she swung her legs to the floor, sitting up now as she looked across at him with enquiring eyes. It had been this way between them since—since that night, he acknowledged wearily.

He hadn't left her apartment that night only because she'd asked him to. No, he had also seen the shocked dismay in her face when she'd realised what they had just done, a wishing that it had never happened.

He had left her that night knowing they could never go back now, that the easy friendship that had existed between them was no more. That it never would be again.

He hadn't gone straight to his own apartment but had parked his car and walked. And walked. And walked. Desperately trying to find a way back from the dark abyss they had fallen into. There wasn't one, he had finally accepted.

That conclusion had been borne out over the next few weeks, Andie not around whenever he'd visited Rome at the estate. And Andie had returned the flowers he had sent to her office on the Monday morning following that fatal night, having obviously read the card that had accompanied them, her own message written clearly beneath his apology—'Not as sorry as I am!'

Not as sorry as she must have been when she'd found she was pregnant with their child...

Adam moved out of the shadows of the villa, having already removed his jacket on the drive from the airport, the heat of the late August Majorcan sunshine having hit him like a blanket as he'd stepped out of the air-conditioned airport.

'Who told you?' Andie demanded as he came to stand beside her. 'Or do I really need to ask?'

'It wasn't Rome,' Adam assured her softly, looking down at her with hooded eyes, still having difficulty accepting that his child nestled in the warm perfection of her body. It didn't really show yet, only a gentle swell visible to the smoothness of her tummy over the green bikini. 'He is otherwise preoccupied at the moment,' he added derisively.

Andie nodded abruptly, reaching up a hand to the sunglasses that lay amongst her honey-blonde hair, bringing them firmly down over the windows of her eyes. 'I intend returning for the wedding next month,' she revealed.

The two of them had pushed Rome in the right direction where Audrey was concerned and, having proposed and been accepted, Rome was now wasting no time in making Audrey his wife!

Adam's mouth tightened as he thought of the battle he

had in front of him to do the same where Andie was going to fight against accepting that, probably with the last breath of her body!

'So who did tell you, Adam?' Andie prompted.

He wished she didn't have those sunglasses covering the usual candidness of her eyes, wanted to reach out and remove them—but he already knew, from the experience of last weekend, that she would recoil away from him if he tried to touch her. She had done it so many times already...

'I called into your office in the week to see you—'

'Why?' she queried flatly.

Because he hadn't been able to stay away from her any longer! Because he knew she would never voluntarily make a move to see him. Ever again!

'You left last weekend without saying goodbye,' he granted, remembering all too clearly his heart-sinking disappointment the previous Sunday when Audrey had told him Andie had left earlier that morning. Before the two of them had been able to talk any further...

Andie's mouth turned down at the corners. 'I hadn't realised you were such a stickler for good manners, Adam!' she taunted.

He drew in a harsh breath before dropping down onto the lounger next to hers. It hadn't been easy to come here at all, the delays at the airport and subsequent two-hour flight not helping his feelings of trepidation—and his legs were now shaking so badly they wouldn't support him any more!

It hadn't seemed this complicated when he'd been in England. Away from Andie...

He had been shocked to his core when he'd learnt of Andie's pregnancy. But once over that shock, his own part in that pregnancy acknowledged, the way had seemed clear and simple. Andie would have to marry him...

But looking at her now, the unsmiling line of her mouth, the stubborn jut of her chin, Adam knew there was going to be nothing clear or simple about persuading her that a marriage between the two of them was the only answer!

'I'm not,' he answered her taunt, running a hand through the slight dampness of his silver-blond hair. 'I—your assistant editor explained that you're away on—on maternity leave.' And his shock on hearing that hadn't yet receded! 'May I?' he indicated the jug of iced lemonade that sat on the table at her other side, the accompanying glass empty.

'Help yourself,' she invited, standing up before he could reach across her, slipping lightly by him to go and stand at the railing of the terrace, gazing out over the calm blue-green of the Mediterranean Sea.

Adam drank the lemonade thirstily, wishing, as he looked over at the rigid set of Andie's back, that it were whisky. He definitely felt in need of something stronger than lemonade!

'It's beautiful here, isn't it?'' she murmured as he joined her beside the rail.

It was beautiful, the villa built into the terraced hills on the west coast of the island, a one-hundred-and-eighty-degree view of the sea visible as far as the eye could see.

'Peaceful, too,' Andie added with a faint sigh.

It must have been peaceful for her—until he'd arrived, Adam acknowledged heavily. He had been to the villa with Rome and Barbara in the past, its remote spot appealing to the other couple. A woman came in from the village every day with the necessary shopping, staying on to cook and clean, meaning that they didn't have to stir from the villa at all if they didn't want to. As Andie didn't seem to have done...

'I'm sorry, Andie,' Adam said.

Her profile suddenly became rigid as she stared out to

sea, her hands tightly gripping the metal rail. 'I was too, to begin with,' she admitted jerkily. 'But now—somehow I don't seem to mind any more,' she acknowledged softly, her face still averted. But one hand moved protectively to the soft swell of her tummy...

His heart leapt at the admission. Although he knew only too well, from her lack of pleasure in his arrival a few minutes ago, that her feelings towards the baby had nothing to do with him, that maternal instinct was probably the reason for her change of heart.

'I actually meant I was sorry to have interrupted your peace and quiet,' he told her dryly.

Andie glanced at him now, lips twitching as she held back her smile at his humorously raised brows. 'How silly of me.' She shook her head self-derisively.

Adam became serious again. 'I— It seems a little early for maternity leave.' He frowned. 'Is there anything wrong? With you? Or the pregnancy?' His knuckles showed white on the rail as he waited for her answer.

'No,' she assured him lightly. 'I did have a little scare early on—it's okay,' she quickly soothed. 'But Jonas has advised it might be best if I don't continue to work through the pregnancy.'

'So that's how Danie met the man!' he realised. 'She didn't waste any time, did she?' he added ruefully; Andie was only three months pregnant.

Andie laughed. 'Jonas didn't realise what had hit him!'

Adam knew how he felt! The Summer women were absolutely lethal. 'What are we going to do, Andie?' he prompted.

She stiffened defensively, her mouth once again unsmiling. 'I have no idea what you are going to do, Adam,' she said. 'But I am going to soak up the sun for several more weeks, before I have to return for Daddy and Audrey's wedding, and then I will probably stay at the estate until after the baby is born.'

'Not "the" baby—*ours*!' he corrected more harshly than he had meant to.

He couldn't help it; the thought of Andie having their baby still made him shake with reaction. Possessive reaction. He wanted to just gather Andie up, her and the baby, and keep them safe for the rest of their lives.

But one look at Andie's determinedly set features told him it wasn't going to be as easy as that!

'Andie.' He turned to her, gently grasping her shoulders and turning her to face him. Although those damned sunglasses still hid her eyes from him!

'Don't!' she cried, shying away as he would have reached up and removed the sunglasses. 'Why have you come here, Adam? What do you want?'

What did he want? If he told her *that*, she would start running and never look back!

Stay cool, Munroe, he instructed himself severely. Hadn't he already done enough to this woman, without scaring the life out of her with the intensity of his feelings concerning her and their expected baby?

'It's not a question of what I want, Andie,' he ground out. 'It's a question of what is necessary.'

Her chin tilted challengingly. 'And that is…?'

'Marriage!' The word burst out of him forcefully. 'The two of us have to get married, Andie,' he added with grim determination.

She stiffened even more in the grip of his hands, her face first flushing and then becoming translucently pale.

Almost as if he had physically struck her with his suggestion…!

CHAPTER FIVE

MARRIAGE...

How ironic.

How amazingly, incredibly, unbelievably ironic. Marriage was a word Andie had never associated with Adam, and certainly had never matched with her own name.

And it wasn't now. Adam didn't want to marry her, he didn't want to marry anyone. He just felt that he had to...!

'Why are you smiling?' Adam broke harshly into the silence.

Smiling? Was she?

Probably, Andie conceded. What else was there to do in the face of such irony? She loved this man, carried their baby inside her, and he had offered to marry her only because of that baby.

She had known this would happen, of course, had known from the minute he became aware of her pregnancy that Adam would feel compelled to make such an offer.

What alternative did he have? Her father was far from stupid, and, even if neither of them ever revealed to him that it was Adam's baby, their strained manner towards each other, over the months—years?—ahead, would eventually become obvious to Rome. Especially to Rome...! Besides, the baby—son or daughter?—could just look so much like Adam when it was born that there would be no doubt that he was the father.

She looked up at him. 'Poor Adam,' she murmured ruefully.

'Poor—!' His hands tightened on her arms. 'What do you mean by that?' he demanded suspiciously.

She gave a humourless smile. 'A wife would be bad enough, but a child as well! However would you survive, Adam?' she taunted.

'The same way every other father does, I suppose,' he replied. 'With little sleep and a lot of heartache.' He bit out harshly at her questioning look.

That was exactly the way her father had described his own daughters' childhood! Somehow Andie had never thought of Adam in that light...

'You forgot the warmth and laughter,' she told him huskily.

His mouth twitched. 'According to Rome that comes later—once the sleepless nights have stopped! He assures me he walked around in a daze for five years while the three of you were babies!'

Andie gave him a sharp look. 'You haven't talked to my father about—'

'I very much doubt I would be here to tell the tale if Rome knew it was my child!' Adam cut in drily. 'I went to see Rome once I left your office—I needed to know where you had gone—and he assured me he's going to strangle the man if he ever finds out who fathered your baby. Apparently you have been less than helpful on that score...?'

'I have no wish to see you dead—or my father in prison for murdering you!'

Adam's laugh lacked any real humour. 'That could still happen,' he admitted. 'Although I understand your lack of enthusiasm for the latter,' he added grimly.

But not for the former, his words implied. However, despite what he might think to the contrary, she had no wish to see anything happen to Adam. She loved him, for goodness' sake! She just knew it was an emotion he would never reciprocate.

But that didn't mean he couldn't, wouldn't, love their baby. In fact, she was sure that he would. Adam had no family of his own, at least, none that he had ever spoken of, and this baby was his own flesh and blood. His only flesh and blood.

Andie just wasn't sure she could live with him, knowing he loved their child but could never feel anything but affection for her! She wasn't sure—but it was something she had known was going to be offered from the moment when she had decided, a month ago, that she wanted this baby, after all, already loved it with a fierce protectiveness that would allow no harm to come to it. Ever.

But did that include avoiding the emotional trauma that a legal battle with Adam, over his own rights where his child was concerned, would incur...? Did it include standing united with Adam in an effort not to alienate the baby's grandfather from the man who had been his best friend for the last twenty years? Did it include marrying Adam to avoid all that?

She still didn't have the answer to that!

She spoke again, sounding resigned. 'You don't want to marry me, Adam—'

'I don't think what I want—or, indeed, what you want, either!—is of particular importance at this moment,' he shot back, releasing her abruptly to walk determinedly to the other end of the terrace.

Andie swallowed hard, his words having put a chill into her heart. 'It isn't...?'

'No,' he told her firmly, a nerve pulsing in the tightness of his jaw. 'We have to think of the baby—'

'And you think I haven't been?' she cut in angrily, a flush to her cheeks now. 'How dare you?' she accused resentfully. 'Why else would I have given up a job that I love doing, if it weren't because it's safer for the baby if I don't work? Why else would I—?'

'Andie, I wasn't implying—'

'Yes, you were, damn you!' There was something to be said for the emotion of anger. It precluded any others—such as love!—from surfacing. 'And you have no right! You—'

'Andie, I didn't come here to fight with you,' Adam interrupted, eyes glittering silver as he glared across the terrace at her.

'Then why did you come?' Her head went back challengingly.

He gave a heavy sigh. 'I've already told you—I came here to ask you, to plead with you if necessary,' he added hardly, 'to consider marrying me.'

How it pained him to have to say it! What sort of marriage would it be, could it be, when it wasn't what either of them really wanted?

Her chin rose proudly. 'I've considered it, Adam, and—'

'Consider it again!' he advised harshly. 'And this time think of it from another angle but your own!' he continued scathingly, hands clenched at his sides now—as if he might strangle her if he didn't...?

She had been considering *every* angle since the moment she had decided, a month ago, that she loved this baby above everything else; her child's wants and needs were of paramount importance to her now. But she wasn't sure that having parents who didn't love each other was the best thing for her baby...

She gave Adam a narrow-eyed look. 'How can you be absolutely positive this baby is yours, Adam?'

His mouth twisted mockingly. 'I'm sure, Andie.'

'I don't see how—'

'I doubt that experience with me was enough to send you out on a life of bed-hopping conquests,' Adam declared. 'And if it wasn't—! You were a virgin that night, Andie,' he stated flatly. 'Or did you think my life was so debauched I wouldn't recognise a virgin if I met one?'

Andie swallowed hard, turning away, heated colour in her cheeks now. He hadn't said anything at the time—she had thought—

She had spent the last few years of her life living and working amongst a casual permissiveness that simply hadn't appealed to her. Maybe that was because she'd already been in love with Adam, and no other man would do for her; she simply didn't know. But he was right; she had been a virgin that night three months ago...

'You're right.' She sighed defeatedly, not wanting to continue discussing the subject of her virginity—or lack of it now! 'It is your child.'

'I never doubted it,' he bit out forcefully.

'What sort of marriage are you offering me, Adam?' she asked levelly, giving no indication that what he said in the next few minutes could be the deciding point for the rest of their lives.

He looked puzzled. 'I don't understand...?'

'In the circumstances, Adam, surely it's a perfectly straightforward question,' she replied, walking over to sit back down on the lounger. 'Oh, don't worry, I'm not asking for you to pretend you're in love with me. Any more than I could pretend to be in love with you.' How could she pretend something that was already a fact?

His puzzlement deepened. 'Then what are you asking for?' he returned.

Affection—if not love. Respect—surely she deserved that, at least? Fidelity—the one thing she wasn't sure Adam was capable of giving her!

She gave a shaky sigh at the thought of suffering years of women, like Elizabeth King, in the background of Adam's life. She couldn't bear that! But, at the same time, was it really feasible to expect the two of them to live out their lives in a loveless marriage? Oh, not that it would be true of her, but for Adam—!

She took a deep breath. 'The thing is, Adam, I grew up in a large family, and because of that I—I've never believed in having only children.'

He blinked, obviously trying to assimilate her words—and failing. 'You aren't expecting twins, are you?' he gasped.

'Not that I'm aware of, no,' she assured him.

'Then—' He broke off, frowning, his gaze searching on the paleness of her face. 'I see,' he finally said slowly.

'Do you?' She held her breath now as she waited for his answer.

'I think so.' Adam nodded. 'You know, Andie…' he strolled across the terrace to stand beside her '…a lot of what is said, and printed—' he grimaced '—concerning my private life, isn't necessarily all that it appears—'

'If only half of it's true—!' Andie gave a snort of derisive laughter.

'Oh, probably half of it's true,' Adam conceded, sitting down beside her on the lounger, his thigh only inches from the bareness of her own.

Andie was aware of him with every particle of her own body. She had lain naked with this man, made love with him, made a child with him—how could she not be aware of him? She knew she couldn't spend the rest of her life living in close confines with him without—without—

Even so, she flinched as Adam reached out to touch the creamy softness of her cheek, his hand dropping ineffectually down to his side.

He turned to stare grimly across at the tranquil sea. 'It doesn't augur well for those future children you mentioned if you're going to do that every time I try to touch you,' he said bitterly.

Andie paused. He was right, it didn't, but— 'The last time you touched me I got pregnant, remember?' she reminded him.

His mouth quirked. 'Well, that isn't likely to happen again, now, is it?'

She stood up suddenly, moving jerkily away from him. The problem was, just that light touch of Adam's hand on her cheek was enough to make her burn with wanting him, her heart pounding so loudly in her chest she was sure he had to hear it!

Why couldn't she hate this man? It would make life so much simpler. But what had happened between them three months ago precluded her life ever being simple again!

Could she marry Adam, knowing that he didn't love her, but felt forced, because of the baby and his long relationship with all of her family, into offering her marriage?

In retrospect, what had happened between them that night three months ago, seemed so childish, the two of them facing angrily up to each other like a couple of disgruntled children, their lovemaking a result of that immature temper rather than desire.

If she hadn't become pregnant, would they eventually have fallen back into that easy friendship that had been so much a part of their lives for so long?

Somehow she doubted it. But, in reality, it was a question, Andie knew she would never have an answer to...

She drew in a ragged breath, knowing that Adam was still waiting for her answer.

Yes. Or no.

Such simple little words, but one of them would shape the rest of her life. And her baby's...

She was going to say no, he knew it!

Adam had sat watching Andie as the conflicting emotions had flickered across her face: the anger, the sadness, and lastly the resolve. He didn't need a crystal ball to know she was going to turn down his marriage proposal...!

Whatever did he do then?

He would have no choice but to publicly announce the baby was his, not if he wanted to be the baby's father. And he was surprised himself at how much he wanted that. He had never given any thought to having children—you had to be with the woman you loved to think about things like that!—but the mere thought of his child growing inside Andie filled him with pride, and a strange need to be the sort of man the baby deserved as a father.

But if Andie refused to marry him, Adam knew that all hell was going to break loose when he tried to claim his rights as the baby's father. Not that he was bothered about that on his own account; he had struggled through much worse—and lived never to tell the tale, to anyone! No, it was Andie he was worried about. As her husband he could protect her from any, and all, adversity concerning her pregnancy. He didn't think she would allow him to do that if the two of them weren't married. In fact, he would probably become a part of that adversity!

He didn't want ever to hurt Andie—again, that was!—it was just that, circumstances being what they were, he—

'I really have given your suggestion careful consideration, Adam—' the huskiness of her voice interrupted his racing thoughts '—and I've come to the conclusion that—'

'Don't be too hasty, Andie,' he interrupted forcefully. 'As a single mother—even one from an obviously wealthy family,' he added, knowing Rome would never see any of his daughters in financial trouble of any kind, 'there will still be the problems of coping with the child more or less on your own, trying to fit work and motherhood together, of—'

'I've decided to accept your offer, Adam,' Andie put in gently.

'Trying to be everything to the baby and ending up ragged and—' Adam broke off as he realised exactly what Andie had just said.

She was saying yes!

He stared at her, knowing his mouth must literally be hanging open in his shocked surprise. But he couldn't help that; he *was* surprised.

He had expected to have much more of a fight on his hands, knew exactly how independent and strong-willed Andie could be. He had even booked a one-way ticket over here because he hadn't been sure how long it would take him to persuade Andie that marriage to him was by far the best solution. For all of them...

Instead she had said yes to his marriage proposal, not exactly instantly, but not with too much delay either.

He looked across at her with narrowed eyes, suspicion in their silver depths. 'What's the catch?' he murmured slowly, sure there had to be one. Although for the life of him he couldn't think what it could be!

Andie laughed softly, shaking her head, her hair a honey-coloured tumble over the bareness of her shoulders. 'I'm sure that isn't the normal reply when a woman has just accepted your marriage proposal!'

Adam remained unsmiling. 'This isn't a normal marriage proposal,' he pointed out gruffly.

'No,' she sobered, turning away. 'However, I do accept,

Adam,' she told him flatly. 'And there is no catch,' she added. 'Except—'

'Aha,' he pounced. '"Except" is definitely a catch.' He was frowning darkly now. 'What are your conditions for accepting, Andie?' he asked warily.

If she gave their marriage a time period, he couldn't accept; it was either for ever or not at all. If she asked for a marriage of convenience, again he couldn't accept; that one time with Andie had shown him that he couldn't promise never to make love to her again.

He wanted her now, couldn't even look at her without feeling aroused by her beauty and the smooth perfection of her body. Not that he did intend making love to her again until they were married, he just knew there was absolutely no way he could agree to a platonic marriage—because he would break that promise the minute she was his wife!

She stilled awhile before turning to look at him. At least, Adam presumed she was looking at him; those wretched sunglasses made it impossible to see exactly where she was looking!

'Take off the sunglasses, Andie,' he instructed harshly before she could speak. 'I want to see your eyes, damn it,' he ground out at her surprised expression.

'The windows to the soul, hmm, Adam?' she responded. But she reached up anyway and pushed the dark glasses back up into her hair.

'Something like that,' he said distractedly, looking searchingly into those deep green depths. And learnt nothing. Andie was deliberately keeping all expression out of her face and eyes… 'You were saying…?' he prompted gently, finding himself tensed as if waiting for a blow.

Perhaps he was. If Andie's conditions included either of those two things he knew he simply couldn't accept, then they were going to be in trouble.

She gave him a wry look. 'Now it's your turn to give this serious thought, Adam,' she taunted. 'We obviously aren't marrying for the reason people usually decide to spend the rest of their lives together. So far, it would appear that neither of us has met that one person we simply can't live without—'

'If you're talking about falling in love, Andie, then say so!' he interrupted, not liking the way this conversation was going at all.

She gave a taut smile, shrugging slightly. 'Okay, I'm talking about falling in love,' she confirmed with sarcasm. 'And until such time as either of us actually does that, I would want our marriage to be on a one-to-one basis—'

'Hell, I'm sure you never used to be this evasive!' Adam exploded as he stood up. 'What you're really trying to say is that if we get married you would expect me to be faithful—'

'*Both* of us to be faithful,' she corrected, her expression strained now.

'Until such time as either one of us meets that one person we can't live without,' Adam scathingly echoed her earlier words, shaking his head as he came to stand beside her, hands clenched tensely at his sides. 'I'm sorry, but your condition isn't acceptable to me, Andie,' he stated.

She paled, her cheeks suddenly looking translucent, giving her a fragile appearance that Adam instantly found alarming. But he couldn't agree to her condition; it would be like living with a sword hanging over his head. He had decided long ago, if marriage was ever for him, then it would have to be for ever. He couldn't—wouldn't—accept less. There was simply no way he could spend the rest of his life living in fear that Andie, of all people, might one day fall in love with someone else, and consequently leave him! No way…!

'Try to see it from my point of view, Andie,' he cajoled, still alarmed by her paleness. 'You're being unreasonable—'

'I should have known I was asking too much,' she cut in, giving him a disgusted glance before dropping those concealing sunglasses back down on the bridge of her nose. 'You're offering only half a commitment, Adam, for the sake of our child. I'm sorry, but I couldn't live that way.' She turned away, her face set in rigid lines.

Adam grasped her arms, turning her back to face him. 'You couldn't live that way?' he echoed disbelievingly. 'Then why the hell should you expect me to?' He shook her slightly in his agitation. 'From what I understand, marriage can be difficult enough, without having to sit there waiting for your partner to fall in love with someone else!'

Andie opened her mouth to say something. And then closed it again, looking up at him frowningly.

Adam coldly withstood that searching gaze. He would do a lot for Andie, agree to almost anything she asked of him, but he could not agree to committing himself to sitting there wondering when she would leave him. He just couldn't do that.

She hesitated. 'I didn't—I wasn't—Adam, I think there's been some sort of misunderstanding—'

'No misunderstanding, Andie,' he bit back. 'Either you agree to marry me, on the understanding it's a lifetime commitment—with no third parties involved. Ever,' he added grimly. 'Or we forget the whole thing.'

His heart was beating so loudly in his chest he could almost hear it, the blood rushing through his veins at breakneck speed as he felt his future balanced on the knife-edge of Andie's reply. He hadn't meant to issue her with an ultimatum, but in the circumstances he didn't feel he had any option. Even so, he stopped breathing as he waited for her to speak.

A nerve pulsed erratically in the slender column of Andie's throat. 'Adam,' she began slowly. 'Just now, when you said those terms were unacceptable to you, I thought you meant that fidelity to me was unacceptable to you, not—' she licked the dryness of her lips '—not the—the fact that the marriage might eventually fail because one of us fell in love with someone else!'

Adam's lips thinned. 'I may have come into the idea of marriage a bit later than most people, Andie, but that doesn't mean I don't have my own views on what it should be. And it shouldn't be a relationship that has the sword of Damocles hanging over it!'

That nerve was still pulsing in her throat, but some of the colour seemed to be returning to her cheeks now. Thank goodness, Adam noted with relief. He had come here to offer a solution to their problem, not to make Andie ill.

Her body relaxed slightly beneath the tight hold Adam still had of her arms. 'I agree,' she finally said softly.

Adam was perturbed. What did she agree to? This was turning into a nightmare; his emotions were like a roller coaster, one minute up, the next minute down.

Andie drew in a steadying gulp of air, her chin raised determinedly. 'On the understanding that it won't be a temporary thing. No half commitments, no third parties involved. Ever,' she repeated his words clearly. 'I agree to marry you.'

That knife-edge was suddenly no longer there, the sword no longer threatening. Andie was going to marry him!

And for the moment, that would have to be enough…

CHAPTER SIX

THE angry bellow could be heard throughout the whole house. Although the house staff, thank goodness, were used, over the years, not to react to their employer's occasional bouts of temper, apparently carrying on with their daily chores.

Something Andie was most grateful for as she shot Audrey a pained grimace. The two of them were in the sitting-room, supposedly drinking coffee together. Although, so far, that coffee had remained cooling in the cups as the two of them sat tensely waiting for Rome's reaction to Adam's news.

They had just heard it!

'It's gone very quiet,' Andie murmured a few seconds later, straining her ears trying to hear any further reaction from her father. The house remained silent with expectation. Unlike Andie, who was expecting, but certainly couldn't remain silent. Especially if her father were now in the process of doing Adam some physical damage. After all, she had been there three months ago too...! 'Do you think I should—?'

'No, I don't,' Audrey answered calmly, finally reaching forward to pick up her coffee-cup and sip at the now tepid liquid.

'But Rome might—'

'He won't,' Audrey assured her with certainty, looking serenely beautiful as she sat in one of the armchairs.

Andie wished she had the older woman's control! But she didn't, standing up to pace agitatedly up and down the room, glancing towards the doorway often, the two men ensconced in Rome's study down the carpeted hallway.

'How can you be so sure?' Andie finally burst out, the lack of any noise whatsoever coming from the direction of the study grating on her already frayed nerves. 'I realise that your engagement, and the wedding next month, have calmed Daddy down a lot, but even so, he isn't going to be pleased by what Adam's telling him, is he?' A frown marred her creamy brow.

'You might be surprised,' Audrey came back dryly. 'Oh, not by his reaction to your and Adam's news,' she added at Andie's obvious surprise at the remark. 'His reaction to that is anyone's guess, I'm afraid. No, I was referring to Rome's calmness.' She shook her head. 'He isn't calm at all since I told him that I had lived here, and worked for him, for twelve years, without going to bed with him, and that now I intended to wait until our wedding night!'

Andie gave a choked laugh, her own worries temporarily forgotten. 'You told Rome that?'

'I certainly did.' The older woman returned her smile. 'My assurance that anticipation is half the fun didn't go down too well, either!' she confided mischievously.

'I'm sure it didn't.' Andie laughed out loud now, easily able to imagine her father's frustration with such a decision. Although he still looked a lot happier than Andie had seen him for years. At least, he *had* looked happier... Her smile faded, to be replaced by her previous frown. 'But you must have some idea of what Rome's going to say about— about—' She still had trouble formulating the words herself. 'I wanted to tell Daddy myself, but Adam insisted he had to be the one to do it,' she went on, irritated beyond words at what she considered Adam's chauvinist behaviour.

In fact, what she had really wanted to happen was for Adam to return to England after their talk, while she stayed on in Majorca for another week. But Adam wouldn't hear of it. They either both stayed in Majorca, or they both returned to England. And he had been absolutely adamant that he would be the one to talk to Rome.

'Quite right too.' Audrey nodded. 'It's his responsibility, Andie,' she added firmly before Andie could protest.

'Don't be ridiculous, Audrey. I'm almost twenty-six years old; I knew exactly what I was doing when I made love with Adam.'

Just once, she had promised herself at a point in their lovemaking when she had known she could have stopped it if she had wanted to. Just once, to be held in Adam's arms, to be loved for herself, and not for her resemblance to her mother. Just once—and it was turning into a lifetime commitment for both of them!

It was going to be no easy thing to be Adam's wife, to know that she could only ever be second best. But any woman would have been second best after her mother, so why not let it be her? After all, she loved Adam, and maybe one day—one day, he might be able to love her a little in return. Better, Andie had decided in Majorca, to be with the man she loved, than spend the rest of her life doing what she had already done for so long: watching and loving him from afar…

Audrey gave her a searching look. 'I'm sure you did,' she finally said. 'As did Adam. Which is why he should be the one to tell your father.' She gave a smile. 'Rome is so overjoyed at the idea of being a grandfather, he might just decide to overlook the fact that the two of you didn't get married first. I—' She broke off as a door could be heard opening down the hallway. 'I think we're about to find out,' Audrey revised quickly.

Andie could feel her tension growing as the two men made their slow progress down the hallway. At least, it seemed slow to her, they could actually have been running for all she knew!

Her father was the first to enter the sitting-room, a quick search of his rigidly set features telling her nothing, her gaze quickly passing to Adam, her heart sinking as he gave a slight shake of his head.

Whatever did that mean? Even if her father wasn't agreeable to them getting married, they were adults, for goodness' sake, could do as they pleased. They had done exactly that three months ago, which was why they were here together today at all! They had only come here to tell her father of their plans; they weren't asking his permission!

Having agonised as she had over accepting Adam's marriage proposal in the first place, she certainly wasn't about to let her father put a dampener on it now!

'I won't have it, Andie,' her father's angrily grated comment broke the tense silence. 'It's just not on. No daughter of mine—'

'Daddy, this has nothing to do with you,' she broke in determinedly; having made her decision where marrying Adam was concerned—painfully so!—she wasn't about to have her father now telling her what she could and couldn't do! 'I'm over eighteen, have been making my own decisions for years now, and Adam and I have only come here today to pay you the courtesy of letting you know what our plans are. You—'

'Very kind of you, I'm sure!' Rome exclaimed sarcastically.

'Andie—'

'Leave it, Adam,' the older man told him sharply as he would have interrupted. 'I don't believe my daughter has finished speaking yet.' Rome turned pointedly back to Andie. 'You were saying…?'

She drew in a ragged breath. 'Adam and I—' She

stopped, wondering if she would ever get used to hearing their two names linked together like that. 'We have decided to get married. We would naturally like you and Audrey to be there, but—'

'How kind of you again,' her father drawled, lowering his lean length into one of the armchairs, chilly blue gaze fixed on Andie.

She shifted uncomfortably under the intensity of that gaze. 'We intend getting a special licence, and the wedding will be organised in a register office for the end of next week—'

'No,' her father stated decisively.

Andie's cheeks flushed mutinously. 'It isn't your decision, Daddy,' she burst out incredulously, looking across at Adam appealingly. Instead of just standing there, why didn't he do something, say something? 'I am going to marry Adam, Rome,' she began again. 'With or without your approval. Although, of course, I would rather have it—'

'Again, how kind,' Rome said dryly.

Her cheeks flushed fiery red at his obvious continued sarcasm.

'But I don't need it,' she told him determinedly. 'And your permission I certainly don't need.'

'Andie.' Adam spoke quietly as he crossed the room to her side, his arm moving protectively about her shoulders. 'Rome, stop playing with her,' he turned to tell the older man. 'Andie, your father is perfectly in agreement with the two of us getting married,' he told her gently.

'How kind of *you*!' she snapped rebelliously at her father.

'He just isn't happy,' Adam continued, 'with the two of us going to a register office to do it!'

'My exact words were, sneaking off to a register office

to do it,' Rome said. 'Harrie and Danie have had full white weddings,' he continued. 'You and Adam will have the same.'

Andie stared at her father. He—they—what—? 'You don't disapprove of my marrying Adam...!' she realised dazedly.

'Certainly not,' Rome came back instantly. 'I'm actually amazed you've shown such good taste.'

'Thanks!' She was still dazed at his reaction.

'I'm not too pleased by the way the two of you have been creeping about meeting each other in secret,' Rome commented. 'But other than that, I couldn't have chosen a better husband for you myself!' he added with satisfaction.

Andie had turned to give Adam a sharp look at her father's mention of the two of them meeting each other in secret, the tightening of Adam's arm about her shoulders, and his warning glance, telling her he would explain later. When the two of them were alone...

Not that he needed to explain; she could already guess how the conversation had gone between Adam and her father. Adam could hardly have told the older man that the two of them had actually only been out together once, and that Rome's grandchild was the result of anger with each other over the way that evening had turned out!

She just wished Adam had taken the trouble to explain to her exactly how he was going to broach the subject to her father! Although, in truth, the two of them had barely spoken to each other on the flight back to England earlier in the day.

She turned back to her father. 'We can't get married in church, Daddy,' she told him huskily. 'I— It wouldn't seem right. In the circumstances I certainly can't get married in white!' She was slightly pale now, the strain of this meeting finally getting to her.

'Sit down,' Adam told her firmly, pushing her gently down into a chair before pouring some fresh coffee into her cup and handing it to her. 'Drink it,' he instructed evenly, standing over her.

After a rebellious moment of stubbornness, Andie did exactly that, her eyes flashing deeply green as she glared at her future husband over the rim of the cup.

Rome chuckled gleefully. 'Out of the frying pan, hmm, Andie?' he teased with obvious enjoyment of the situation.

She shook back her hair as she turned to include her father in that glare. Adam was as forceful as her father, all right. And as domineering. Which meant the two of them were probably going to have more than their fair share of arguments before they came to some sort of compromise. But that would probably be preferable to the two of them continuing to behave like polite strangers!

'Andie, you don't have to wear white for the wedding.' Audrey was the one to step tactfully into the rising tension. 'Most women wear cream nowadays, anyway. Or almond, even. It's a sad reflection on society, I know, but I'm afraid there aren't too many virgin brides left any more!'

Andie deliberately didn't look at Adam as her cheeks coloured fiery red, but she could sense his searching glance on her. Except for that one act of heated impetuosity between the two of them, they both knew she *would* have been a virgin bride.

'Don't you think I'll look slightly ridiculous?' Andie began sharply. 'Floating down the aisle on the arm of my father, over three months pregnant!'

'No.' Adam was the one to answer. 'You'll just look beautiful. As you always do,' he added emotionally.

This was going to be a nightmare, Andie decided. They had overcome the hurdle of her father's anger and disapproval, only to find themselves confronted with the prospect of a church wedding rather than the register office Andie would have preferred— That *she* would have preferred...?

She turned sharply to look at Adam, his deadpan expression telling her nothing of his thoughts. Deliberately so? He hadn't said anything in Majorca when she had told him she wanted a quiet wedding, as unobtrusive as possible, with only close family in attendance. At the time she had assumed his silence on the subject had been agreement, now she wasn't so sure...

'It just seemed better to tell your father we had been meeting in secret,' Adam defended wearily at her attack. 'After thinking about it—'

'For all of two seconds,' Andie accused, the two of them sitting in Adam's car as he drove them back to London.

Adam accepted it had been an evening of tension for the two of them, the subject of the wedding—in church—the only conversation over dinner.

'What would you rather I had done, Andie?' Adam challenged, hands tightly gripping the steering wheel. 'Explain to Rome that we only went out together for the evening once—and his grandchild is the result of that evening?'

Of course Andie wouldn't want that. And Adam had known that only too well. But Adam could also understand Andie's problem with that; this way Rome, and the rest of her family, were going to assume this was a love-match...

'Of course not.' She sighed wearily. 'But how do you expect the two of us to keep up this obligation we now feel to act as if we're in love with each other?'

His mouth set grimly. 'We would have had to do that anyway, Andie, you know that,' he said. 'Rome wouldn't accept anything less for one of his daughters.'

If Rome so much as guessed this situation was at all contrived, then he wouldn't have given his blessing to their marriage. Despite what Andie might have claimed earlier, Adam knew her well enough to know she would find any estrangement from her father extremely stressful. And, in her condition, that simply wasn't on as far as Adam was concerned.

'It wasn't so bad this evening, was it?' he asked teasingly, sensing rather than seeing the sharp look she gave him in the dark confines of the car. 'I thought we managed quite well,' he opined with satisfaction.

'And I think you went too damned far when you tried to tempt me into eating dessert by actually feeding it to me yourself!' Andie replied impatiently.

That was a pity; he had quite enjoyed that part of the evening! 'But you enjoyed the dessert, after all, didn't you?' he reasoned sardonically, having eventually persuaded her to eat every mouthful of the sherry trifle.

'It isn't a question of enjoying it,' Andie said snappily. 'I simply don't want to end up as big as a house before the baby is born!'

Adam looked at her darkly at his explanation. 'I think your size ten can go to hell for the time being!'

'Size eight, actually,' she came back waspishly. 'And I have no intention of battling for months to regain my figure after the baby is born.'

Adam opened his mouth to tell her once again exactly what he thought about the subject of her weight, and then closed it again. He didn't want to argue with Andie, especially over something he knew, in the long run, he would have very little say in. Andie would do as she pleased. He had enough confidence in her judgement to know she would never do anything that would harm the baby.

'Are we having our first engaged argument?' He finally broke the silence.

'We aren't engaged, Adam,' she came back tautly.

'Oh, yes, we are,' he returned as determinedly. 'We agreed in Majorca that we're both only going to do this the once, Andie, so we're going to do it properly. I've asked you to marry me, you've accepted—'

'You asked because I'm pregnant. And I accepted—'

'For the same reason,' he pointed out. 'But I suggest we both move on from there. I—'

'Adam, was it your idea we get married in church?' she prompted suspiciously.

He drew in a sharp breath. 'Rome—'

'No, not Rome,' she insisted, turning in her seat to look at him. 'Oh, I'm sure he was in full agreement with it, but who was the first one to suggest it?'

She was too damned astute by half, Adam decided frustratedly. 'I was,' he admitted reluctantly.

'I thought so!' Andie exclaimed irritably.

His mouth firmed. 'And can you honestly say you wouldn't prefer a church wedding?'

She sighed. 'In all honesty, no. But—'

'No buts, Andie,' he said with finality. 'A church wedding it will be. Tomorrow we will meet, choose an engagement ring together, before going out for a celebration lunch.'

'No!' Andie gasped protestingly.

'You would rather we had lunch and then chose the engagement ring?' he reasoned thoughtfully. 'I don't see how we can celebrate when we don't have the ring yet, but—'

'No, that isn't what I meant at all, and you know it,' she interjected with reluctant laughter. 'Adam—'

'Yes, Andrea?' he returned mildly.

'Uh-oh,' she said warily. 'Rome only ever calls me by my full name when I've pushed him as far as he's willing to go...'

Adam knew that. 'Yes?' he prompted again.

'Okay, okay.' She held up her hands defensively. 'An engagement ring and then lunch it is.'

Adam reached out and squeezed her hand. 'I knew you would come round to my way of thinking.'

'I'm not sure I had any say in it at all,' she replied. 'I hope you aren't going to be this domineering over everything, Adam. Because if you are—'

'We're going to end up arguing a lot,' he predicted lightly. 'And that isn't going to be good for you or—'

'The baby,' Andie put in dryly.

'Or me,' Adam finished correctly. 'I've never liked arguments, Andie.' Probably because he had witnessed too many of them in his formative years, and the thought of living in that sort of battlefield gave him the shudders! 'Any problems, and I suggest we talk them out rather than resort to a slanging match, okay?'

'I've never resorted to a slanging match in my life—'

'Good,' he cut in with satisfaction over Andie's outraged outburst. 'That's agreed, then.'

The indignant silence emanating from Andie's side of the car told him she didn't think she had agreed to anything!

Adam inwardly acknowledged this new relationship with Andie was slightly odd. Although not in an unpleasant way. No, he decided happily, not unpleasant at all...

In fact, he knew he could get used to it all too quickly!

'Shall I come in with you?' Adam offered once he had parked the car outside her apartment building, getting out to open her door for her.

Andie joined him on the pavement. 'What on earth for?' she asked.

'Now there's a leading question...'' he teased.

'Don't be ridiculous, Adam.' Her cheeks were fiery red as she looked up at him.

'You're probably right,' he agreed. 'Exactly when are Danie and Jonas expected back from their honeymoon?'

'This weekend,' Andie provided with a puzzled frown. 'Why?'

'We'll make an appointment to go and see Jonas on Monday.'

'Monday?' Andie echoed incredulously. 'I'll have you know that Jonas is a very busy man. I very much doubt he will have the time to see us on Monday.'

Adam quirked blonde brows. 'He couldn't make time even for his new sister-in-law and her fiancé?'

Her cheeks flushed fiery red. 'I have never asked for special favours in any part of my life!'

No, he was aware of that. Andie had worked her way up to her now prominent position as Senior Editor of *Gloss*, even though her father had been more than capable of buying her the magazine if she had ever expressed such a wish. Which she never had. But Andie's independence was part of what he admired about her.

'I'll call Jonas's office anyway,' he said purposefully.

'But why do you need to see him?' Andie frowned her consternation. 'I've already told you that the pregnancy is progressing well after that hiccup a few weeks ago.'

Adam's mouth tightened. 'I want to hear more about that "hiccup", and its implications.'

'But—'

'You'll just have to accept, Andie, that I intend being one-hundred-per-cent involved in your pregnancy, and the birth,' he told her. 'Besides, I need to have a chat with Jonas, anyway.'

'Concerning what?' Andie eyed him suspiciously.

'Concerning how and when it's going to be safe for us to indulge in anything like that,' Adam answered mildly.

'Indulge in anything like what?' Andie cried.

'Like that,' he repeated, suppressing the laughter he felt at Andie's obvious indignation, not sure she would appreciate his humour in her present mood. In fact, he was sure she wouldn't.

But he had realised from her flinching reaction to him in Majorca that they had a few barriers to break down on the side of any physical relationship they intended having in the future. And, as husband and wife, they *would* have a physical relationship.

They were two healthy, not unattractive people, about to marry each other; there was no way they could live celibate together. Besides, Andie had told him quite clearly that she wanted more than one child...

Andie stiffened her shoulders, green eyes flashing fire as she glared at him. 'In my opinion, anything like that can wait until after we're married!' she growled.

He shrugged. 'I'm sure Jonas would allow a few kisses and caresses—'

'Maybe Jonas would—but I wouldn't!' Andie told him furiously.

'We don't want to get out of practice,' he drawled mockingly.

Her fingers tightened on the strap of her handbag. 'Some of us have never been *in* practice,' she responded scathingly. 'And a week or so's abstinence won't do you any harm, either!'

A week or so...

How little she knew. Adam hadn't so much as looked at another woman since that night with Andie almost four months ago.

As he looked at the flushed beauty of her face, inwardly indulging himself with the knowledge that she carried their baby, he had a feeling that he never would again...

CHAPTER SEVEN

SHE was being stupid. Ridiculous. Juvenile.

But somehow, no matter what names she called herself, Andie couldn't help her feelings of excitement as she waited for Adam to arrive to take her out to choose their engagement ring.

He had kissed her very chastely on the cheek last night before leaving her with the promise that he would pick her up at eleven o'clock today.

Andie had dressed with care, the Edwardian-style jacket of the bottle-green suit she wore doing much to hide the slighter fullness to her waist and breasts, the cream blouse alleviating its dark colour. Her hair was thick and glossily gold over her shoulders, her make-up light, peach lipgloss emphasising the curve of her mouth.

Power-dressing, her father would have called it. But, as Andie was quickly learning, she needed all the confidence she could muster against Adam's teasing forcefulness.

She had wanted to be the one to talk to her father, but Adam had insisted it had to be him that did that. She hadn't expected a church wedding, but Adam had seen to it that was exactly what they would have. She hadn't expected an engagement ring, either. But again, she had been overruled.

She would have to be very careful in the future that Adam didn't end up making all their decisions for them!

But when she opened the door to him a few minutes later, eyes widening as she took in his handsomeness in the charcoal-grey suit and pale silver shirt, a grey silk tie knotted neatly at his throat, Andie realised it wasn't going to be so easy to withstand his way of charming her into agreement. Not if her knees knocked together like this every time she saw him!

Adam bent his head to lightly brush his lips against hers. 'You look beautiful,' he told her as he straightened. 'I've booked an appointment for us at the jewellers for eleven-thirty, with instructions for them to show us rings that have emeralds in as well as diamonds. And the restaurant is booked for—'

'I can see you've been very busy this morning, Adam,' Andie interrupted. 'But shouldn't you have consulted me first about the type of engagement ring I would like? You—'

'I thought the emeralds would go with your eyes.' He shrugged. 'But if you have other ideas...?'

An emerald and diamond engagement ring sounded wonderful, especially in view of the fact that until yesterday she hadn't known she was going to have one at all. But, even so, Adam instructing the jewellers that was what they were to show her was just another example of his high-handedness.

'Not particularly,' she dismissed, turning to pick up her bag. 'I would just like to do my own choosing, if you don't mind.'

'I don't mind at all,' he accepted, taking a light hold of her arm as they left the apartment. 'Your father has some good news too. He's managed to secure a church wedding for us at three o'clock three weeks on Saturday,' he announced.

'It's not what you know but who you know,' Andie muttered, her earlier excitement giving way to irritation. She had the feeling much like being on a runaway express train—with her merely a helpless passenger!

'Quite honestly, Andie, I don't care how Rome managed

it,' Adam stated as he held the car door open for her to get inside. 'Besides, that extra couple of weeks will allow time for any other arrangements we want to make.'

'It will also allow time for me to look even more pregnant,' Andie pointed out.

Adam turned to smile at her as he got into the car beside her. 'I told you, Andie; you look beautiful. Pregnancy obviously suits you.'

She was also, she inwardly acknowledged, starting to sound like a shrill-voiced harridan. She really didn't have any objection to any of these arrangements—apart from the fact that her father and Adam seemed to have taken over! Besides, she didn't want Adam to think he was getting a shrew for a wife...

'I'm sure it will all work out,' she replied noncommittally.

Adam reached out and squeezed her hand. 'I'm going to be the model husband and father,' he assured her huskily.

Andie couldn't help it, she spluttered with laughter. 'Now that I just have to see,' she chuckled once she felt able to talk again. 'Adam Munroe, one of the world's most eligible bachelors, a model husband and father! Do you have any idea how to go about achieving that?'

Adam arched arrogant brows at her laughter. 'Your father managed it, so why shouldn't I?'

Her humour faded completely. Her father had 'managed' it because Barbara had been his wife and the mother of his children; Adam only had her.

'Perhaps you're right,' she responded flatly, turning to look sightlessly out of the car window.

She had known in Majorca, when she'd accepted Adam's proposal, that this marriage was going to be fraught with emotional tension. But actually living it was completely different from knowing it...

'What did I say wrong now?' Adam asked softly at her continued silence.

Andie forced her panicked feelings back into the recesses of her mind. There was no reason, absolutely none, she told herself firmly, why her marriage to Adam shouldn't be a complete success.

'Nothing.' She reached out and lightly touched his arm.

The choosing of her engagement ring was much more fun than she had imagined it would be, Adam's indulgence knowing no bounds as he encouraged her to try on any ring that took her fancy.

There were no prices on any of the rings—the exclusivity of the jewellers clearly indicated that if you needed to know the price then you couldn't afford it!—but even so some of the jewels were so big as to be garish in Andie's eyes.

The ring she finally settled on was definitely not in that category, an emerald and diamond cluster, one large emerald surrounded by eight smaller diamonds.

'There is a wedding ring to complement this particular ring,' the male assistant told them.

'I—'

'We'll look at it,' Adam answered the man firmly. 'And a plain gold wedding ring is suitable for me,' he added decisively.

Andie turned slowly to look at him as the male assistant moved unhurriedly to get the requested rings. Adam intended wearing a wedding ring?

He looked at her in amusement at her obvious surprise. 'A model husband and father, remember?' he teased.

'And that includes wearing a wedding ring?' She couldn't say she wasn't pleased that Adam intended to wear this public announcement of being a married man; she was just stunned that he was choosing to do so.

'Yes, it does,' he told her with certainty. 'I—'

'Here we are, sir, madam.' The assistant returned with the matching wedding ring to Andie's choice of engagement ring, and another tray containing an assortment of male wedding rings.

Her own wedding ring was shaped to fit around the cluster, also studded with emeralds and diamonds. But, to Andie's amazement, Adam took as much time choosing his wedding ring as she had her engagement ring, finally settling on a thin plain gold band. She had to admit, it suited the long, artistic slenderness of his hand.

Although Adam wasn't quite so happy with his own choice when Andie insisted on buying it for him!

'That was unnecessary,' he told her stiltedly when they left the shop a short time later, Andie's engagement ring firmly on her finger, the two wedding rings packed away in their respective boxes.

Andie reached out and touched his arm. 'Not to me,' she assured him. If he intended wearing a wedding ring, then it was going to be one that she had bought for him. Otherwise it just wouldn't mean the same thing.

He seemed about to say something else, but then thought better of it. 'Thank you,' he finally accepted.

She gave a mischievous smile. 'You're welcome. Not very good at accepting gifts yourself, are you?' Her own rings must have cost several hundred times more than Adam's wedding ring had cost her.

He grimaced. 'Probably because I've very rarely been given any.'

Andie looked up at him thoughtfully. 'Not even when you were a child?' she probed gently, realising, and not for the first time, just how little she really knew about his early years.

Adam gave a bitter laugh. 'Especially not then!'

'But—'

'Leave it, Andie,' he grated. 'I promise I'll try to be a little more gracious about accepting the next time you give me a gift, okay?' he added with deliberate lightness.

But Andie wasn't fooled for a moment. What sort of parents had he had not to know the joy of receiving gifts from them at Christmas and on his birthday…?

There was still so much about Adam she didn't know, so many facets she wasn't aware of that had made him the man he was today. Well, maybe she didn't know them now. But she would. Oh, yes, in time she most definitely would!

Adam watched her face as they entered the dining-room of the restaurant he had booked for lunch, knowing by the pleasure that lit up her features as she saw her father and Audrey already seated there, along with Andie's sister Harrie and her husband Quinn, that he had done the right thing in inviting them here to share in their celebration.

Up until this moment, he could only hope that he was doing the right thing in organising this surprise for her. Although he had also realised that by presenting a *fait accompli* to her family today it was going to be less awkward for Andie in the future; the last thing she wanted, or needed, at the moment was to go around explaining herself to all of them.

'We'll go out with Danie and Jonas separately once they're back from their honeymoon,' he assured Andie as they went to join the rest of her family at the table.

She turned to give him a glowing smile, emerald-coloured eyes over-bright with unshed tears. 'Thank you.' She squeezed his arm gratefully.

They might have started this off all wrongly, Adam had decided as he'd lain alone in his bed the previous evening, but that stopped right here. Andie deserved to have the best, and a celebration lunch for their engagement was going to be the start of it.

'My, my, my,' Harrie said as she stood up to congratulate them both. 'Some people will go to any lengths to throw a party!'

Andie laughed softly. 'It's Adam's party.'

'Our party,' he corrected firmly.

Harrie reached up to kiss him warmly on the cheek. 'You've been an honorary member of our family for so long, it will be nice to make it official.' She smiled at him.

Adam glanced at Andie, realising she was very close to letting those tears overflow and spill hotly down her cheeks. 'Show Harrie and Audrey your ring, Andie,' he instructed teasingly. 'While us men get down to the more serious matter of studying the menus!'

Lunch was a resounding success, Andie relaxing completely in the company of her family, laughingly happy, even indulging in a sip of the champagne Adam ordered for a celebration toast.

Now all he had to do was try to get her to become that relaxed in his own company. *All* he had to do...! That wasn't going to be so easy.

But they had made a start. He had managed to kiss her lightly a couple of times today without her jumping like a startled doe. In time he hoped they would be able to find that easy friendship that had once existed between them.

Even if being Andie's friend was the last thing he wanted to be!

Being pregnant definitely suited Andie, that nausea she had experienced initially having all but gone now, leaving her with a contented glow that made her infinitely desirable. In fact, he was going to find great difficulty in containing that desire until after their wedding in three weeks' time.

'I forgot to tell you,' he said casually as he drove her

back to her apartment later that afternoon. 'I called Jonas's office earlier too—'

'You did have a busy morning,' Andie murmured derisively, her smile totally relaxed as she looked across at him.

'It's the way I am,' he admitted ruefully. 'If something needs fixing, then do it. Now. Not later. I spoke to someone called Dorothy. Jonas's secretary, I presume—'

'And watchdog.' Andie laughed. 'Danie swears that if Dorothy hadn't approved of her she may have had a fight on her hands where marrying Jonas is concerned. She's talking nonsense, of course. It's obvious to anyone with eyes in their head that Jonas absolutely adores Danie.' She frowned wistfully.

Adam wasn't unaware of her wistfulness. As he wasn't unaware of the fact that Andie had to wish their marriage was going to be the love-match her sisters' were.

But a lot of couples had started life together on less than they had between them; there was absolutely no reason why their own marriage shouldn't be as happy and successful as Harrie and Quinn's obviously was—Danie and Jonas's too, he shouldn't wonder.

He reached out and briefly touched her hand. He would make this marriage right for them. For Andie's and the baby's sake, he had to!

'Dorothy didn't seem to think there would be any problem with our seeing Jonas on Monday,' he continued lightly.

Andie quirked teasing brows in his direction. 'The Munroe influence wins out again!'

'Actually—' he grinned '—it was the Summer influence this time! It seems that, as Danie's sister, you come in for preferential treatment where Jonas Noble is concerned.'

Andie snorted. 'I told you Dorothy is in charge!'

Adam didn't particularly care who made the decisions,

as long as he got to share this pregnancy with Andie. 'We have an appointment to see Jonas at two o'clock on Monday. Apparently he isn't usually available on Monday afternoons, but for you he'll make the exception.'

Andie nodded. 'Jonas runs a free clinic twice a week for women who need his professional help but can't afford to pay for it.'

Adam felt himself bristle with resentment at the undoubted admiration for the other man in Andie's tone. He had met Jonas Noble at the wedding a couple of weeks ago, had found him charming enough. But, knowing how difficult Danie could be on occasion, Adam didn't doubt the other man had a lot more to him than that surface charm. He just didn't like the fact that Andie obviously thought so too!

'We can have lunch together again, if that suits you,' Adam said stiffly. 'And then go on to the clinic.'

She paused. 'I can't think of anything else I have to do on Monday. Or any other day, for that matter,' she muttered, obviously alluding to the fact that she was no longer working, her diary remarkably empty after years of being tied to a tight working and social schedule.

'Try to keep three weeks on Saturday free, too, hmm?' he teased.

'I'll try.' She laughed huskily, obviously mellowed by the success of their engagement luncheon.

And it had been a success, the others taking their cue from Adam, and treating their engagement and impending marriage with all the excitement it should have. There had even been a couple of jokes about two matrons of honour; Harrie was sure that Danie wouldn't want to be left out.

After years of putting any thoughts of marriage from his own mind, Adam found he was quite looking forward to the wedding in three weeks' time too. Andie was going to be his wife, and that was something he had never thought would happen!

'Would you like to come to dinner this evening?' Andie offered as they reached her apartment, Adam having already reluctantly explained that he would have to at least show his face in his own office this afternoon. Reluctantly because, now that Andie had agreed to marry him, he found he didn't want to let her out of his sight!

'You mean you can cook, too?' he said with mock—surprise.

Andie's eyes gleamed in the confines of the parked car. '"Too"?'

'You make love rather beautifully,' he told her.

Her gaze no longer met his, heated colour in her cheeks now. 'Don't patronise me, Adam,' she said. 'I was awkward and inexperienced.'

'You could never be awkward in anything you do, Andie.' He reached out and gently touched one of her hot cheeks. 'And you were lovely in your inexperience. I'm only sorry—'

'I have to go, Adam,' she announced abruptly, reaching out to open her car door before getting out onto the pavement. 'Don't get out,' she said as he would have done exactly that, bending down to speak to him. 'I'm making dinner for seven-thirty, if you would care to join me.'

Too far, too soon, Adam acknowledged heavily as he drove away. Obviously that night was still something Andie would rather not talk about. Even if she now carried the physical proof of that night inside her.

But he wished she had let him finish saying how part of him wished he could have given her the same gift she had given him that night three months ago, that his own experience hadn't far outweighed her own. There was nothing he could do to change it now, but how he now regretted all those other relationships that had meant nothing to him.

The last thing he wanted, or needed, after the enjoyable lunch with Andie and her family, was to see that familiar figure waiting for him outside his office.

Not here.

Not now, he wanted to cry.

The woman arched an eyebrow. 'You don't look pleased to see me, Adam,' she said.

He was never pleased to see her. How could he be?

'Aren't you going to invite me in, Adam?' she demanded as someone brushed past them in the corridor on their way to the office further down.

She knew, damn her, that the last thing he wanted was for anyone to see him talking to her. To add two and two together, and come up with—

'I suppose you had better,' he rasped, pushing open the outer door, nodding tersely to Andrew, his assistant, as he walked straight past him and through into his own office.

All the time knowing she would be following him. He could hear the softness of her breathing, smell her perfume.

That perfume. He had smelt it in his sleep for years. Until Andie's perfume had replaced it…!

He sat down behind his desk, eyes steely grey, totally unmoved by the faded beauty this woman had become. 'What do you want?'

She tilted her head, giving him a considering look. 'There's something different about you…' she commented thoughtfully.

Adam felt himself stiffen. How could she tell! How did she know? Had just the thought of having Andie for his wife really made him look different?

Because if it had he would have to do everything in his power to hide that difference from this woman. At least until three weeks on Saturday. When his marriage to Andie would be a *fait accompli*.

When this woman could no longer do or say anything to change that!

CHAPTER EIGHT

THERE was something different about Adam this evening.

Andie had noticed that difference as soon as he'd arrived shortly before seven-thirty to join her for dinner at her apartment. For one thing there had been no smile on his face. And for another, he hadn't even attempted to kiss her hello...

Strange how she had already become used to those light kisses of his, and how much she had missed that casual intimacy this evening.

She watched him below lowered lashes as they ate the avocado and prawns with marie-rose sauce she had pre-pared for their first course. Adam ate the food automati-cally, not even seemingly aware of what he was eating. Although he complimented her on the choice once his plate was empty.

Andie removed the plates, looking down at him thought-fully. 'What did you just eat?'

Adam blinked up at her. 'I—well—it was prawns and—and something, wasn't it?' he said falteringly.

'And something,' she agreed, becoming more and more convinced that Adam's thoughts were definitely elsewhere.

Unless he had finally realised that they were going to be married in a matter of weeks, that they would spend a lot of their evenings together like this...?

'I'll go and get the second course,' she announced abruptly.

'We'll go and get the second course,' Adam told her decisively as he stood up. 'I have no problem with eating

111

at home, but I do object to having you wait on me.' He followed her out to the kitchen.

Despite the fact that Andie had known this man for most of her life, she realised that they really knew very little about each other's private lives. For one thing, she had no idea whether Adam usually ate at home in the evenings, or whether he went out to a restaurant. There was no doubting the fact that he could afford to do the latter if he chose to, but restaurant food, although enjoyable, could become tiresome on a regular basis.

At least, that was what she told herself as she served the lamb chops, baby potatoes and peas that were their main course, knowing she had only provided cheeses to follow.

Maybe she was expecting too much of Adam. Maybe it was a little early in their new relationship to be bombarding him with domesticity!

The thing was, she actually quite enjoyed cooking, although it was her sister Danie who was the trained cook. Amongst other things.

'I hope you like lamb,' Andie said awkwardly as she served the sauce to go with it.

'I'll eat anything,' Adam replied distractedly. 'Sorry—I didn't mean that quite the way it sounded.' He groaned as he realised what he had just said. 'I'm sure the meal is going to be just fine,' he added reassuringly.

She frowned across at him. 'Adam—'

'Would you like me to open the wine?' he prompted, holding up the bottle that stood on the side, his expression once again unreadable.

She had forgotten all about serving the wine earlier! Not that she would drink any herself, but she had put out a nice bottle of red wine for Adam to enjoy—and promptly forgotten all about it.

She knew why she had, of course; Adam's distant behaviour when he'd arrived having thrown her into a state of confusion...

In fact, this evening wasn't going at all as she had thought it would. They had seemed so relaxed with each other earlier today, the engagement lunch with most of her family a complete success.

She had been touched that Adam had gone to so much trouble on her behalf, and this evening's meal came in the form of a thank-you for that thoughtfulness. But since his arrival half an hour ago Adam had given every impression that this was the last place he wanted to be.

Was she the last person he wanted to be with?

Well, what else had she expected? Until a few days ago, Adam hadn't even thought about having a wife, let alone taking on a baby as well. She had been in shock herself for weeks after realising she was pregnant, had denied it to herself for the same amount of time; it was going to take Adam time to get used to this idea too...

'I hope you don't mind if I opt for an early night once we've had our meal.' She spoke brightly once they were seated back at the dining-table. 'It's been rather an—exciting day, one way or another,' she said with a rueful glance at the engagement ring that twinkled and glittered on her left hand.

Adam's ring. A ring she had thought never to own.

She had dreamt of one day being with Adam. Of course she had. She couldn't be in love with him and not have her dreams. But those dreams had involved Adam realising that he was in love with her too, that he wanted to spend the rest of his life with her. Even in her wildest dreams she had never envisaged being with him under these circumstances!

Adam paused in the act of sipping his red wine, giving

her a sharp look. 'You're feeling okay, aren't you? Today hasn't been too much for you?'

Poor Adam; he was the one who had found today too much!

'Not at all,' she reassured him soothingly. 'I just tire easily still. Jonas assures me that soon I'm going to blossom with vitality and good health,' she added dryly. 'I keep waiting for the day!'

There was no answering smile on Adam's face. 'I'll feel better myself once I've spoken to him on Monday.'

She shrugged. 'He isn't going to tell you much more than I already have. I was nauseous to the point of incapacity to begin with,' she recalled with a grimace. 'But that's mainly passed,' she added quickly as she saw Adam's dark frown. 'There really is no problem with the pregnancy, Adam.' She reached out and lightly touched his hand, hastily removing it again when she felt the tingling sensation that ran heatedly up her arm.

Adam still looked grim. 'So you keep telling me. I'll just feel better once Jonas has confirmed that for me.'

Andie looked at him beneath lowered lashes. 'I hope you aren't going to be an over-protective father-to-be,' she remonstrated playfully.

Adam gave up any pretence of eating the lamb, carefully placing his knife and fork on the plate before looking across at her. 'I'm sorry.' He indicated the half-eaten food. 'I think I'm still full from lunch.'

Andie believed that, for the moment, he had taken as much of the Summer family as he could take. But especially her and their baby...

'Me too.' She put down her own cutlery and stood up, unaware of the fact that she was nervously twisting her engagement ring round and round her finger. 'I really am rather tired, Adam...' she told him, her nerves stretched out almost to breaking point now.

She had thought earlier, when they'd chosen the rings together, during the lunch with her family, that perhaps this was going to work out after all. But alone with Adam like this, with him so obviously finding the situation such a strain, she wasn't so sure...

'Of course.' He nodded abruptly. 'I—let's go back to the sitting-room for a while, hmm? I know you're tired, but it is only eight-fifteen.'

Though the last hour, since his arrival, had seemed more like eight!

'We still have a few things to discuss,' he said gruffly.

Andie stiffened warily, making no effort to move into the sitting-room, as he suggested. 'Such as?'

'Such as where we're going to live once we're married, for one thing,' he pointed out.

She stopped to think. Where they were going to live? Why, London, of course. Her own work was here, and, although Adam travelled extensively in his work as a film producer, his office was based here. Besides, as they all knew in the Summer family, Adam hated the countryside, had never made any secret of the fact that visiting the family there was something of a chore. She didn't understand what he meant about where they would live once they were married. Maybe they did have things to discuss, after all...

'Perhaps we should go through to the sitting-room,' she agreed.

'I'll make us some coffee. You can still drink coffee, can't you?' Adam paused on his way to the kitchen.

'I can now,' she acknowledged distractedly, still thinking as she followed him into the kitchen with their used plates. 'You don't know where anything is,' she explained at his questioning look.

'I can find it.' He took a firm hold of her shoulders and turned her back towards the sitting-room. 'You've done enough for one day,' he declared as he gave her a gentle push towards the adjoining room.

She might have done, but the next few minutes alone in the sitting-room, still with only her thoughts, was something she could have done without at the moment.

No one had said this was going to be easy, she told herself impatiently. As long as she and Adam at last kept talking they should be all right.

'This is good,' she said to him once she had sipped the strong coffee he had just made.

'Don't sound so surprised.' He smiled, stretching out his own length in the chair opposite hers. 'A man who has lived on his own for as long as I have should at least have learnt how to make good coffee!'

She swallowed hard, wondering if that were the point here; a man who had lived on his own for as long as Adam had...

She moistened dry lips. 'Adam—'

'Don't take that comment any further than it was meant,' he said astutely. 'I'm sure you're as aware as I am that living alone isn't all it's made out to be.' He looked at her with narrowed grey eyes.

Of course she was aware of that. Sometimes the hours she wasn't working could be too lonely, the silence in her apartment too heavy and still. But she had always had the Summer estate to return to if she felt in the need of company. As had Adam himself...

'But—'

'No buts, Andie. I've lived on my own most of my life,' he explained grimly. 'And I'm sure you're going to find I have some annoying habits, such as leaving the bathroom untidy, or squeezing the toothpaste from the middle rather than the bottom of the tube—'

'I always use the dispenser type myself,' she put in quickly.

'You see,' Adam rejoined. 'That's one problem solved already.'

But, like Adam, she realised it was a minor one in comparison with some of the others they were going to come up against. Such as where they were going to live!

'I'm sure we're both going to have to make adjustments,' she accepted.

'But…?' he guessed.

'Where do you want to live once we're married?' she asked guardedly.

'In a house. With a garden,' he came back unhesitantly. 'And preferably somewhere our son or daughter can breathe fresh air,' he added.

Andie was taken aback. Adam hated the country, had always been extremely vocal on the subject. What—?

'I want our child to have the things I didn't,' he continued flatly, his expression remote. 'Air to breathe. A garden to play in. Trees to climb.'

Presents on birthdays and at Christmas…

Oh, how she wished she knew more about Adam's early life. But from an early age she had been told by her mother that she was never to intrude in that part of Adam's life, that if he ever wanted her, or any of the sisters, to know, he would tell them. He never had.

Would it still be intruding, as his future wife, to ask him about it…?

Andie was looking at him as if she had never seen him before. And he couldn't exactly blame her.

She had accepted his proposal, was obviously trying to

make the best of the fact that the two of them were soon
to be married, but it wasn't what she had planned for her
life, was it? Harrie and Danie both had careers too, very
responsible ones, but Andie had always been the sister who
put her work before everything else. It was the existence
of their baby that had put that career indefinitely on hold.

Andie had come to terms with her pregnancy, now she
needed time to come to terms with becoming his wife.

'Just think about it,' Adam encouraged. 'It doesn't have
to be too far out of London, can easily be in commuter
distance. I just—the idea of bringing a child up in an apartment in the middle of London just doesn't appeal.' He
pulled a face.

Andie still looked troubled.

Damn it, this was all his fault. If he hadn't lost his head
that night. If—

If. If. If!

It was too late for ifs. He really would do everything in
his power to make this marriage and motherhood as enjoyable as possible for Andie.

Well…as enjoyable as it could be when she was obviously marrying a man she didn't love.

'Andie, I have to go away tomorrow for a few days,' he
decided abruptly. 'some filming in Germany has hit a few
financial snags the director wants to discuss with me. I
should only be away a few days.' He couldn't seem to stop
talking as she just looked at him with those deep green
eyes. 'Three or four at the most,' he concluded lamely.

Because until a few moments ago, he hadn't given the
filming in Germany another thought, not since he'd received the director's message this afternoon. If he had
thought about it at all he had been considering asking the
director to come to London for discussions. Until a few
moments ago…

Andie looked very much in need of some breathing space. Just space, really. From him.

And after his visitor earlier today, he needed some time to think too. Oh, not about Andie; he had no doubts where marrying Andie was concerned. She was everything he could ever want in a wife.

It was getting through the next three weeks to the wedding that was consuming most of his thoughts. If that woman got so much as a hint that he was going to be married—!

His mouth tightened angrily, grey eyes bleak. She had done her best to ruin his life once before; he would not let her have the chance to do so again. He still couldn't believe the bad luck that had made her appear back in his life today, of all days. But then again, why couldn't he believe it? The woman was his nemesis.

She didn't appear for months at a time usually; once it had been almost a year. That time he had almost convinced himself that he wouldn't see her again. Then she had appeared at his office, much as she had today, almost as if no time had passed at all since he had last seen her.

She always wanted the same thing. Money. And like a fool, because of some deeply buried memories of having once loved her, he always gave her what she came for.

He knew, now that Andie was to be his wife, one day he would have to tell her about the other woman, of what she had once been to him. But he wanted Andie already safely established as his wife before he did that.

Coward, an inner voice taunted him.

Yes, he was a coward. But if being a coward now meant he kept Andie in the future, then he would choose being a coward every time!

He sat forward in his seat, attempting a smile that he knew didn't quite come off. But how could it? He had been churned up with conflicting emotions ever since he'd returned to his office this afternoon and found that wretched woman there. Half of him was looking forward to having Andie as his wife, and to being her husband, and the other half of him was terrified, after this afternoon, that the wedding would never take place!

'I'll make sure I'm back in time for our appointment with Jonas on Monday afternoon,' he promised.

Andie swallowed hard, her expression bland—deliberately so, it seemed to Adam. 'Of course you must go. I understand completely. After all, it's your work.' She smiled.

But her eyes didn't. Those beautiful sparkling green eyes were completely emotionless.

Adam just wanted to sweep her up into his arms, tell her everything, plead for her patience and understanding over a situation that had caused him much heartache over the years. But he knew he couldn't do that, that he had kept his own counsel for too long. He had only ever spoken to one person about Glenda, and he had known Barbara well enough to trust that she had taken his secret to the grave with her.

How he wished Barbara were here now!

'I really am rather tired now, Adam.' Andie spoke quietly, her gaze not quite meeting his. 'And I'm sure you must have things to do if you intend flying to Germany tomorrow,' she added pointedly.

He could feel the distance between them, a distance that seemed to be widening, not lessening. He didn't know what to do or say to stop it happening…!

'What will you do while I'm away?' he questioned, knowing by the way her eyes widened indignantly that he had once again said the wrong thing.

'I believe I managed to keep myself occupied before you

came into my life, Adam,' she replied scornfully. 'And that I will continue to do so,' she continued, green gaze flashing a warning.

He winced. 'I didn't mean—I was just taking an interest—I—'

He had sounded patronising! When, in reality, he was desperately trying to find some common ground between them before he took his departure. He didn't want to go away for three or four days feeling that things weren't right between them.

Andie stood up, moving to lightly stroke his arm. 'It's all right, Adam,' she told him. 'I do understand. This is going to take time to get used to. For both of us.'

His expression softened as he looked up at her. She really was so very much like Barbara. Perhaps if he just explained everything to Andie—

No!

It was a risk he dared not take. Not until after they were married, anyway. When he would have no choice.

He stood up, aware of Andie's move away from him as he did so, his smile slightly tinged with bitterness. If Andie didn't love him now, shied away from being close to him, how much more difficult was this going to be once they were married?

'I'll call you from Germany,' he said as the two of them walked to the door.

'You will?' Andie sounded doubtful.

'Of course I will.' He turned and grasped her arms, bending slightly so that he could look into the magnolia beauty of her face. 'I'll need to know that my fiancée is well,' he teased.

'Your pregnant fiancée,' Andie amended.

Implying that was the only reason he would be telephoning, to make sure that their baby, rather than Andie herself, was still well!

Adam wanted to assure her that it was her he cared about, her health and welfare that concerned him. But he knew she wouldn't believe him even if he tried to tell her that. Because without the existence of that baby, Andie would never have agreed to marry him...

The next three weeks, until he could make Andie his wife, stretched out before him like a minefield. And each step he took could be the one that made his future with Andie blow up in his face...!

CHAPTER NINE

'THIS is what you've always wanted, isn't it?' Harrie asked indulgently as Andie paraded in front of her in yet another wedding dress.

Andie pulled a face. 'To find a wedding dress that hides the fact I'll be almost four months pregnant when I walk down the aisle on Rome's arm as the blushing bride?'

'Good try, Andie,' her sister replied. 'But you know very well that isn't what I'm referring to.'

Of course she knew. But had she really been that transparent in her feelings towards Adam? She had thought, over the years, that she had hidden them rather well. But not, it seemed, from her eldest sister, who knew her so well...

Harrie had telephoned her yesterday and suggested the two of them went shopping today to look for a wedding dress, and, feeling Adam's absence in Germany as deeply as she was, Andie had been only too happy for the suggested diversion from her own troubled thoughts.

Adam had telephoned her yesterday evening, as he had promised he would, but their conversation had been stilted and brief, Adam finally giving her the name and telephone number of his hotel in Berlin, in case she should need to contact him over the weekend. Andie knew it was a telephone number she would never use.

She blandly met Harrie's affectionate gaze. 'I don't think I've ever given marriage too much thought, either,' she said truthfully. Mainly, because she had never been able to envisage marrying the man she loved!

123

'You're being deliberately obtuse, Andie,' her sister commented.

Andie sighed, giving up all pretence of studying this latest silk and satin wedding dress in the full-length mirror provided. 'Harrie, I'm sure you must have realised at the engagement luncheon that this isn't exactly a love—'

'I think I preferred the cream satin,' Harrie cut in, turning to the assistant who had just entered the large private fitting-room. 'My sister would like to fit the cream satin again,' she told the other woman lightly.

'Of course, Mrs McBride.' The middle-aged woman smiled politely before leaving in search of the cream dress.

Harrie grinned. 'I still get a delicious thrill down my spine every time someone calls me that!'

Mrs Munroe. Mrs Adam Munroe. Yes, Andie felt a similar thrill at the thought of being Adam's wife.

'It will all work out, you know,' Harrie continued, watching her intensely.

Andie gave her a sharp look. 'Will it?'

Harrie stood up, moving to put her arms about Andie and give her a hug. 'Adam is a kind and considerate man.' She held Andie at arm's length.

She swallowed hard. 'I know that. It's just—'

'I don't think this is the place to talk about this,' Harrie warned as the assistant returned with the requested wedding dress. 'We'll go and have some tea somewhere once we've finished here, hmm?' She gave Andie's arms an understanding squeeze before moving away.

The cream satin dress, with its Empire line that did much to hide her pregnancy, was beautiful, Andie agreed a few minutes later, the choice of matching veil and satin shoes much easier to make.

'We'll go back to my house for tea,' Harrie decided as

they stepped into a waiting taxi. 'It will be much more private there.'

Andie wasn't sure she wanted to have a private chat with Harrie. Her sister knew her far too well, was sure to get the truth of this sudden engagement out of her without too much trouble.

Harrie observed Andie as they waited for the tea things to be brought through to her luxuriously comfortable sitting-room. 'You look as if you're sitting in the waiting room of the dentist—or, in your case, doctor!' she commented affectionately.

Andie knew she looked far from relaxed as she perched on the edge of one of Harrie's armchairs. But she and Adam had an agreement, and confiding the truth to her sister was not part of that agreement.

'Are you missing him very much?' Harrie prompted softly.

Strangely, yes, she was. Her life so far had been one of independence, making her own decisions, answerable to no one. Yet, in a very short time, Adam's absence, even for a few days, had left a huge gulf in her life...

'Don't answer that; I can see that you are,' Harrie told her as the tea things were brought in and placed on the table between them. 'Andie, I'm not going to pry,' she assured once they were alone again. 'Your relationship with Adam is your own affair, and no one else's. Not even a big sister's! I do have one thing I want to say to you, though...'

'I thought you might have.' Andie sighed, accepting her cup of tea.

Her sister shook her head, dark hair loose around her shoulders. 'I doubt it's anything like you think it is,' she said gently. 'It's something Quinn said to me a week after we were married.'

Andie smiled. She liked and approved of her brother-in-law.

Harrie nodded. 'He was almost Adam's age when we got married, and I wondered—stupidly, as it turned out—whether he would regret it, whether he would long for his freedom, resent the ties of marriage—'

'But Quinn loves you!' Andie protested.

Her sister shrugged. 'He had still been a bachelor for almost forty years. But when I said those things to him, do you know what his reply was…?'

Andie couldn't even begin to guess. Just as she didn't see what bearing this had on her impending marriage to Adam.

Harrie sipped her tea before answering. 'Quinn told me that men of his age do not marry unless they are absolutely sure they're doing the right thing—that they are marrying the right person,' she qualified.

Andie gave another humourless smile. 'That doesn't exactly apply in this case, does it?' she said in reply.

Her sister looked sympathetic. 'Well, of course, I realise that story about the two of you dating in secret isn't true—we've always been close, Andie; you would have told me if you were seeing Adam. But that doesn't change the fact that it's Adam's baby you're expecting. Or that you are marrying the person you love.' She looked challengingly across at Andie.

She sighed. 'And Adam?'

'He wouldn't marry you either if he didn't feel you could both make a success of it,' Harrie said with certainty.

'But he doesn't love me!' Andie heard herself groan, the relief of at last being able to talk to someone about this surprise engagement and hasty marriage proving too much for her. 'He's only marrying me because of the baby.'

Harrie looked startled momentarily. 'Has he said that…?'

Andie avoided her sister's compassionate gaze. She-did-not-want-to-cry. If she started, she might not be able to stop!

'He doesn't need to.' She shook her head. 'I—he—he's in love with someone else!' The words came out in a flood, as quickly shocking her into silence as she heard their stark reality.

She had told herself that she wouldn't think of Adam's feelings for her mother, that it could only lead to unhappiness. But, without Adam's confident support, those doubts had set in once again.

Harrie looked at her with assessing eyes. 'Are you sure?'

Andie easily remembered Adam's devastation when her mother had died, his continued bachelor state as the years had passed. 'Oh, yes, I'm sure.'

Close as she was to both her sisters, Adam's feelings for her mother were something she had never discussed with either of them. It had somehow seemed disloyal. To her mother—because she knew, fond as her mother had been of Adam, that she had not returned his feelings, that she had been totally in love with Rome. And to Adam—because it had been a futile love that must have caused him deep pain over the years.

Her sister stood up. 'I don't believe it, Andie. I've seen the way Adam looks at you—'

'Well, he doesn't find me unattractive, if that's what you mean!' She put her arms protectively about the slight swelling that was their child.

'It isn't,' Harrie said reprovingly. 'You were always his favourite. When we were all little—'

'Harrie, you're talking about twenty years ago,' she interrupted wearily. 'We're big girls now—remember?'

Her sister paused. 'He has to have remained a bachelor all these years for a reason.'

'And you think I'm it?' Andie asked incredulously.

'I think it's a possibility,' Harrie said slowly.

She shouldn't have spoken, should never have confided her doubts to her sister, could see that Harrie was really worried now. If Harrie became worried enough, then she would discuss this with their father. If Rome got in on the act…!

Andie made a concerted effort to erase the frown from between her eyes, her expression altogether brighter as she gave a slightly self-conscious laugh. 'I think I'm having a touch of wedding nerves,' she excused lightly.

Harrie gave her a searching look, but Andie managed to meet that gaze unwaveringly. She shouldn't have said anything, should never have voiced her fears to Harrie. Because Harrie had always been the big protective sister, and her own marriage to Quinn hadn't changed that.

'A husband and a baby!' Andie reflected. 'Is it any wonder I'm panicking?'

'No…'

But Harrie still wasn't convinced!

She laughed softly. 'Didn't you have any nerves before you and Quinn were married?'

'I've just told you that I did…' Harrie still looked serious.

'I'll be fine once Adam is back home again,' Andie told her decisively. 'I miss him, that's all.'

And, surprisingly, she did. How quickly he had become a part of her life, and how easily those doubts set in when his physical presence wasn't here to reassure her!

'I had better go now.' She picked up her shoulder-bag. 'He said he would ring me this evening.'

'It's only five o'clock,' Harrie teased.

'He may try and ring me before he goes out this evening,' Andie insisted determinedly.

In fact, she knew it was doubts about what Adam was actually doing in Germany that had fuelled her uncertainties. They had agreed they would be faithful in their marriage to each other—but they weren't married yet! With the sudden way Adam's circumstances had changed, he could have a few loose ends in his life to tie up. A few women he had to break the sad news to!

Although he sounded cheerful enough when he rang her at seven o'clock. Early enough to still allow him to go out to dinner?

Stop this, Andie, she told herself firmly. She had never been jealous in her life—and she wasn't about to start now!

'I'm coming home tomorrow,' he told her cheerfully. 'Do you feel like meeting me at the airport?'

He was coming home a day earlier than expected! She was so thrilled by this news that she almost missed what he had said next. Almost...

'You want me to meet you off the plane?' she said uncertainly.

'Well, only if you want to. Of course, it's a long way to go. And you probably have other plans. Forget I even suggested—'

'What time does your plane land?' she cut in excitedly. Adam wanted her to meet him at the airport! Which meant he was coming back alone.

One of her imaginings in the last couple of days Adam had been away was that this business trip was perhaps a little too convenient, that perhaps Adam had taken someone else away with him, with the idea of softening the blow when he told the woman of his impending marriage. As far as she was aware Adam had never been seriously involved in any of the relationships he had indulged in over the years. But if there were someone in his life at the moment... He wasn't cruel either.

However, if he wanted her to meet him at the airport…!

'Some time in the afternoon,' he supplied distractedly. 'But it was a stupid idea, Andie. An hour's journey out to the airport, the stuffy atmosphere there. And then I could be delayed—'

'I'll be there, Adam,' she declared, knowing she needed to see him. If only to reassure herself he really was going to be her husband.

'You will…?'

She almost laughed at his own uncertainty. But she didn't. Because she had a feeling Adam was as insecure in their present relationship as she was. Hopefully it would be different once they were married.

'I will,' she told him steadfastly. 'I'll be the one that slightly resembles a balloon!'

Adam laughed softly. 'You look absolutely beautiful—and you know it!'

She knew no such thing. But if Adam thought so, that was all that mattered. 'I'll see you tomorrow afternoon,' she assured him before ringing off.

Now get a grip, Andie Summer, she told herself. She was one of the Summer sisters, Jerome Summer's youngest daughter, had never lacked for confidence in her life.

And she couldn't start now.

Adam felt like a giddy schoolboy. Anticipation tinged with excitement. And all because Andie was going to be waiting at the airport for him.

He wasn't sure what had prompted him to suggest she meet him off the plane. In all the years he had been travelling all over the world, for pleasure as well as work, there had never been anyone waiting for him to arrive home before.

But now he had Andie. His fiancée. Shortly to be his wife. How good that sounded!

His had been a relatively lonely life, the Summer family the closest he had ever come to having one of his own. But now he would have a wife. And shortly a child too. He had never realised before how good it felt to belong with someone, to someone.

Which made Andie and their child all the more precious...

No, he wouldn't think of Glenda today, wouldn't let her spoil this for him. As she had spoilt so many things in the past.

Andie looked absolutely gorgeous as she waited in Arrivals for him; her hair was an abundance of loose gold curls, just as he liked to see it, green eyes sparkling, her face flushed and beautiful. So much so that he noticed several other men looking at her admiringly.

He scowled darkly as he caught, and held, the gaze of one of those men, grey eyes communicating a warning; Andie was his!

'Adam?'

He turned back to find that Andie had walked over to join him, looking up at him questioningly. He forced himself to relax, putting down his case and briefcase to sweep her up into his arms and give her a lingering kiss.

'Wow,' she murmured throatily as they broke the kiss but still stood in each other's arms. 'Perhaps you should go away more often, Adam.'

He had decided, during the long dragging hours in Germany, that he wouldn't go away in future at all if Andie couldn't go with him. He had missed her too much.

His arms tightened briefly before he released her. 'No more travelling until after we're married, at least.' And even then it was questionable; Andie's advancing pregnancy meant that she probably wouldn't be able to fly anywhere within a matter of weeks.

He looked down at the small case and briefcase, cursing the fact that he wouldn't have a hand free to hold Andie's hand; he wanted to keep this closeness between them, had missed her more than he had thought it possible to miss anyone.

Andie solved that particular problem by picking up his briefcase for him, smiling at him companionably as he linked his hand with hers, the two of them walking outside into the autumn sunshine.

It felt good to be alive, Adam decided happily.

'Where shall we go for our honeymoon?' He turned to Andie as she drove the two of them back into London.

She looked surprised. 'I didn't know we were going to have one.'

Adam had thought of little else but having Andie as his wife while he'd been away. In fact, he had probably agreed to all that film director's demands simply so that he could get back to Andie as quickly as possible! Their honeymoon, having Andie completely to himself for a few days, had been paramount in those thoughts...

'Oh, I think we should, don't you?'

'If you can spare the time.'

Not exactly enthusiastic, but then it was still early days between them. 'As we're only going to do this once, I think the least we owe ourselves is a honeymoon,' he said firmly.

'I'm told that Paris is the place for honeymoons,' Andie murmured huskily.

'Then Paris it shall be,' he decided. 'Leave all the arrangements to me.'

Andie tilted her head as she turned briefly to look at him. 'You like organising things, don't you?'

Adam shrugged, not altogether sure of her reason for the

statement. 'It's certainly a fact that if I didn't organise things in my own life then they would never get done.'

'Hmm.'

His eyes narrowed. 'What does that mean?'

'"Hmm"?' Andie repeated mildly.

'Yes—"hmm"!'

It was Andie's turn to shrug. 'I'm pretty used to making arrangements for myself too.'

He was overstepping an invisible line by choosing to make all their decisions for them! Andie hadn't exactly said that, but it was obvious what she meant. Adam foresaw some delicate manoeuvring between them over the next few months, while they adjusted to each other. Oh, well, no one had told him marriage was easy. In fact, he knew it wasn't!

'We'll make the Paris arrangements together,' he amended.

Andie laughed softly. 'Did that hurt?'

He gave a self-deriding grin. 'Not too badly, no,' he acknowledged, looking around them. 'You know where my apartment is, don't you?' They had reached the city, but his apartment was in the opposite direction to the one in which Andie was driving.

'I know where it is,' she conceded slowly. 'I just wasn't sure where you wanted to go.'

'Home. So that I can wash the travel dust off me.' He grimaced. 'There's something particularly—dirty, about air travel. I always get off the plane feeling as if I need a shower!'

'I went out with Harrie yesterday and bought my wedding dress,' Andie told him suddenly.

'You mentioned that on the telephone last night,' he reminded her watching her carefully.

They were talking for the sake of it, he realised. Trivial

conversation. Because they were both wary of it becoming a serious one…?

Or was it the thought of coming to his apartment with him that was making Andie seem so distant suddenly?

Close as his relationship had been with all the Summer family over the years, only Rome had actually ever visited him at his apartment. There had never been any reason for any of the three sisters to go there.

Until now.

He reached out and lightly stroked Andie's hair, knowing by the way she flinched that things were still far from relaxed between them. The kiss they had shared at the airport had given him hope that—

It was the thought of going to his apartment that was now making Andie so jumpy!

'Perhaps you would like to make us both some coffee?' he suggested once they had arrived in his penthouse apartment. 'It will give me time to hide the whips and chains!'

Andie had been looking curiously around at her surroundings, but she turned to him sharply at this last comment.

'I'm joking, Andie!' he assured her exasperatedly as he lightly grasped her arms. 'You've looked as if you expect me to pounce on you at any second ever since I suggested we come here. I thought the mention of the whips and chains might confirm all your worst fears about the man you've decided to marry.'

'Very funny,' she snapped.

Adam grinned. 'Disappointed?'

'Not in the least,' she said. 'I'm just a beginner—remember?'

Oh, yes, he remembered. Every creamy, untouched inch of her. It kept him awake at night remembering!

Adam released her arms to hold her gently against him.

'So am I when it comes to you,' he whispered huskily. 'I ache with wanting you, Andie!'

She gave him a startled look. 'You do?'

His answer was to pull her even closer, knowing the physical evidence of his desire must be obvious—even to a beginner!

Andie looked confused before turning away. 'I'll make the coffee while you take a shower.'

He laughed at the blush in her cheeks, slowly releasing her. 'That's probably the safest plan—although not the one I would personally have opted for!'

'Audrey told Rome that anticipation of their wedding night is good for him,' Andie observed.

'Good for her,' he replied approvingly. 'I—' He broke off as the telephone began to ring, frowning darkly. Who the hell could be telephoning him at this time on a Sunday?

Very few people actually had his private telephone number, which limited the identity of the caller to a handful of people. And at least one of them was someone he did not want to talk to in front of Andie...

'Shouldn't you answer that?' She eyed the ringing telephone.

'Officially I'm not here,' he denied, his expression grim. His relationship with Andie was still too tenuous to risk answering that call.

'But—'

'There, it's stopped now,' he said with relief as the telephone suddenly went silent. 'I'll take that shower, and then we can decide where we would like to go for dinner.'

'And if the phone rings again?' Andie prompted softly.

He drew in a ragged breath. 'Don't answer it.'

She looked at him searchingly for several long seconds before going to the room he had told her was the kitchen.

Damn, Adam muttered to himself as he stripped off in

his bedroom in preparation of taking his shower in the adjoining bathroom.

Andie, he knew, had drawn her own conclusions about his refusal to answer the telephone call. While he might not like having her believe it was another woman, someone he was—or, now that the two of them were to be married, had been!—involved with, he knew that the truth was even less acceptable.

Three weeks, until the wedding, that was all he asked. Then he would have to tell Andie everything…

CHAPTER TEN

'SOMEHOW I was expecting that to be cold,' Andie said with some surprise.

Jonas smiled at her as he continued to smooth the clear-warm-gel over her bare abdomen. 'I like to make this as pleasant an experience as possible for you mothers-to-be!'

Andie knew she was talking for the sake of it. But it hadn't occurred to her, when they had made this appointment to see Jonas, that he would suggest doing an ultrasound scan for them, so that they could actually see the baby inside her on what was the equivalent of a television screen.

She was talking because she felt embarrassed at being naked from sternum to thighs in front of the watching Adam!

It had been different the night they had made love, emotions and passion high. Just as it hadn't seemed the same thing at all when he'd come upon her sunbathing in her bikini in Majorca. Actually lying here on the medical bed, baring the slight swell of her tummy, somehow felt very intimate. Even with Jonas present!

Jonas hadn't seemed in the least surprised that it was Adam, a man he had met only briefly before, who had accompanied Andie on this visit as the baby's father. Danie and Jonas had arrived back from their honeymoon yesterday, and Andie could only assume that they had seen Rome and he had told them of the wedding in three weeks' time. No doubt Danie would have something to say—to both of them!—when they next saw her!

Jonas sat back, smiling at Andie before looking across her to where Adam sat on her other side. 'Are you ready for this?' he prompted gently.

Andie suddenly felt extremely nervous. What if she were mistaken? If Jonas were mistaken? If there wasn't a baby at all? Adam wouldn't want to marry her then, and—

'We're ready.' Adam was the one to answer the other man gruffly, reaching out to tightly grasp one of Andie's hands as they lay at her sides.

'Right.' Jonas's voice was businesslike now. 'Your abdomen is ultra-sensitive at the moment, so the scanner may feel a little strange as I move it around to give you the full picture,' he warned. 'But I'm sure the end result will be worth it,' he added warmly.

Adam's hand tightened around hers, but Andie couldn't look at him, concentrating her attention on the television screen that stood beside them.

Her breath caught and held in her throat as she saw the shape of a tiny skull and body on the right-hand side of the screen. A baby. It really was there. Their baby. Hers and Adam's!

There was a definite tiny face there too; eyes, a little snub nose, and a slightly open mouth.

'My God…!' She heard Adam breath emotionally at her side.

She did turn to look at him then, her own emotions getting the better of her as she saw the tears falling unashamedly down his cheeks.

She reached out to smooth them away, her fingertips gentle against his skin.

It wasn't until Adam reached out and touched her own cheeks that she became aware of her own tears. But seeing the baby like that, so small and helpless, but so safe and secure inside her, suddenly made it all real. And so incredibly beautiful.

'Er—I hope you two are concentrating on this,' Jonas broke in lightly.

Andie and Adam shared a smile of complete intimacy before turning back towards the screen.

Just in time to see the shape of a second head and body on the left-hand side of the screen!

'What—?'

'Twins,' Jonas answered Adam calmly. 'I had my suspicions, but—well, this confirms it. There they both are.' He looked at the screen with satisfaction.

'Twins?' Andie broke out of her stupor long enough to gasp disbelievingly. 'You mean there are two of them?'

'Twins usually implies two, Andie,' Jonas teased her, freezing the picture onto the screen before removing the scanner. 'And everything present and correct, as far as I can tell.'

'But—I don't—how—are you—sure?' she finally gasped weakly; it had never occurred to her that she could be carrying more than one baby, her earlier embarrassment completely forgotten in the face of this revelation.

'Very sure,' Jonas answered confidently. 'As long as there isn't another one hiding behind these two. In which case, it's triplets.'

Andie's eyes widened 'You don't think—'

'No, I don't.' Jonas laughed softly at Andie's disbelieving gasp. 'But it briefly diverted you both from your obvious surprise that you're expecting twins!'

'I'm sure Danie appreciates your humour, Jonas,' Andie said irritably. 'But I'm not sure that we do.'

She glanced nervously at Adam. He hadn't said a word since Jonas had first shown them those two tiny human beings on the screen, that picture frozen there now, totally indisputable.

'I'm going to leave the two of you alone with your children for a few minutes,' Jonas told them, obviously aware of how emotional all this was for them both. 'Let you become acquainted with each other. I still need to do some more scanning before you leave, but I can come back and do that in a few minutes.' When you've both got over your shock, his tone implied. 'And you'll be able to take some photographs away with you when you leave,' he added warmly.

Neither of them noticed, Andie was sure, when Jonas stood up to leave, they just heard the closing of the door behind him.

Andie and Adam stared at the screen. Two babies, one on either side, facing each other.

Would they be identical? Two boys or two girls? Or could it be that they were two entirely separate entities, a boy and a girl? No doubt Jonas would be able to tell them that, too, if she were willing to have a test. But did Andie really want to know? More to the point, did Adam?

She turned slowly to look at him, to find his own eyes still fixed on the screen. The tears had stopped falling now, but his eyes had taken on a silver sheen where moisture still gathered there.

'I can't—it's—they're ours, Andie!' Adam suddenly ground out possessively, his hand tightly gripping hers now. 'I never imagined I would ever have one child, let alone two!'

'Do you mind?' Andie voiced her uncertainty. After all, he had never envisaged being married, let alone being presented with a ready-made family several months later.

He looked at her steadily. 'Do you?'

She glanced back at those two tiny creatures on the

screen, a flow of maternal love already reaching out to them both. 'No, of course I don't,' she denied fiercely.

'Neither do I,' he assured her with emotion. 'It's like Christmas and Easter all rolled into one!'

But not those barren Christmases, Easters, and birthdays he had known as a child. Perhaps, only perhaps, their children would help to alleviate some of that awful loneliness he had known then. She hoped so!

She gave a shaky smile. 'I can't imagine how this could have happened. There are no twins in my family, and— What is it, Adam?' She became concerned as she saw the way his mouth suddenly tightened grimly.

'Nothing,' he muttered. 'Absolutely nothing.'

But Andie wasn't convinced. It was—something. 'Do you have twins in your family?' she asked, aware that he didn't like talking about his family.

The two of them had made a list of people they wanted to invite to the wedding as they'd lingered over dinner the evening before. Not one of the names Adam had given her had appeared to be a member of his own family. Knowing how sensitive he was on the subject, Andie hadn't questioned it; after all, it was up to Adam who he wanted as guests at his own wedding.

He released her hand, standing up abruptly to walk over to stare out of the window, although there was no way he could actually see anything; the glass frosted so that no one could peer in.

'Adam?'

His shoulders hunched defensively, but he didn't turn to face her. 'I didn't think. But—yes, there have been twins in my family,' he finally confirmed unhelpfully.

Andie watched the tenseness of his back, sensing that he wasn't about to add anything to that statement. But there was no reason why he should, she decided. This was here and now and the two of them were expecting two wonderful babies.

'Adam…?' She reached out a hand to him, relieved when he turned and saw it, crossing the room in two strides to stand by the bed tightly gripping that hand. 'I can't wait to see Rome's face when we tell him, can you?' she said mischievously, determined not to let any sort of dampener fall on the magic of this incredible day.

Some of the tension left Adam as he smiled. 'You do realise that if they're two girls, he's never going to forgive us?'

Andie grinned at the thought. 'I'll just suggest that it isn't too late for him and Audrey to have a son of their own.'

Adam chuckled, shaking his head. ''You, my dear, have a decidedly wicked streak! Even if it's true,'' he added slowly. ''How would you feel about that?''

''Absolutely fine,'' she replied unhesitantly, knowing that Harrie and Danie would feel the same way. After all, why shouldn't Audrey want a child of her own?

Andie smiled, mainly with relief that the brief moment of tension between herself and Adam was completely dispelled. She would make sure it never returned. If Adam ever wanted to talk to her about his family, then he would do it in his own way and time; she wouldn't press him.

'Do you think we should invite Jonas back in now?' she suggested. 'After all, this is his clinic.'

'I think I quite like Danie's Jonas,' Adam said thoughtfully.

Jonas seemed to quite like the other man too, Andie thought, as a few minutes later he explained to them both exactly what they were seeing on the screen, shaking Adam warmly by the hand before the two of them left the clinic a short time later.

'Don't tell Danie, will you?' Andie requested of Jonas excitedly. 'I want to tell her myself.'

Jonas shook his head. 'Doctor and patient confidentiality precludes that,' he assured her. 'Even if the patient is my wife's sister!' He grinned. 'Besides, your pregnancy has already made Danie broody; the fact that it's twins will send her into hyperdrive!'

Andie's eyes widened. 'Danie is broody?' Somehow she couldn't quite see her I-can-do-anything-a-man-can-do-and-probably-better sister in that particular role. But, then, she had never quite been able to envisage Danie as anyone's wife, either...

Maybe it was always that way with your own siblings, memories of your childhood together making marriage and pregnancy seem slightly unreal? Their family had certainly changed a lot—grown—in the last six months. When the twins were born it would be even larger!

'She is,' Jonas confirmed, although he didn't look particularly bothered by the fact. 'I believe Quinn is having a similar reaction from Harrie,' he continued conversationally. 'It could have something to do with the fact that their baby sister will be the first one in the family to have children of her own.'

Andie was sure that it was, Harrie and Danie were protective of her when they were all children together, that protective air still there, despite their maturity.

'By the way—' Jonas walked down the corridor with them '—have either of you seen the newspaper today?'

'I was in the office all morning,' Adam rejoined. 'Andie?'

'I'm afraid I lazed half the morning away in the bath, and then I felt too lethargic to bother going down for a newspaper,' she admitted, having lain in the bath dreaming impossible dreams—mainly that Adam would fall madly in love with her! 'Why?' She frowned up at Jonas as he held the door open for them.

'Your father put the announcement of your forthcoming marriage in the newspaper today,' Jonas told them happily.

'He did what?' Adam exclaimed.

Andie turned to look at him, a sinking feeling in her stomach as she saw the unmistakable anger in his face.

She had believed Adam had spent some of this past weekend away dealing with any loose ends that still remained from his bachelor existence, but as she looked at him now she knew there was still someone out there that Adam didn't want to read in the newspaper about his forthcoming marriage!

'Where's Danie today?' Andie changed the subject to something more neutral. 'I telephoned her earlier, but she wasn't at home.'

Jonas smiled at the mention of his wife. 'Your father needed to go up to Edinburgh today. He asked Danie to fly him up there. She left at about eight o'clock this morning. But she assures me she'll be back in time to cook us both dinner.'

'Danie has always loved flying,' Andie said.

Once again Andie knew she was talking for the sake of it. But this time it was to give Adam time to recover from the fact that Rome had announced their marriage in the newspaper. A fact that seemed to have disturbed him…

Adam wasn't listening as Andie and Jonas talked affectionately of Danie for several minutes, glad of the respite. Today was turning out one shock on top of another, he acknowledged grimly. He and Andie were having twins. Which was amazing, incredible, wonderful! And now Rome had put the announcement in the paper without consulting either of them. Which was far from wonderful…!

He forced himself to relax slightly as Andie looked at him warily. His three weeks' grace, it seemed, had been swept away by Rome's announcement, and he couldn't say he was pleased by the fact, but that was still no reason to worry Andie. Especially when she was expecting twins!

It hadn't even occurred to him when he'd learnt of Andie's pregnancy that she could be carrying two babies. In the circumstances, maybe it should have done. But it hadn't.

The two of them walked outside into the sunshine, Andie speaking after several minutes' silence. 'I'm sure Daddy thought he was doing the right thing by putting the announcement in the newspaper,' she said.

He was sure Rome had thought so too, didn't for a moment think the other had acted maliciously. Why should he have done? Rome had no idea of the tangled mess Adam's life could sometimes become. Only Barbara had known that.

'Of course he did.' Adam gave Andie a reassuring smile. 'With the amount of weddings in the Summer family needing to be announced in recent months, the newspaper editor must be rubbing his hands with glee.'

Andie grinned. 'Six months ago none of us had even thought of marriage!'

Adam took her hand in his as they walked along side by side. 'I think we should go out to celebrate tonight, don't you? Possibly with Danie and Jonas? Jonas did say that Danie will be back in time for dinner.'

Andie's smile showed that she was pleased by this suggestion. 'I think that's an excellent idea,' she confirmed. 'This way Danie may have missed out on the engagement, but she'll be the first to hear about the twins.'

Adam's stomach seemed to rise up, turn a somersault, before falling back into place again. He had seen the two babies on the screen, even had a photograph of his very own showing those two tiny beings curled up together in foetal bliss—and he still found it incredible to believe that he was going to be a father soon, not to one baby, but two.

'You really don't mind?' He looked down intently at Andie.

'Of course not,' she answered instantly.

'But it's going to be more difficult with two,' he persisted, needing to be absolutely sure that Andie was happy with the way things were. It could be disastrous if she weren't.

Andie shook her head. 'Harder work, maybe. In fact, I'm sure it will be.'

'It might make it harder for you to return to work afterwards,' he pointed out.

Andie's laugh had a slight catch in it. 'I have a feeling I won't want to go back to work! Awful, isn't it?'' She screwed her nose up endearingly.

Adam would be perfectly happy with Andie staying at home to care for their children. In fact, he would prefer it. But there was no way he would ever make that decision for her. 'Wait and see how you feel,' he advised cautiously. 'You may find you miss all that glamour after a few months.' After all, Andie had always been extremely fashion-conscious herself.

'Motherhood may not be glamourous, but I'm sure the twins will keep me more than busy. In fact, it will probably be infinitely more fun than a job that now seems frivolous and unimportant.'

'We could always employ a nanny—'

'No way,' Andie told him determinedly. 'None of us ever had a nanny, Mummy always looked after us herself, and she said that, no matter how hard and difficult it could sometimes be, it was worth it, if only in the fact that we each knew we were totally loved.' A slightly wistful look came over her beautiful face. 'She also said that no matter how many children you have there's always enough love to go round.'

Barbara would say something like that, Adam realised sadly. She would also have been overjoyed at the prospect of grandchildren.

'Do you still miss her?' Adam heard himself ask. And then wished he hadn't, as Andie's beautiful face clouded over. 'Forget I said that,' he told her hastily. 'It was a stupid question. What I suggest we do now, if you have no other plans,' he added softly, aware that he could be domineering in his decisions without actually meaning to be; he had been in charge of just his own destiny too long, it would take time to adjust to the three—no, four—of them, as a unit!

'I have no other plans, Adam,' Andie answered him, obviously fully aware of what he was endeavouring to do.

'I just have to pop back to my office to check on a contract my secretary was preparing when I left earlier, and I thought you could come with me. Once I've dealt with the contract we could perhaps go on to an estate agent and make some enquiries about houses?' He looked at Andie questioningly.

She nodded. 'That space and garden you mentioned seems all the more appealing now that we know there will be two babies and not one. A visit to an estate agent's sounds like a very good idea,' she agreed happily.

Adam felt such a sense of ecstatic happiness himself, at the thought of their future life together, that for a moment he couldn't speak. He could see the four of them now, out in the garden together, Andie laughingly happy, the two babies gurgling merrily on a blanket on the lawn.

But, as always happened when he imagined that complete happiness, a shadow loomed. A dark, ugly shadow that he wanted nowhere near his future life with Andie.

The same shadow that loomed as they approached his offices!

Once again there was that familiar figure, patiently waiting, a newspaper tucked under one arm!

Adam didn't need to be told that Glenda had seen the announcement. He had spoken to her only last week, dealt with that situation—for what he had hoped at the time would be several months; there was absolutely no reason for Glenda to be here now, other than the fact she had seen the marriage announcement in the newspaper she so conspicuously carried.

'Adam...?' Andie looked up at him uncertainly as she seemed to sense his sudden tension.

What did he do now? He could hardly turn tail and run. But to actually speak to Glenda, with Andie at his side, was even more unacceptable.

Why was there never a bus to walk under when you needed one?

CHAPTER ELEVEN

THEY had come to an abrupt halt on the pavement after getting out of Adam's car outside his offices, Adam's sudden tension a tangible thing as Andie looked up at him worriedly.

She followed his line of vision, but there was really nothing to see, just a blonde woman in a poppy-red suit, reading some notices in an office window.

But Adam was staring at the woman as if he had seen a ghost!

Andie turned back to look at the woman herself. Tall and very slender, that blonde hair resting silkily on her shoulders, she had a sensual beauty that sometimes came with age, a beauty Andie was sure men would find attractive.

That Adam had found attractive?

It suddenly occurred to Andie that this woman could be one of those loose ends she had expected Adam to deal with now that he was marrying her.

She felt tense herself now. The last thing she wanted, today of all days—the incredible news of their twins still uppermost in her feelings!—was to have to deal with one of the legion of women who had at some time been part of Adam's life!

Although it seemed, as Adam tightly gripped her arm as they slowly began to walk towards the building that housed his offices, that she was going to have little choice in the matter.

The woman had turned now, was watching their approach with speculatively narrowed eyes.

Andie instantly felt an unexplained animosity welling up inside her!

She hadn't even spoken to the other woman. She had no proof that she was someone Adam had been involved with. Nevertheless, Andie knew that she disliked the other woman intensely.

'Adam,' the woman greeted.

'Glenda,' he bit out harshly, his hand falling away from Andie's arm now.

Andie watched the two of them, swallowing hard, knowing that if Adam ever looked at her with such contempt she could want to curl up in a corner and die.

'Aren't you going to introduce me to your fiancée, Adam?' the woman Glenda said archly. 'I take it this is your future wife?' She looked speculatively at Andie.

'I'm Andrea Summer, yes,' Andie was the one to answer stiffly, reaching out to curl her fingers about Adam's hand. A hand that was surprisingly very cold. Or perhaps not so surprising; Adam looked as if he were carved out of ice at this moment.

The woman Glenda gave her a sweeping glance before turning her attention back to Adam. 'Adam...?' she said pointedly.

His expression was grim, his mouth a thin angry line, grey eyes narrowed chillingly. Andie felt a shiver down her own spine just looking at him. Although the woman Glenda seemed unperturbed by Adam's lack of welcome, smiling at him confidently...

He drew in a harshly angry breath. 'Andrea Summer. Glenda—Howarth.'

Was it her imagination, or had there been the slightest hesitation in Adam's voice before he'd stated the other woman's surname? As if he would rather not have said it!

Although Andie couldn't imagine why not. As far as she

was aware, the other woman's name meant nothing to her. Although the same obviously wasn't true of Adam...

'Mrs Howarth,' Andie responded stiltedly, actually having no idea of the other woman's married state. The too-slender hands were bare of rings, but in this day and age that didn't mean anything; lots of women chose not to wear a wedding ring.

'Miss Summer,' the other woman drawled derisively before once again turning back to Adam. 'And the wedding is to be two weeks on Saturday, I believe?'

Adam's nostrils flared as he looked at the newspaper tucked beneath the woman's arm. 'That is one of the few newspapers I know that actually print the truth,' he replied tautly.

The woman continued to smile undauntedly. 'I trust I will be receiving an invitation?' she queried.

Andie saw raw anger flare in Adam's tightly set features, that silver gaze sending out shards of light. Whoever this woman was—whatever she had once been to Adam—he obviously did not want her at their wedding!

'It's going to be a very quiet wedding.' Andie was the one to answer the other woman. And not exactly truthfully; their guest list had added up to fifty at the last count. 'With family and only a few very close friends,' she finished firmly.

Blonde brows arched. 'Really? In that case—'

'We're actually in rather a hurry, Glenda.' Adam cut her short, fingers tightening about Andie's hand. 'So if you wouldn't mind—'

'So it would seem.' The woman looked at him for several seconds before her slightly contemptuous eyes passed on to Andie.

This woman knew, or had at least guessed, that Andie was pregnant!

Andie didn't know how she was so sure the other woman knew, she just knew that she did. Because Adam had told her? Had he excused his sudden marriage by explaining that he really had little choice in the matter, that it was literally a shotgun wedding; Rome would have taken a shotgun to Adam if they weren't married and Rome recognised the baby as being the other man's!

Andie felt slightly sick, those moments of deep emotional intimacy she and Adam had shared, as they'd gazed at their babies, disappearing like a puff of smoke.

Adam was being forced into marrying her by the circumstances of his long-standing friendship with her family, her father in particular, and, no matter how much she loved Adam, she knew she must never lose sight of that fact.

She turned blindly to Adam. Blindly, because of the tears threatening to fall. Something she would not allow to happen in front of Adam, let alone this brittle, but beautiful woman.

'If you don't mind, Adam, I think I'm really too tired to bother with the estate agents today.' To her surprise her voice sounded lightly dismissive, instead of how she really felt—heartbroken! 'In fact, I think I'll return home and rest for a while if we're going out this evening with Danie and Jonas.'

Something she was no longer looking forward to, Andie acknowledged heavily. Half an hour ago the world had seemed bright and full of promises, now it only consisted of two tiny innocent beings caught at the centre of what was, after all, merely a loveless marriage! Carrying out what now seemed nothing but a charade, in front of her sister and Jonas, was going to take every ounce of courage she possessed!

'Andie—'

'I'll call Danie and Jonas later this afternoon, and let you know where and at what time we're meeting them for dinner,' Andie pushed smoothly into what she knew was going to be Adam's protest at having her cut their afternoon together short like this. She did it with all of her old authority; she was perfectly capable of choosing to make decisions without consulting Adam first! 'I'll leave you to talk to Mrs Howarth, Adam.'

'I hope I haven't interrupted something?' Glenda Howarth said cattily.

Telling Andie that she hoped no such thing at all! The other woman was enjoying herself at the expense of Adam's marriage to Andie—and Andie, for one, had taken enough of it.

'Not in the least, Mrs Howarth,' she came back smoothly. 'Adam and I will have the rest of our lives together, I certainly don't begrudge you a few minutes of his time.' Her emerald-hard gaze told Glenda Howarth that if it amounted to anything more than that, begrudging a few minutes of Adam's time would be the least of the other woman's problems.

Blue eyes returned to hers unflinchingly. 'That's very gracious of you.'

Gracious was the last thing Andie felt—she could cheerfully have wiped that condescending smile off the other woman's face! But, having no idea what this woman meant to Adam, that was something she couldn't do.

She turned to Adam. 'I'll give you a ring later.' She reached up and placed a light kiss on his rigidly clenched jaw. 'Goodbye, Mrs Howarth,' she added with more than a little force.

'Miss Summer.' The other woman was still confidently unperturbed.

Adam seemed stunned by the suddenness of her decision to leave, Andie realised as she turned away from them to signal a passing taxi to stop. He hadn't come out of that stupor by the time she had climbed into the waiting taxi and turned to give him a dismissive wave through the window.

She gave the taxi driver her address before sinking wearily back into the seat, realising as she did so that her legs were actually shaking.

She hadn't liked Glenda Howarth on sight, and further acquaintance hadn't changed that opinion, the other woman proving to be hard and brittle. Worst of all, she seemed to have some sort of hold over Adam...

That was the thing that bothered Andie the most about that unexpected meeting.

Adam hadn't been at all pleased earlier when Jonas had told them Rome had put their marriage announcement in the newspaper, and at the time Andie had guessed there was someone that Adam didn't want to see that announcement.

She now knew, with sickening clarity, that person was Glenda Howarth!

Who was Glenda Howarth?

More to the point, what did the other woman mean to Adam...?

Andie had a feeling she wouldn't like the answer to either of those questions!

Adam watched Andie as she chatted happily with Danie across the dinner table.

As promised, Andie had telephoned him at five-thirty to tell him she had managed to contact Danie, and that the four of them were meeting up for dinner at Cleo's at eight o'clock.

Andie had sounded bright and cheerful enough on the telephone, just as she had looked stunningly beautiful in a knee-length black dress when he'd called at her apartment for her shortly after seven-thirty so that they could drive to the restaurant together. And she seemed happy enough in Danie and Jonas's company now too.

But for all that bright happiness Andie portrayed, Adam knew that something had subtly changed between them this afternoon. Andie was politely gracious when he told her how beautiful she looked this evening, politely considerate of everything he said, politely distant! In fact, Andie was just too damned *polite*!

He knew the reason for it, of course. Andie was puzzled, if not a little hurt, by that strained meeting with Glenda earlier this afternoon. The problem was, he wasn't sure, without telling Andie everything, how he could make things right between them again. It was something he had hoped to avoid until after he and Andie were safely married.

Although he had had the satisfaction, after Andie had left so abruptly, of leaving Glenda in no doubt that if she tried to interfere in his life again in the way she had today, then she would get nothing else from him. Absolutely nothing.

As Glenda's interest in him had only ever been a financial one, he was pretty sure she would take note of that warning.

Which took care of Glenda, for the immediate future, but did absolutely nothing to put things right between himself and Andie. If he tried to touch her, put his arm about her waist, hold her hand, she found some way of eluding that touch. When he had moved to kiss her on arrival at her apartment earlier, she had turned her face slightly so that he'd ended up kissing her cheek.

In other words, he was back to square one as far as Andie was concerned!

It wasn't acceptable to him! Being with Andie was the best thing that had ever happened in his life—and he wasn't about to lose it.

He reached out and took her hand in his, his grasp tightening as she seemed to instinctively move away. 'Isn't it time you told Danie our news...?' he prompted as Andie turned to look at him questioningly.

Her cheeks became slightly heated, her gaze shifting uncertainly away from his.

Andie didn't want to tell Danie they were expecting twins!

Adam knew that as clearly as if Andie had shouted the words out loud, feeling a sudden sinking feeling in the pit of his stomach. Andie had seemed as excited as he was earlier when Jonas had shown them the two babies on the screen. Obviously it was something that had happened since that had changed that.

Glenda had happened!

His mouth tightened at that realisation. Glenda was responsible for much of the unhappiness in his own life; he would not allow her to be the cause of any in Andie's.

'We already know about the wedding.' Danie was the one to break what was becoming an uncomfortably long silence following Adam's question.

'Andie?' Adam prompted again, his hand tightening reassuringly about Andie's now.

She drew in a sharp breath before smiling across at her sister. Adam just hoped he was the only one who could tell how strained that smile was!

'Jonas did a scan for us today,' Andie told Danie lightly. 'It was—very illuminating,' she added with a return of some of her mischievous humour.

Danie turned to her quietly listening husband. 'You didn't mention that,' she rebuked playfully.

Jonas shrugged. 'Doctor and patient confidentiality still stands, even from the patient's sister. Even if that sister happens to be my own wife. As you very well know.'

'Can you believe this man, Adam?' Danie turned to him, her eyes twinkling humorously. 'For several weeks after Jonas and I first met, I thought he was a heart specialist, or, at worst, a cancer specialist!' She shook her head. 'I even got the patient wrong!'

Adam smiled. 'Sounds like an interesting story,' he said.

He had always rather liked the red-haired Danie; of the three sisters she was probably the most spirited. Although Jonas didn't seem to be having any problems as her husband, looking confidently relaxed as he sat beside his wife.

The other man had a quiet strength of character that was more than a match for Danie's more extrovert one, Adam was quickly learning. The other man was also highly intelligent. Jonas was a very capable obstetrician. And obviously deeply in love with Danie. It was the latter that made Adam like him the most.

'Oh, it is,' Danie confirmed. 'So tell me your news,' she demanded. 'Obviously Jonas already knows it.' She gave her husband a playfully chastising look.

Adam could see that Andie was still having trouble sharing their news. 'How about if we show you instead of telling you?' he suggested, taking out his wallet to remove the photograph Jonas had given him earlier.

Danie's reaction to the two babies was as joyful as expected, the two men sharing an indulgent glance as the two women launched into conversation about twins, baby buggies, cots, clothes, everything that could possibly be needed for the arrival of two babies instead of one.

'I'm afraid this evening must have been very boring for you,' Andie said shyly on the drive back to her apartment later—much later—that evening. 'All that baby talk,' she explained.

Adam raised blond brows, his mouth tight. 'And why should I be bored talking about our babies?'

Andie tensed beside him. 'Most men would be.'

'I'm not most men, Andie,' he returned. 'You should know that by now.'

Two steps forward, and one step back, he inwardly acknowledged. He hoped it wasn't always going to be like this between them.

But Andie hadn't mentioned that earlier meeting with Glenda so far this evening, and Adam was loath to do so earlier. Except that he knew that was what was putting this particular barrier between them.

He drew in some air. 'About Glenda—'

'I don't want to know, Adam,' Andie rebuked him.

'No?' He blinked his surprise.

She gave a decisive shake of her head. 'She's obviously someone from a different part of your life, a life I have no part of, which makes her none of my business, either.' But that slightly emotional quiver to Andie's voice implied she didn't really believe that.

Adam was stunned for a few seconds after this announcement. Andie believed—she thought—Andie believed he had been *involved* with Glenda!

Why should she have thought otherwise? Came the immediate question. To look at, Glenda was a beautiful woman—even if that wasn't true inside! He hadn't offered any explanation about his relationship with Glenda, so what else was Andie to think?

Involved with Glenda?

He would rather be involved with a snake; it would probably be less deadly!

But without telling Andie the truth, he couldn't very well contradict that impression...

'You won't be seeing her again,' he told Andie.

'I don't think that's the point here, Adam—do you?' Andie insisted.

'Then what *is* the point?'

'Whether or not *you'll* be seeing Glenda Howarth again, of course!'

His breath caught, and held, in his throat. Could he make Andie that particular promise, and keep it?

CHAPTER TWELVE

WITHOUT Adam having to say anything, Andie knew she was asking him something he couldn't, in truth, agree to!

Which left the two of them precisely where?

They had agreed there would be no one else in either of their lives, that they were going to give their marriage every chance of success. Adam had agreed to that. In fact, he had insisted on it.

But not where Glenda Howarth was concerned, obviously.

What hold did the other woman have on him? There had to be something. Because there certainly wasn't any love between them; there was no way Andie could forget the contemptuous way Adam had looked at the other woman earlier today.

So why couldn't he agree not to see the other woman again?

If Adam wasn't prepared to tell her that—and by the stubborn set to his mouth, he obviously wasn't!—then she would have to ask someone else.

Glenda Howarth…?

Andie quivered with distaste just at the thought of having to see the other woman again.

Not Glenda Howarth, then.

But someone else. Because there was no way they could have the spectre of Glenda Howarth standing between them when they were married in just over two weeks' time.

'Never mind, Adam,' Andie said sharply. 'You obviously need to give that suggestion some thought.'

'It isn't that—'

'Do you want to come up for a cup of coffee?' she invited as they arrived outside her apartment block, not particularly wanting this evening to end with obvious strain between them. One evening like that had been enough as far as she was concerned.

Adam turned to look at her in the dark confines of the car. 'I would love to—if you're sure you aren't too tired?'

'I had a nap this afternoon,' she explained as she got out of the car. She knew it wasn't a very gracious invitation, but it was the best she could do for the moment.

Adam seemed happy enough with it, anyway, accompanying her up to her apartment, helping her to prepare the coffee in the kitchen before carrying the tray into the sitting-room.

However, that awkward silence fell between them again as they sipped their coffee.

Finally, Adam drew in a heavy breath. 'Andie, I know you don't want to hear about Glenda—'

'I don't,' she agreed.

'Any more than I want to talk about her,' he continued, his expression grim. 'However, I do have one thing to say on the subject...'

Andie briefly closed her eyes, a vision instantly coming to mind of Adam's face this afternoon, as they'd looked at the screen that had shown them their two babies. It had been a face full of love.

She had known Adam most of her life, knew that he was an honourable man. Whatever he chose to tell her about Glenda Howarth, she would believe him.

She opened her eyes, looking across at him. 'Yes?' she pressed gently.

Adam put his coffee-cup down before standing up, coming over to crouch down next to her chair, reaching out to grasp both her hands in one of his. 'I want you to know that Glenda Howarth means nothing to me. Is nothing to me.'

Andie looked at him, could see the worry in his silver gaze, the dark frown to his brow. It was very important to him that she believe him...

She swallowed hard. 'All right, Adam.' She nodded.

'Is it?' His frown was pained now. 'Is it really all right?'

Her expression softened as she saw the raw uncertainty in his face, reaching out a slightly trembling hand to lightly caress the hard curve of his jaw. 'Yes, Adam, it's all right,' she told him, feeling relieved herself at a partial return to the closeness they had known earlier today; she loved Adam too much to be able to stand the desolation of that distance between them!

'God, Andie...!' He reached forward and pulled her into his arms, his face buried in the perfumed silkiness of her hair. 'This evening has been—awful!' he groaned achingly.

She reached up and touched his silver-blond hair. 'I won't tell Danie and Jonas you said so!'

He pulled back slightly to look at her. 'It had nothing to do with Danie and Jonas, and you know it.'

Yes, she knew it. It had been as if there were an invisible barrier between them most of the evening. Even though Andie had known she was responsible for most of it, that she'd flinched away from Adam every time he'd touched her, she hadn't seemed to be able to do anything about it. But she had hated that distance between them as much as Adam obviously had.

Adam's hands cradled either side of her face. 'I will never do anything that might put my relationship with you and our children at risk,' he promised her.

Tears suddenly glistened in her eyes. Their children...

It all still seemed somehow like a dream. A wonderful dream, but a dream nevertheless.

Adam bent his head, kissing her gently on the lips, sipping and tasting their sweetness, until Andie gave a low groan in her throat and deepened the kiss, her arms moving up about his shoulders as she pressed herself against him.

She loved this man, loved him so deeply, that she knew in her heart that she would forgive him anything.

'Andie...?' Adam raised his head to look down at her with needy grey eyes.

She wanted him, needed him, loved him. There was nothing else.

'Adam!' she breathed, heated colour in her cheeks as she knew she wanted him more than she had ever wanted anything in her life.

He looked at her searchingly for several long seconds before standing up to bend down and sweep her up into his arms.

'I'm too heavy for you,' she protested, at the same time clinging tightly around his neck.

He grinned down at her. 'Maybe in a couple of months or so, you might be!' he conceded. 'At the moment you're still as light as air.'

'Where are we going?' she asked as he strode across the room.

'Wonderful as it might have been the first time, I don't think we should make love on the floor a second time!' He softly kicked open the door that led to her bedroom, pulling back the bedclothes to gently lay her down on top of the bed, before joining her there.

Andie turned into his arms, a bedside lamp their only illumination as they gazed hungrily at each other. She would never have believed, at the beginning of this evening, that the two of them would be here together like this!

She reached up to curl her fingers into the thick blondness of his hair, loving the silky feel of it, suddenly feeling slightly shy. What if that one time together had been a fluke? What if this time it all went—?

Adam laughed softly as he gazed indulgently down at her. 'Have a little faith, Andie,' he chided affectionately.

As he began to kiss her, her body suddenly alive with a hundred senses, her mind went completely blank, and there was only feeling left, vein-tingling, spine-thrilling sensation.

Adam's hands roamed restlessly down the length of her body, even as his lips trailed an erotic pattern down the creamy column of her throat to the hollows below, the curve of her breasts visible above the rounded neckline of the black dress she wore.

'You are so beautiful, Andie.' The warmth of his breath caressed her heated skin as he slid the zip down the back of her dress. 'So incredibly beautiful.'

It was impossible to feel in the least self-conscious in the face of such warm admiration, her dress completely discarded now, only black lace bra and matching panties covering her nakedness.

'Let me,' she said, reaching up to unbutton his shirt, smoothing the material back to run her hands caressingly over the smoothness of his skin, fingertips tingling over the silky hair that covered his chest.

There had seemed no opportunity, the last time they'd been together like this, to actually touch and feel, to learn the contours of each other's body.

Adam's body was lean and hard, his legs long and muscular, skin lightly tanned—obviously not all of his time was spent behind a desk, on the telephone, or on a plane!—and covered with fine silver-blonde hair.

As he pulled her in tightly against his body, only thin

garments still between them, Andie could feel the hard evidence of his desire.

She moved sensuously against him, her senses raised to fever pitch, her eyes deeply green as she looked up at him pleadingly. She wanted more—so much more!—wanted to be completely naked against him, wanted—

'Not until we're married—remember?' Once again Adam seemed able to read her thoughts, regret in his voice.

She shook her head, reaching out to caress him. 'That doesn't seem important any more.'

'It is to me,' he told her firmly, his hand tightly gripping her wrist.

But as if to take any sting out of his words, his head lowered, lips closing hotly over one bra-covered nipple, sucking the sensitive tip into the moist cavern of his mouth.

Andie's head went back, her eyes closing as she groaned low in her throat, her body feeling on fire as Adam released her hand to caress her other breast, heated pleasure now coursing through her body.

Her breathing was short and shallow as she felt the sensations building up inside her, sure that she was going to completely explode as she felt Adam's caress against her panties.

Waves of pleasure washed over her with ever-increasing pressure, until she felt as if she couldn't stand any more, her body arching in aching ecstasy.

The aftermath of that pleasure left her weak and exhausted, lying limply in Adam's arms now.

He raised his head to look at her as she still trembled in his arms. 'Are you all right? I didn't hurt you?'

If that was hurting—!

'No, you didn't hurt me,' she assured him, knowing that Adam had taken her to the plateau of complete pleasure. 'Although I did feel as if I had died and gone to heaven.'

Adam laughed huskily, smoothing back the blonde tangle of her hair from the heat of her face. 'That's how I hoped you would feel!' He reached beneath them to pull the bed-clothes up over both of them. 'And now I would like a pleasure that was denied me last time,' he said.

She looked up at him, unsure of what he meant. She was pregnant as a result of their last lovemaking, so what—?

He looked down at her with laughing grey eyes. 'The pleasure of having you fall asleep in my arms,' he explained with playful rebuke.

Andie stared at him in the glow from the bedside lamp. 'But—'

'Sleep, woman,' he commanded, his arm about her as he put her head on his shoulder before reaching out to turn off the lamp.

Andie lay beside him in the darkness. But he hadn't— He had given her pleasure, and yet he—

'We have the rest of our lives, Andie,' he murmured beside her in the darkness as he sensed her troubled thoughts. 'Tonight I wanted to give you pleasure.'

And he had.

He certainly had!

Complete. Utterly. Unselfishly…!

'Will you stop pacing up and down on the same piece of carpet, Adam? You'll wear it out!'

He paused to give Rome a glowering glare. But he changed the direction of his pacing, nonetheless.

He had known, after that meeting with Glenda yesterday, Andie's reaction to it, that he had to talk to someone. Unfortunately, the person he was closest to in the world— apart from Andie, herself!—was Rome. Who, of course, also happened to be Andie's father!

Which explained why he was pacing impatiently up and

down the sitting-room at the estate house. He had no idea how to even begin telling Rome about Glenda!

Rome sighed. 'Is this going to take long, Adam? Because I have a wedding of my own to go to next week, you know!' he added satirically, perfectly relaxed as he sat in one of the armchairs watching Adam.

'Very funny!' Adam grimaced.

'I doubt Audrey would share that sentiment if I failed to appear at the church simply because it took you a week to get round to what you want to say!' Rome drawled.

Adam stopped his pacing. 'It's all very difficult…'

Rome looked concerned. 'You aren't thinking of letting Andie down, are you?' He spoke mildly enough, but there was a definite edge to his tone as he looked far from relaxed now.

'Don't be ridiculous,' Adam came back impatiently.

'That's okay, then.' The older man settled back into his chair. 'Because you would seriously be stretching the bounds of our friendship if you were to even consider doing that.'

'I've just said I'm not,' Adam snapped irritably.

'I heard you. Just as I heard you the day you came here to explain to me that you and Andie had been secretly involved with each other for months, and that you were the father of her baby,' Rome continued softly, blue eyes narrowed now.

Adam looked at the other man warily. 'It's true, I am. And by the way, it's babies. Plural,' he added.

Rome gave an abrupt nod of his head. 'Andie came to see me this morning to tell me the good news.'

Andie had been here this morning…?

Adam had left her apartment shortly after eight o'clock this morning, the two of them sharing a pot of coffee before he'd gone back to his own apartment to shower and change ready for going to his office.

Except that he hadn't gone to his office, had spent the morning at his apartment thinking over what he should do about Glenda, finally telephoning Rome and asking if he could come and talk to him.

But Andie had already been here today.

Why? Oh, obviously she would want to tell her father about the twins, but even so…

Adam frowned. 'I didn't realise that.'

Rome shrugged. 'There's no reason why you should have done. I'm pleased for both of you, of course.'

But.

The other man hadn't actually said that, but it was there in the tone of his voice.

Adam also questioned why Rome hadn't told him he knew about the twins when he'd arrived a short time ago. Surely it would have been the most natural thing in the world for Rome to have talked excitedly of the fact that he was now expecting two grandchildren and not one?

Rome stood up. 'I said I heard you last week, Adam— that doesn't mean I believed you. Most people who meet me for the first time believe—as they are supposed to!— that I am just an easygoing man who happened to make a couple of lucky business decisions early on in my career, and that I have built on those decisions because of that earlier success. That's most people, Adam,' he repeated. 'I didn't count you amongst their number!'

He had told Andie only yesterday that he wasn't most men!

But he knew that wasn't what Rome meant at all. Rome was right; Adam had never been fooled by that happy-go-lucky philanthropic guise Rome wore for the general public. Rome had achieved his success by shrewd intelligence, accompanied by kid-glove ruthlessness.

'Audrey told me I should leave the subject alone,' Rome continued. 'And while I accede to my future wife's views on most subjects—' he smiled tightly '—Andie's future happiness is not something I intend letting anyone play around with.'

He looked across at Adam with narrowed blue eyes, the two men of similar height and build, the fourteen years' difference in their ages noticeable only in the lines of experience beside Rome's eyes and mouth. But it was a difference Adam had always known he should be wary of...

'I am as concerned for Andie's future happiness as you are,' Adam told him shortly.

'Are you?' Rome returned in measured tones. 'Then let me tell you that I was never fooled for a moment by that story of the two of you keeping your relationship a secret. Not one single minute, Adam,' he repeated firmly as Adam would have spoken. 'My daughters were simply not brought up to be secretive,' he declared with proud affection. 'However,' he went on, 'at the time, I considered the details of your earlier involvement none of my business.'

'"At the time"...?' Adam echoed.

Rome nodded abruptly. 'I'm still not going to pry, Adam; the two of you have decided to marry, and that is the end of the matter as far as I'm concerned.'

There was still a but. Adam sensed it.

'However,' Rome said, 'Andie's visit here this morning changed things somewhat.'

'It did?' Again Adam looked at the other man warily. This wasn't turning out at all as he had imagined it would!

Rome gave a stiff inclination of his head. 'My daughter is under the impression that there's a—complication in your life that may affect your married life together.'

Adam drew in a harsh breath. He had come here for the very reason of talking to Rome about that complication. But now he felt on the defensive.

He moistened dry lips. 'Did she tell you what that complication was?'

Rome gave a humourless smile. 'As it happens, yes, she did. But she didn't need to. I already knew.'

Adam stared at him dazedly. Rome knew? But how—? The only person he had ever told about Glenda had been Barbara, and he couldn't believe—

Rome softly broke into his racing thoughts. 'Adam, when you came to me twenty years ago with your business proposal, I was a man of thirty-four, with a wife and very young family; I took risks, but I wasn't stupid. I had your background thoroughly checked out before I agreed to finance you.'

Adam could only stare at the other man. Rome really did know! All this time he had known—and never said anything!

Rome gave an impatient sigh, moving over to the drinks tray to pour them both a glass of brandy, handing Adam one of those glasses before sipping at his own.

'What are you so afraid of, Adam?' Rome looked at him over the rim of his glass.

Losing Andie! He was so close, so close to having her for all time, and the thought of losing her now—!

Rome briefly closed his eyes. 'Do you have so little faith in Andie that you think she won't want to marry you once she knows about your past?'

Adam swallowed hard, dropping down heavily into a chair. 'You don't understand,' he groaned. 'Andie doesn't love me. And once she knows—'

'Andie doesn't love you!' Rome repeated with incredulous disbelief. 'Are you stupid, Adam? Or just blind? Andie has worshipped the ground you walked on since she was seven years old!'

Adam took a gulp of the brandy. 'You're wrong. She—'

'Take my word for it, Adam,' the older man broke in. 'Andie loves you. She always has.'

Adam looked across at him. Could Rome possibly be right? Did Andie care for him?

No! He couldn't believe that. He didn't dare take the risk of believing that.

'Adam, this morning I told Andie that if she had any doubts, if she had changed her mind about marrying you, that it was all right with me,' Rome told him gruffly. 'That I would stand by whatever decision she made.'

Adam's breath caught and held in his throat. 'And?' he finally gasped weakly.

Rome smiled. 'She told me that if she didn't marry you she would never marry anyone—'

'That's because of the babies—'

'No, it isn't, damn it!' Rome rasped harshly, blue eyes blazing. 'Adam, I know how difficult it's been for you,' he continued more gently. 'But you aren't responsible for your past. You were a child—'

Adam's eyes clouded. 'Don't you see? My past makes me the man I am!'

Rome sighed. 'I accept that, unlike my own children, you were brought up in a world that didn't have any affection, let alone love. I can even understand how it must be difficult for you now to accept having someone love you. But the Summer family have always loved you. And Andie more than all of us.'

Was Rome right? Was he just unable to believe that anyone could love him?

Could Andie ever love him...? Was Rome right, and she already did love him?

He thought back over the last couple of weeks, their initial awkwardness together, and the closeness they had known last night...

He looked across at Rome, only to find the other man looking right back at him, his gaze steadily challenging. 'What else did Andie say to you this morning?'

The other man hesitated. 'As you might suppose, she asked me if I knew anything about a woman called Glenda Howarth.'

Adam tensed. 'And?'

'I had to answer her honestly and say no,' Rome came back easily.

'But—'

'Adam, I would never lie to Andie,' Rome assured him. 'I have never lied to any of my children, and I'm not about to start now. The truth is I don't know anything about Glenda Howarth. Glenda Munroe is another matter, however. But that isn't what Andie asked me.'

Glenda Munroe...

Yes, that had once been her name. The same surname as his. Before she'd remarried.

'I also happen to believe, Adam,' Rome said, 'that it is for you to tell Andie about the past. About Glenda.'

It was. He knew it was.

He was just so terrified of losing Andie when he had done so, of her pity, if not her disgust.

Despite Rome's assurances that Andie loved him...

CHAPTER THIRTEEN

ANDIE watched Adam as he walked restlessly up and down her sitting-room.

He looked terrible, his face pale, a grimness about his eyes and mouth that she had never seen there before.

She had no idea why. Last night, sleeping in each other's arms, had been wonderful. As had sitting drinking coffee together this morning before he'd left.

But Adam had telephoned her late this afternoon and suggested he come over to her apartment this evening, turning down her offer to cook them both dinner. Andie had an idea why that was now; Adam didn't look as if he would be staying long enough to eat dinner!

Finally she could stand the silence no longer. 'Adam—'

'Andie, I have something to tell you,' he burst out. 'It isn't something I'm going to enjoy telling you, but I know it has to be done.'

Glenda Howarth...?

Surely it had to be something to do with the other woman; Adam had changed since that meeting with Glenda Howarth outside his office yesterday.

Andie had been to see her father this morning, in the hope that he might be able to shed some light on the other woman's role in Adam's life; after all, the men had been close friends for years. But Rome had been less than helpful, his expression completely blank at the mention of the other woman's name. Although he had promised to see what he could find out about her.

But from the expression on Adam's face, Rome wouldn't

need to bother; Adam was going to tell her about the other woman himself.

She moistened suddenly dry lips. Adam looked so unhappy about all this that she just knew it was going to be awful.

But what on earth could be so terrible about his relationship with Glenda Howarth that it made him look like this? Andie had given a lot of thought to the other woman today—and the only thing she had been able to come up with, the very worst scenario, was that Adam had once been married to Glenda Howarth. After all, she knew little or nothing about his life before twenty years ago.

But even so, such a young marriage, a marriage that must have gone terribly wrong to have ended before Adam was even twenty, would have no significance in his life now.

Not that Andie would like the idea of Adam ever having been married to anyone else—and especially a woman like Glenda Howarth, a woman she had disliked on sight!—but it wasn't so terrible that Adam had to be reluctant to tell her about it. Was it…?

Or perhaps she had it all wrong, and Adam wasn't going to tell her something awful about Glenda Howarth, perhaps he was going to tell her of his feelings for her mother. That, she most certainly did not want to hear!

She stood up. 'Do I really need to hear this, Adam? Is it going to help anything?' she reasoned.

He gave a slightly bitter smile. 'Probably not,' he conceded. 'In fact, I'm sure not. But Rome has convinced me it isn't something you should learn about after we're married.'

'Rome has?' Her eyes widened. When had Adam spoken to her father about this? Before or after her own visit this morning? How had Rome reacted to being told that Adam had been in love with Barbara all these years?

Adam went on with his explanation. 'He doesn't believe it would be fair to you not to tell you before we're married. And after thinking about it, I know he's right,' he acknowledged.

Fair to her? Had it been fair to Rome, even if he were finding happiness a second time in marrying Audrey, to burden him with the truth of Adam's feelings towards Barbara?

'How did my father react?' she asked worriedly. After all, such knowledge was sure to put a strain on Rome and Adam's friendship. That was the last thing any of them needed just now!

Adam sighed. 'Apparently, he already knew.'

Well, she had guessed that much, her father was far from stupid. But actually hearing the words must have made it seem so much worse.

Andie was puzzled. 'I don't know what you hoped to achieve by talking to my father about this.' Any more than he expected to achieve anything positive by telling her either! It might succeed in easing Adam's conscience, but it certainly wouldn't do anything to help their own marriage.

'I didn't hope to achieve anything,' Adam protested. 'I just needed someone to talk to, and Rome was the only person I could think of. It helped that he already knew.'

'I'm sure it did,' Andie snapped.

'He mentioned that you had been to see him this morning, too.' Adam looked at her searchingly.

'That was about something else completely,' she dismissed impatiently.

Adam frowned. 'I don't think so...'

Andie was becoming more and more confused the longer this conversation continued along these abstract lines. 'Maybe if you just say what you feel you have to say,

Adam…?' she prompted, anxious to get this over with now, her nerves already strung out to breaking-point.

He gave another deep sigh. 'It's been buried inside me for so long—! Would you like to sit down again?' he invited.

Maybe she had better; she didn't want to fall down!

'There,' she told him once she was back in her chair, looking up at him expectantly.

'Right. Well. To start at the beginning, we have to go back thirty-five years—'

'Thirty-five years?' Andie echoed incredulously. 'But you would only have been four at the time!'

'Yes,' he agreed, no longer looking at her, no longer looking at anything it seemed, his expression blank, his thoughts all inwards.

If this thing—whatever it was—went back to when Adam was four, then this couldn't possibly be anything to do with her mother. Or Glenda Howarth either, that Andie could see…?

'I was four,' Adam confirmed gruffly. 'And so was my— my brother. Harry.'

Andie had never known he had a brother, let alone—

Twins! If Adam and Harry had both been four, then that meant they had to be twins. The twin connection in Adam's family that he had told her about.

But where was Harry now?

Adam looked at her with pained eyes. 'Harry is dead.'

Andie's gasp of dismay caught and held in her throat at Adam's next comment.

'And I killed him.'

She stared across at him with incredulous green eyes. He couldn't have just said— He had been four years old, for goodness' sake!

'Oh, not with my own bare hands,' Adam assured her bitterly. 'But I was still responsible for his death.'

Andie swallowed hard, shaking her head. 'I'm not sure a four-year-old has enough awareness of life to be held responsible for anything, let alone—let alone—Adam—'

'No, don't touch me!' he instructed harshly as she would have stood up and gone to him.

Andie subsided back into her chair. But only because he'd asked her to. What she most wanted to do was cradle him in her arms while he told her the rest of what he felt he had to say.

Adam turned away, swallowing convulsively. 'Harry was my identical twin to look at, but we were completely different in personality. I was the extrovert, the outgoing one. Harry was shy, liked to sit quietly looking at books. But at the same time, he would always follow where I led. My mother—our mother,' he amended, 'was twenty when we were born. We never knew our father. They were married, but he—he walked out when he found out they were expecting twins. Too much responsibility, I suppose.' Adam took a gulp of air. 'By the time we were six months old our mother had begun to go out in the evenings. She couldn't afford to pay for babysitters,' he added bitterly as Andie would have spoken. 'By the time we were three, she was out almost every night. I was left in charge, because I was the oldest—'

'By how much?' Andie gasped, horrified at what he was telling her. She had read about things like this in the newspapers, of course, but had never guessed that this could be Adam's childhood.

'Five minutes,' Adam answered flatly. 'Anyway, one night, when we were four, our mother had gone out as usual, and—the money ran out in the electricity meter.' He moistened dry lips. 'I couldn't find any money to put in it, so I—I lit a candle in our bedroom. Harry had never liked the dark, and I—I fell asleep!' he continued emotionally. 'The candle must have fallen over, caught the curtains alight, and within minutes the place was an inferno. I couldn't find Harry amongst the smoke! I looked and I looked, but I couldn't find him. Then a neighbour burst in and carried me out. I never saw Harry again.'

Andie's sob caught in her throat. How horrible. How absolutely, heartbreakingly horrible. For Adam.

'By the time my mother returned from her evening out, our apartment was burnt beyond recognition. And Harry was dead,' Adam said numbly.

A sudden—shocking!—truth hit Andie like a lightning bolt. Glenda Howarth, still beautiful but older than she actually looked, was Adam's mother!

Andie didn't know how she knew, couldn't even have said where the idea had come from. But she knew it with blinding certainty.

Andie stood up, determined to go to Adam now whether he wanted her to or not, putting her hand tentatively on the rigidness of his arm. 'Glenda Howarth is your mother, isn't she, Adam?' Andie said evenly.

His mouth twisted with distaste. 'She is,' he confirmed. 'And I've hated her from the day Harry died.'

Andie felt choked. She understood his feelings, even while she ached with the pain he must have suffered at his twin's death.

She also understood now why he was so determined to be a good and loving father to his own children. Even if he couldn't love their mother, he would love and take care of his children.

Adam looked searchingly at Andie. He knew she was tender-hearted enough to empathise with his trauma at

Harry's death. It was his mother that was the real skeleton in his cupboard. After all that had happened, all the years of hating her, she was still his mother. Much as he hated it, her blood ran in his veins.

He had decided very early in his life that he would never love anyone again. When his mother had come back into his life fifteen years ago, he had known it was the right decision; how could he ever offer any woman Glenda as a mother-in-law? Certainly not Andie, who had only ever known love and sunshine in her own life.

He grasped Andie's arms now, putting her firmly away from him, still not sure how this conversation was going to turn out. 'It was so hard for me to believe Harry was really gone. He was the other half of myself.' His expression softened. 'You would have liked him, Andie—'

'Don't!' she choked, tears glistening on her lashes.

'No,' he accepted heavily. 'It doesn't help, does it? I go to his grave sometimes, talk to him, but that doesn't help, either.' He swallowed hard.

'I'll come with you next time,' Andie told him huskily. 'We can tell him about our own twins. He would probably like that.'

She understood that, at least! He had hoped that she would, but been so afraid that she wouldn't...!

'It's been so long since I was able to share Harry with anyone,' he admitted, his own throat choked with tears. 'Your mother understood, but—'

'My mother?' Andie repeated. 'She knew about all this?'

'I told her,' he admitted, sensing a sudden distance widening between Andie and himself. A distance he didn't understand. 'Your mother was one of the most beautiful people I have ever known, gave me back my belief in human love and kindness, a belief that had been missing from my life for so many years—'

'Adam, I don't want to hear how you felt about my mother!' Andie protested emotionally.

He blinked his surprise at her vehemence. 'But—'

'If we're to stand any chance of building a future together, Adam—and I believe from this conversation that you still want that—then it has to be with no emotional baggage,' Andie told him firmly. 'Oh, I don't mean Harry,' she assured pleadingly at his pained frown. 'Losing Harry, an identical twin, must have been like losing half of yourself.'

'Worse,' he confirmed bleakly. 'We were so close we could finish each other's sentences, read each other's minds. After Harry died I completely withdrew into myself, refused to speak. To anyone. There was an inquest on Harry's death, of course, a social services report on my mother.' He looked steadily at Andie. 'The report showed that my mother's evenings out were spent with a number of different men. Men who gave her money.'

He watched as the truth dawned on Andie, the absolute horror on her face.

His mother, selfish, irresponsible, totally incapable of caring for anyone but herself, had been little better than a prostitute!

Oh, no one had actually used that word at the time, and Adam wouldn't have understood what it meant if they had, but he hadn't even been in his teens when he had worked out for himself that was what his mother had actually been. There was no denying the fact that the men his mother had seen had been on a regular basis, but the plain truth of the matter was, his mother had taken money from those men. Which made her only one thing in his eyes.

In Andie's eyes too...?

This was what he had dreaded Andie finding out: the horrible truth about his mother...

He was unable to look at Andie now. Frightened of what he might see in her face!

'The authorities decided that Glenda wasn't a fit mother to look after me. But with typical selfishness, my mother refused to even think of agreeing to adoption, so I was put into care—'

'No!' Andie protested brokenly.

He gave a humourless smile. 'It was the best thing anyone could have done for me. Away from her, from the place where Harry and I had known such unhappiness, I at last began to respond to people, to talk again. On the few occasions when my mother came to visit I refused to see her. Her birthday and Christmas presents were always sent back unopened, until she finally stopped sending them.' He at last explained the lack of them in his childhood; it had been an act of deliberate denial on his part! 'In fact, I didn't see her again until I was twenty-five or so. When I had begun to make a name for myself—and obviously money, too!—as a film producer,' he explained bitterly.

'After all that had happened, she came to you and asked for money?' Andie gasped disbelievingly.

He still clearly remembered that first meeting with Glenda after twenty years of inwardly denying she had ever existed. She had looked exactly the same, still beautiful—and still the same selfishly grasping woman she had always been.

He nodded. 'That was when I talked to your mother about her. I had to tell someone.' He had hated Glenda. But at the same time, she was his mother, his only living relative, and those two emotions had been at war inside him.

'Adam—'

'Andie, I don't understand this problem with your mother?' he protested. 'She's the one who helped me to see the past objectively, helped me to understand that no one is all black, just as no one is all white. My mother had been barely twenty when we were born, abandoned by her husband, left alone with two babies to bring up as best she could. Barbara never tried to excuse Glenda's behaviour, but she did at least succeed in helping me to pity her,' he recalled heavily.

'You loved my mother!' Andie burst out forcefully.

'Well, of course I loved her,' he confirmed. Barbara had helped him retain his sanity fifteen years ago when Glenda, recently divorced from her second husband, had suddenly appeared back in his life. Without Barbara's gentle guidance his reaction to Glenda might have been completely different! 'How could I help but love her?' He shook his head. 'Barbara was everything a mother should be: loving, caring, giving. Everything my own mother wasn't, and never could be!'

Andie was very pale now, eyes hugely green against that paleness. 'She was also another man's wife!'

'Well, of course she—' Adam broke off his exclamation, suddenly still as he looked searchingly down at Andie. She returned that gaze unflinchingly, but once again there were tears glistening in her eyes. 'Andie, I loved Barbara like the mother I had never had, the mother I never would have.' He firmly grasped the tops of her arms. 'And Barbara being the woman she was, she took me in as if I were one of her own children.'

'How could she possibly seem like a mother to you?'' Andie scorned in a pained voice. 'She was only twelve years older than you!'

'Andie—' He paused disbelievingly. 'Tell me if I'm understanding this correctly; do you believe I was in love with your mother…?'

She raised her chin proudly. 'And weren't you?'

'Good God, no,' he answered unhesitantly, shaking his head dazedly. 'I told you, she was like a mother to me, gave me the gentleness and love, the acceptance for who and what I am, that had been missing from my life for so long. Rome instinctively understood that. I always thought you girls did, too,' he said. 'Obviously I was wrong...'

Very, very wrong, if Andie had believed all this time that he was in love with her mother!

But if Andie believed that, had always believed that, why had she agreed to marry him? He couldn't believe it was just the pregnancy.

Hope began to burn deep inside him as he looked at Andie's palely intense face. Hope that perhaps Rome had been right about Andie's feelings towards him, after all...?

He knew that he was about to take the biggest risk of his life, bigger even than telling Andie the truth about his mother. But if he and Andie were ever to know any happiness together, it was a risk he had to take.

'Andie,' he began shakily, 'there's a very good reason why I was never in love with your mother...' He paused, clenching his hands at his sides so that she shouldn't see the way they were trembling. 'And that reason is because I'm very much in love with someone else. And have been for more years than I care to think about.'

Andie's throat moved convulsively. 'Do you really think I want to hear this?' she cried emotionally. 'We're supposed to be marrying each other in two weeks' time!'

'Do you still want to go ahead with that? Now that I've told you about my own childhood? My mother,' he asked hardly. 'You won't be seeing her again, by the way,' he continued grimly. 'That last meeting with her was exactly that.' He had told Glenda in no uncertain terms exactly what he thought of her, what he had always thought of her. As Barbara had told him he would feel strong enough to do one day. He did not want Glenda anywhere near Andie or their two children.

'You aren't your mother, Adam—'

'Her blood runs in my veins!' he bit out.

Andie gave a shake of her head. 'You were practically a baby the last time you lived with her. And I've known you most of my life, Adam, don't believe there is a single part of her in you. You're good, and kind, and—'

'So much in love with you it hurts!' he groaned, giving a self-deprecating laugh as her eyes widened disbelievingly. 'I decided years ago that I would never love anyone again, never need anyone again; Harry had died, my mother had never done a single thing to deserve that title—' He broke off, nervous at going on with this.

But he had started now, he had to go on!

'Over the years, as I worked to build up my company, I convinced myself that was what I was doing, why there was never anyone permanent in my life. It wasn't until your eighteenth birthday that I realised I had only been deluding myself, that there was a much simpler explanation as to why I had never been seriously involved with anyone. Do you remember your eighteenth birthday, Andie?' He looked at her intently.

Andie was still staring up at him, but it was impossible to tell by her dazed expression whether she was merely still disbelieving or just reluctant to hear what he had to say.

'You didn't like the red dress I was wearing,' she finally answered.

He gave a snort. 'I *loved* the red dress you were wearing!' he corrected. 'It was the thought of any other man seeing you in that dress that made me so damned insulting to you that night. I suddenly realised you were no longer a child but a beautiful woman—and that other men would think so too. I also realised,' he continued, 'that I was in love with you. Completely, head over heels, for ever, in love with you.'

Andie blinked. 'You were so horrible to me that night...'

He gave a grimace. 'You would have been horrible too if you had just seen all your carefully laid plans for a care-free bachelor life disappear at the sight of you in a red dress!'

'But I—you—you never said anything! Adam, in all these years you have never given any indication—'

'Andie, you're fourteen years younger than me.' He sighed. 'You had the perfect childhood, a wonderful family, a university degree, a successful career; what did I ever have to offer you—?'

'Yourself!' she cut in emotionally. 'My childhood was perfect,' she acknowledged. 'My family is wonderful. The degree was Rome's idea. My career—for the last five years my career has taken the place of what I really wanted in life!'

Adam tensed. 'And that is?' He held his breath, almost afraid of her answer.

Andie moved towards him, putting her arms about his waist, resting her head against his chest. 'What I have now,' she told him gruffly. 'You. Children. Marriage. Slightly out of the normal order of things,' she acknowledged with a small laugh. 'But I would have settled for just you!'

It was incredible that Andie loved him, too.

Amazing.

But as he gathered her possessively close to him, held her tightly against him, he knew that he accepted that love with open arms, that he worshipped this woman, with every particle of his being.

That he always would.

EPILOGUE

'DO YOU think we will ever get them back?'

Andie followed Adam's amused gaze to watch her family as they oohed and aahed the two babies they held, one in Harrie's arms, the other in Danie's, their two husbands standing beside them smiling indulgently, Rome and Audrey already protesting the two sisters had already held the babies long enough, that as the doting grandparents it was their turn now.

'Eventually.' Andie chuckled, stretching with satisfaction as she turned back to look at Adam.

Her husband.

The love of her life.

As she was his.

She still had to pinch herself occasionally to make sure that she wasn't dreaming, that all the misunderstandings were really over, that she and Adam loved each other.

Even more so since the twins had been born yesterday. She hadn't believed they could possibly be any happier than they already were, their marriage turning out to be everything, and more, that she could ever have hoped for. But as they had shared the experience of their children's birth, held their two tiny sons in their arms, she knew she had been wrong. This was total bliss.

'Although I'm afraid Harry and Peter are going to end up being very spoilt,' she murmured unworriedly.

The names, two boys' and two girls', had been chosen long before the birth. But Andie was inwardly ecstatic that Adam now had another Harry in his life. It could never make up for the loss of the first one, nothing could ever do that, but it was a fitting tribute to the brother Adam had loved so much.

Adam reached out and took one of her hands into his, the love he no longer took pains to hide blazing brightly in his eyes. 'Did I remember to thank you?' he asked.

'For the twins?' She laughed softly. 'I believe we have each other to thank for them!'

Adam shook his head. 'Not for the twins—although God knows I already love them so much I ache with it,' he admitted. 'But it isn't them I thank you for. It's the wonderful family you have given me for them. I—I always wanted—I never believed—'

'They are your family too, Adam.' She squeezed his hand tightly in understanding. They hadn't seen Glenda since that day at Adam's office, never spoke of her, and Andie knew that was the way Adam wanted it to remain. 'They can't love you as much as I do,' she told him. 'But almost!'

As Rome and Audrey finally returned their two sons to them, one in Andie's arms, one in Adam's, the two of them still looking at each other over the babies' heads, and she knew that love would only grow over the years, grow and deepen.

It was for ever.

One

"Making a sock by hand creates a connection to history; we are offered a glimpse into the lives of knitters who made socks using the same skills and techniques we continue to use today."
—Nancy Bush is the author of Folk Socks (1994), Folk Knitting in Estonia (1999) and Knitting on the Road, Socks for the Traveling Knitter, (2001), all published by Interweave Press

Knitting saved my life. It saw me through two lengthy bouts of cancer, a particularly terrifying kind that formed tumors inside my brain and tormented me with indescribable headaches. I experienced pain I could never have imagined before. Cancer destroyed my teen years and my twenties, but I was *determined* to survive.

I'd just turned sixteen the first time I was diagnosed, and I learned to knit while undergoing chemotherapy. A woman with breast cancer, who had the chemo chair next to mine, used to knit and she's the one who taught me. The chemo was dreadful—not quite as bad as the headaches, but close. Because of knitting, I was able to endure those endless hours of weakness and severe nausea. With two needles and a skein of yarn, I felt I could face whatever I had to. My hair fell out in clumps, but I could weave yarn around a needle and create a stitch; I could follow a pattern and finish a project. I couldn't hold down more than a few bites at a time, but I could knit. I clung to that small sense of accomplishment, treasured it.

Knitting was my salvation—knitting and my father.

After he died, I realized I had a choice: what to do with the rest of my life. I wanted to honor my father in whatever I chose, and that meant I was prepared to take some risks.

I opened a yarn store on Blossom Street in Seattle. That might not seem earth-shattering to anyone else, but for me, it was a leap of faith equal to Noah's building the ark without a rain cloud in sight. I had an inheritance from my grandparents and gambled every cent on starting my own business. Me, who's never held down a job for more than a few weeks. Me, who knew next to nothing about finances, profit-and-loss statements or business plans. I sank every dime I had into what I *did* know, and that was yarn and knitters. Naturally, there were a few problems. At the time, Blossom Street was undergoing a major renovation—in fact, the architect's wife, Jacqueline Donovan, was one of the women in my first knitting class. Jacqueline, Carol and Alix, my original students, remain three of my closest friends to this day.

I didn't get the support you might expect from my family. Mom, bless her, tried to be encouraging, but she was in shock after losing Dad. She still is. Most days, she wanders around hopelessly in a fog of grief and loss. When I mentioned my plan, she didn't discourage me, but she wasn't actually cheering me on, either.

My older sister, Margaret, on the other hand, had no qualms about drowning me in tales of doom and gloom. The day I opened my doors for business, she marched in with a spate of dire forecasts. The economy was down, she told me; people were hanging onto their money. I'd be lucky to stay afloat for six weeks. Ten minutes of listening to her ominous predictions, and I was ready to rip up the lease and close my door—until I realized this was my first official day on the job and I had yet to sell a single skein of yarn.

As you might've guessed, Margaret and I have a complicated relationship. Don't get me wrong; I love my sister.

But Margaret, to put it mildly, isn't the warm, spontaneous type. I didn't understand how much she cared until I had a third cancer scare just a few months after I opened A Good Yarn. *Scare* doesn't come close to describing my feelings when Dr. Wilson ordered those frightening, familiar tests. It was as if my entire world had come to a sudden halt. The truth is, I don't think I could've endured the struggle yet again. I'd already decided that if the cancer *had* returned, I would refuse treatment.

My come-what-may attitude disturbed Margaret, who wouldn't accept my fatalism. Talk of death unsettled her, the way it does most people, but when you've been around death and dying as much as I have, it's as natural as turning off the lights. I don't look forward to dying, but I'm not afraid of it either. Thankfully, the tests came back negative and I'm thriving, right along with my yarn store. The only reason I mention it now is that it was during those few weeks that I discovered how deeply my sister loves me. In the last seventeen years, I've only seen her cry twice—when Dad died and when Dr. Wilson gave me a clean bill of health.

Once I returned to work full-time, Margaret bullied and cajoled me into contacting Brad Goetz again. Brad, who drives the UPS truck that makes deliveries to A Good Yarn, is the man I'd started seeing last year. He's divorced and has custody of his eight-year-old son, Cody. It would be an understatement to say Brad is good-looking; the fact is, he's drop-dead gorgeous. The first day he came into the store, wheeling several cartons of yarn, it was all I could do to keep the drool from dripping down my chin. I got so flustered I could hardly sign for the delivery. He asked me out three times before I finally agreed to meet him for drinks. Given my experience, male-female relationships fluster me and I was sure I'd be completely out of my element dating Brad. I would never have found the courage to say yes if not for Margaret, who harassed me into it.

I always say that A Good Yarn is my affirmation of life, but according to my sister I was afraid to really live, afraid to venture outside the tiny comfortable world I'd created inside my yarn store. She was right and I knew it, but still I resisted. The truth is, it'd been so many years since I'd spent any amount of time with a man other than my father or my physician that I had the social finesse of a dandelion. But Margaret wouldn't listen to a single excuse, and soon Brad and I were having drinks together, followed by dinners, picnics with Cody and ball games. I've come to love Brad's son as much as I do my two nieces, Julia and Hailey.

These days Brad and I see quite a bit of each other. We're cautious—okay, I'm the one who's taking things slow, but Brad's fine with that. He was burned once when his ex-wife walked out, claiming she needed to "find herself." There's Cody to consider, too. The boy has a close relationship with Brad, and while Cody loves me too, I don't want to disrupt that special bond between father and son. So far, everything is going well, and we're talk-

ing more and more about a future together. Brad and
Cody are so much a part of my life now that I couldn't
imagine being without them.

The bell above my door chimed as Margaret stepped
inside. She's actually working with me three days a week
now. It was the first Tuesday morning in June, and a lovely
day.

"Good morning," I greeted her, turning away from the
small coffeemaker I keep in the back room that's officially
my office.

She didn't answer me right away and when she did it
was more of a grumble than an actual response. Knowing my sister and her moods, I bided my time. If she'd had
an argument with one of her daughters or with her husband, she'd tell me eventually.

"I've got a pot of coffee on," I announced as Margaret
walked into the back room and locked up her purse.

Without commenting, my sister pulled a freshly
washed cup from the tray and reached for the pot. The
drip continued, sizzling against the hot plate, but she
didn't appear to notice.

Finally I couldn't stand it any longer and my resolve
to give her a chance to get over her bad mood disappeared. "What's wrong with you?" I demanded. I have to
admit I felt impatient; lately, she's brought her surly
moods to work a little too often.

Facing me, Margaret offered a tentative smile. "Nothing…sorry. It's just that this feels a whole lot like Monday."

Because the shop is closed on Mondays, Tuesday is
technically our first work day of the week. I frowned at
her, trying to figure out what the real problem was. But

she'd assumed a perfectly blank expression, telling me nothing.

My sister is a striking woman with wide shoulders and thick, dark hair. She's tall and lean, but solid. She still looks like the athlete she used to be. I wish she'd do something different with her hair, though. She wears the same style she did in high school, parted in the middle and stick-straight until it hits her shoulders, where it obediently turns under, as if she's tortured it with a curling iron. That was certainly part of her teenage regimen—the curling iron, the hair spray, the vigorously wielded brush. The style suits her, I suppose, but I'd give anything to see her try something different.

"I'm going to post a new class," I said, changing the subject abruptly, hoping to draw her out of her dour mood.

"For what?"

Ah, interest. That was a good sign. For the most part, all the classes I'd held had gone well. I'd taught a beginners' class, an intermediate and a Fair Isle, but there was one I'd been thinking of offering for a while.

"It's such a difficult question?"

My sister's cynicism shook me from my brief reverie. "Socks," I told her. "I'm going to offer a class on knitting socks."

With the inventive new sock yarns on the market, socks were the current knitting rage. I carried a number of the European brands and loved the variety. My customers did, too. Several of the new yarns were designed to create an intricate pattern when knitted. I found it amazing to view a finished pair of socks, knowing the design had been formed by the yarn itself and not the knitter.

"Fine." Margaret's shoulders rose in a shrug. "I suppose you're going to suggest knitting them on circular needles versus the double-pointed method," she said casually.

"Of course." I preferred using two circular needles.

Margaret would rather crochet and while she can knit, she doesn't often. "There seems to be a lot of interest in socks lately, doesn't there?" Her tone was still casual, almost nonchalant.

I regarded my sister closely. She always had a list of three or four reasons any idea of mine wouldn't work. It had become practically a game with us. I'd make some new suggestion and she'd instantly tell me why it was bound to fail. I missed having the opportunity to state my case.

"So you think a sock class would appeal to our customers?" I couldn't help asking. Good grief, there had to be something drastically wrong with Margaret.

I was fond of knitting socks for reasons beyond the current popularity. The biggest attraction for me was the fact that a pair of socks was a small project. After finishing an afghan or a Fair Isle sweater, I usually wanted a project I knew I could complete quickly. After knitting for endless hours, I found it gratifying to watch a sock take shape almost immediately. Socks didn't require a major commitment of either time or yarn and made wonderful gifts. Yes, socks were definitely my choice for this newest class. Because of my other classes, I was limited as to the day and time I could do this but I hoped there'd be enough aspiring knitters available on a Tuesday afternoon.

Margaret nodded in answer to my question. "I think a sock class would definitely attract people," she murmured.

I stared at my sister and, for just an instant, thought I saw the sheen of tears in her eyes. I couldn't believe it and stared harder. As I mentioned earlier, Margaret rarely cries. "Are you feeling okay?" I asked, just in case, keeping my voice gentle. I didn't want to pry, but if something really *was* wrong, she needed to know I was concerned about her.

"Stop asking me that," she snapped.

I sighed with relief. The old Margaret was back.

"Would you make a sign for the window?" I asked. Margaret was much better with graphic art than me. I'd come to rely on her for window displays and notices.

With no real display of enthusiasm, she agreed. "I'll have one up before noon."

"Great." I walked over to the front door, unlocked it and flipped the Closed sign to Open. Whiskers glanced up from his perch in the front window, where he lazed in the morning sun. Red Martha Washington geraniums bloomed in the window box. The soil looked parched, so I filled the watering can and carried it outside. From the corner of my eye I saw a flash of brown as a truck turned the corner. A familiar happiness stole over me. *Brad*.

Sure enough, he angled the big truck into the parking spot in front of Fanny's Floral, the shop nextdoor to mine. He hopped out, all the while smiling at me.

"It's a beautiful morning," I said, reveling in his smile. This man smiles with his whole heart, his whole being, and he has the most intense blue eyes. They're like a beacon. I swear I can see those eyes a mile away, they're that blue. "Have you got a yarn delivery for me?" I asked.

"I'm the only delivery I have for you today. I've got a couple of minutes if there's coffee on."

"There is." It was a ritual with us. Brad stopped at the shop twice a week, with or without a load of yarn—more often if he could manage it. He never stayed long. He filled his travel coffee mug, took the opportunity to steal a kiss and then went about his business. As always, I followed him into the back room, pretending to be surprised when he eased me into his embrace. I love Brad's kisses. He started with my forehead, then gradually worked his way down my face until he reached my lips. By the time his mouth moved over mine, I could feel the electricity through every inch of my body. He has that effect on me—and he's well aware of it.

He held me just long enough for my equilibrium to return. Then he released me and picked up the coffeepot. To my surprise he was frowning when he turned around.

"Is there a problem between Margaret and Matt?" he asked.

I opened my mouth to assure him everything was fine, but before I could utter a word I stopped myself. All at once I realized I didn't know. "What makes you ask?"

"Your sister," he said in hushed tones. "She isn't herself lately. Haven't you noticed?"

I nodded. "Something's definitely up with her," I agreed, remembering how she'd declined the opportunity to wage verbal battle.

"Do you want me to ask her?" Brad inquired, forgetting to whisper.

I paused, afraid Margaret would take offense and snap at Brad the same way she had at me. "Probably not." But then I changed my mind. My sister was half in love with Brad herself. If anyone could make it past that protective barrier of hers, it would be him. "Maybe, but not now."

"When?"

"Perhaps we should all get together soon."

Brad shook his head. "It'd be better if Matt wasn't around."

"Right." I nibbled on my lower lip. "Do you have any other brilliant ideas?"

Before he could answer, Margaret tore aside the curtain to the back room and glared at us. Brad and I started, no doubt looking as guilty as we felt.

"Listen, you two lovebirds, if you're going to talk about me I suggest you lower your voices." With that, she released the curtain and stomped into the store.